D...
CODE
BOOK

Published by
Kenneth Mason Publications Ltd
Dudley House, 12 North Street
Emsworth, Hampshire PO10 7DQ

© Kenneth Mason Publications Ltd, 1995

Dialling code compilation © British Telecommunica-
tions plc 1994
Reproduced with permission

BT and the publishers do not accept responsibility for
any errors or omissions in the codes

British Library Cataloguing-in-Publication Data
A catalogue record for this book is available from the
British Library
ISBN 0-85937-400-9

Printed and bound in Great Britain by
Cox & Wyman Ltd, Reading, Berkshire

Section 1
National A–Z dialling codes

This section gives the new national dialling codes listed alphabetically by place name.

On Phoneday, April 16 1995, all national dialling codes changed to include a 1 after the initial 0. For example York (0904) became (01904).

The exception to this is in Leeds, Sheffield, Nottingham, Leicester and Bristol. These 5 cities have been given completely new national codes and one extra digit has been added to individual customer numbers, for example Leeds (0532) becomes (0113) 2.

The changes will not affect –

• 3 figure numbers, such as 999 (emergencies) or 100 (BT operator).

• Individual customer numbers or local calls, except in Leeds, Sheffield, Nottingham, Leicester and Bristol.

• Mobile phone numbers.

• Freephone or reduced rate services, such as 0800 or 0345 numbers.

• Information and entertainment lines, for example 0891 or 0898 numbers.

A full list of the codes which are not affected by the changes can be found on the following page.

Exceptions to Phoneday changes

Code	Operator
0336	Vodafone
0338	Vodafone
0345	BT Lo-call
0370	Vodafone
0374	Vodafone
0385	Vodafone
0399	Vodafone
0426	BT Radio Paging
0459	Mobile Comms
0500	Mercury
0523	Mercury
0585	Cellnet
0645	Mercury
0660	Mercury
0696	Jersey Premium Rate Service
0800	BT Freefone
0802	Cellnet
0831	Vodafone
0836	Vodafone
0839	Mercury
0850	Cellnet
0860	Cellnet
0881	Mercury
0891	BT Premium Rate Service
0893	BT Radio Paging
0894	BT Premium Rate Service
0897	BT Premium Rate Service
0898	BT Premium Rate Service
0941	Hutchison Paging
0956	Mercury
0958	Mercury
0973	Orange
0976	Orange
0979	Jersey Cellular Radio
0990	BT National Call

A

Place	Code
Abbey St Bathans	
3 figure numbers	013614
6 figure numbers	01361
Abbeytown	016973
Abbotsbury	01305
Abbots Ripton	
3 figure numbers	0148 73
6 figure numbers	01487
Aberaeron	01545
Aberchirder	01466
Aberconwy	01492
Abercrave	01639
Abercynon	01443
Aberdare	01685
Aberdaron	
3 figure numbers	0175886
6 figure numbers	01758
Aberdeen	01224
Aberdour	01383
Aberdovey	01654
Aberfeldy	01887

Place	Code
Aberfoyle	01877
Abergavenny	01873
Abergele	01745
Abergynolwyn	01654
Aberkenfig	01656
Aberlady	01875
Aberlemno	01307
Aberlour	01340
Abermule	01686
Abernethy	
3 figure numbers	0173885
6 figure numbers	01738
Aberporth	01239
Abersoch	01758
Abertillery	01495
Aberystwyth	01970
Abingdon	01235
Aboyne	
5 figure numbers	013398
6 figure numbers	01339
Accrington	01254

Place	Code
Achiltibuie	
3 figure numbers	0185482
6 figure numbers	01854
Achnamara	
3 figure numbers	0154 685
6 figure numbers	01546
Achnasheen	
3 figure numbers	0144588
6 figure numbers	01445
Achnashellach	
3 figure numbers	015206
6 figure numbers	01520
Ackleton	
3 figure numbers	017465
6 figure numbers	01746
Acton Burnell	01694
Adbaston	01785
Addingham	01943
Adlington(Chorley)	01257
Advie	01807
Aeron	01570
Aghadowey	01265

Place	Code
Aghalee	01846
Ahoghill	01266
Airdrie	01236
Airshow	01252
Airth	01324
Airton	01729
Albrighton	01902
Albury (Herts)	01279
Alcester	01789
Aldbury Common	01442
Aldeburgh(Suffolk)	01728
Aldeby	01502
Alderley Edge	01625
Alderminster	01789
Alderney	01481
Aldershot	01252
Aldford(Cheshire)	01244
Aldington (Kent)	01233
Aldridge	01922
Alexandria	01389
Alford (Aberdeen)	
5 figure numbers	019755

Place	Code
6 figure numbers	01975
Alford (Lincs)	01507
Alfreton (Derbys)	01773
Alfriston	01323
Alloa	01259
Allonby	01900
Alloway	01292
Almondbank	01738
Almondsbury	01454
Alness	01349
Alnmouth	01665
Alnwick	01665
Alresford	01962
Alsager	01270
Alston	01434
Alstonefield	
3 figure numbers	0133527
6 figure numbers	01335
Altnaharra	
3 figure numbers	0154981
6 figure numbers	01549
Alton (Hants)	
3 figure numbers	01420
6 figure numbers	0183 53
Alva	01259
Alves	
3 figure numbers	0134385
6 figure numbers	01343
Alyth	
4 figure numbers	018283
6 figure numbers	01828
Ambergate	0773
6 figure numbers	
Ambleside	015394
Amersham	01494
Amesbury	01980
Amisfield	01387
Amlwch	01407
Ammanford	01269
Amman Valley	01269
Ampleforth	
3 figure numbers	014393
6 figure numbers	01439
Ampthill	01525
Amulree	01350
Ancrum	
3 figure numbers	0123383
6 figure numbers	01233
6 figure numbers	01835
Andover	01264
Angle	01646
Annaghmore	01762
Annalong	013967
Annan	01461
Annbank	01292
Anstey Mills	
3 figure numbers	013984
6 figure numbers	01398
Anstruther	01333
Antrim	01849
Appin	01407
3 figure numbers	0163173
Appleby	01631
6 figure numbers	0176 83
Applecross	015204
3 figure numbers	01520
Appledore (Kent)	
3 figure numbers	0123383
6 figure numbers	01233
Appleton Roebuck (North Yorks)	01904
Appley Bridge	01257
Arborfield Cross	01734
Arbroath	01241
Arden	
3 figure numbers	0138985
6 figure numbers	01389
Ardentinny	
3 figure numbers	0136981
6 figure numbers	01369
Ardersier	01667
Ardgay	
3 figure numbers	018632
6 figure numbers	01863
Ardglass	01396
Ardgour	
3 figure numbers	018555
6 figure numbers	01855
Ardingly	01444
Ardrossan	01294

Ardvasar
3 figure numbers 014714
6 figure numbers 01471
Ardwell 01776
Arisaig
3 figure numbers 0168 75
Arley (Northwich) 01687
Arley (Worcs) 01565
3 figure numbers 012997
6 figure numbers 01299
Armadale 01501
Armagh 01861
Armathwaite 0169 74
Armitage 01543
Armoy (Co.Antrim) 0126 57
Arncliffe 01756
Arncroach
3 figure numbers 013338
6 figure numbers 01333
Arnside 01524
Aros 01680

Arrochar
3 figure numbers 013012
6 figure numbers 01301
Arundel 01903
Ascot 01344
Ash Bank 01782
Ashbourne 01335
Ashburton 01364
Ashby-de-la-Zouch 01530
Ashcott 01458
Ashdon 01799
Ashford (Kent) 01233
Ashford (Middlesex) 01784
Ash Green 01474
Ashington
(Northumberland) 01670
Ashington
(West Sussex) 01903
Ash (Kent) 01304
Ashkirk 01750
Ashley 01630

Ashreigney
3 figure numbers 017693
6 figure numbers 01769
Ashtead (Surrey) 01372
Ashton-in-Makerfield 01942
Ashurst 01703
Ashwater
3 figure numbers 0140921
6 figure numbers 01409
Ashwell 01462
Ashwicken 01553
Aspatria 016973
Assynt
3 figure numbers 0157 12
6 figure numbers 01571
Asthall Leigh
3/4 figure numbers 0199387
6 figure numbers 01993
Astwood Bank 01527
Athelstaneford
3 figure numbers 0162088
6 figure numbers 01620

Atherstone (Warwicks)
01827
Atherton (Lancs) 01942
Attleborough 01953
Auchenblae 01561
Auchencairn
3 figure numbers 0155664
6 figure numbers 01556
Auchengray
3 figure numbers 0150185
6 figure numbers 01501
Auchenmalg 01581
Auchenleuchries
Auchleuchries 0135 85
Auchnagatt 01358
3 figure numbers 013583
6 figure numbers 01358
Auchterarder 01764
Auchterhouse
3 figure numbers 0182626
6 figure numbers 01382

7

Place	Number
Auchterless	
3 figure numbers	018884
6 figure numbers	01888
Auchtermuchty	01337
Audlem	01270
Aughafatten	01266
Aughnacloy	
3/4 figure numbers	0166252
5 figure numbers	016625
Aughton Green	01695
Auldgirth	0138774
3 figure numbers	01387
6 figure numbers	01445
Aultbea	
Aultguish	019975
3 figure numbers	01997
6 figure numbers	01672
Avebury	01479
Aviemore	01324
Avonbridge	01934
Axbridge	01297
Axminster	
Aycliffe	01325
Aylesbury	01296
Aylsham	01263
Ayr	01292
Ayton	
5 figure numbers	018907
6 figure numbers	01890
B	
Back	
3 figure numbers	0185182
6 figure numbers	01851
Bacton (Suffolk)	01449
Bacup	01706
Badachro	
3 figure numbers	0144583
6 figure numbers	01445
Badingham	01728
Bagshot	01276
Bagworth	01530
Bailies Mills	01846
Bakewell	01629
Bala	01678
Balallan	
3 figure numbers	0185183
6 figure numbers	01851
Balbeggie	01821
Balcombe (Haywards Heath)	01444
Baldock	01462
Balfour	
3 figure numbers	0185671
6 figure numbers	01856
Balfron	01360
Ballachulish	
3 figure numbers	018552
6 figure numbers	01855
Ballantrae	
3 figure numbers	0146583
6 figure numbers	01465
Ballater	
5 figure numbers	013397
6 figure numbers	01339
Ballinamallard	01365
Ballinaskeagh	018206
Ballindalloch	01807
Ballingry	01592
Ballinluig	01796
Ballycastle (Co Antrim)	012657
Ballyclare	01960
Ballygally	01574
Ballygawley	016625
Ballygowan	01238
Ballykinler	01396
Ballymena	01266
Ballymoney	012656
Ballynahinch	01238
Ballyronan	01648
Ballywalter	0124 77
Ballyward	0182 06
Balmacara	
3 figure numbers	0159986
6 figure numbers	01599
Balmaha	
3 figure numbers	0136087
6 figure numbers	01360

Place	Code
Balmedie	01358
Balmore	01360
Balmullo	01334
Baltasound	
3 figure numbers	0195781
6 figure numbers	01957
Baltonsborough	01458
Balvicar	
3 figure numbers	018523
6 figure numbers	01852
Bamburgh	01668
Bampton Castle	01993
Bampton (Devon)	01398
Bampton (Penrith)	01931
Banbridge	018206
Banbury (Oxon)	01295
Banchory	01330
Bancyfelin	01267
Banff	01261
Bangor (Co. Down)	01247
Bangor (North Wales)	01248
Bangor-on-Dee	01978
Bankfoot	01738
Banknock	01324
Bankshill	
3 figure numbers	015767
6 figure numbers	01576
Bannockburn	01786
Banwell	01934
Barbon	015242
Barbreck	
3 figure numbers	018525
6 figure numbers	01852
Barcombe (Lewes)	01273
Bardney	01526
Bardsea	01229
Barford (Warwicks)	01926
Bargoed	01443
Bargrennan	01671
Barkston Ash	01937
Barkway	01763
Barlaston	01782
Barmouth	01341
Barnby	01502
Barnetby	01652
Barnham Broom	01603
Barnoldswick	01282
Barnsley	01226
Barnstaple	01271
Barr	
3 figure numbers	0146586
6 figure numbers	01465
Barrhill	
3 figure numbers	0146582
6 figure numbers	01465
Barrock	
3 figure numbers	0184785
6 figure numbers	01847
Barrow-in-Furness	01229
Barrow-on-Humber	01469
Barry	01446
Barton-on-Humber	01652
Barton-on-the-Heath	01608
Barton-under-Needwood	01283
Barvas	
3 figure numbers	0185184
6 figure numbers	01851
Baschurch	01939
Basildon	01268
Basingstoke	01256
Baslow	01246
Bassenthwaite Lake	017687
Bassingham	01522
Bath	01225
Bathgate	01506
Batley (West Yorks)	01924
Battle	01424
Baumber	01507
Bawdeswell	
3 figure numbers	0136288
6 figure numbers	01362
Bayford	01992
Bayhead	01876
Beaconsfield	01494
Beaford (Devon)	
3 figure numbers	018053
6 figure numbers	01805

Place	Code
Beaminster	01308
Beattock	016833
3 figure numbers	01683
6 figure numbers	01683
Beaulieu (Hants)	01590
Beauly	01463
Beaumaris	01248
Beaworthy	01409
Beccles	01502
Beckermet	01946
Beckley (East Sussex)	01797
Bedale	01677
Beddgelert	
3 figure numbers	0176686
6 figure numbers	01766
Bedford	01234
Bedlington	01670
Bedlinog	01443
Bedworth	01203
Beeford(North Humberside)	01262
Beguildy	
3 figure numbers	015477
6 figure numbers	01547
Beith	01505
Belbroughton	01562
Belcoo	01365
Belfast	01232
Belford (Northumberland)	01668
Bellaghy	01648
Bellarena	015047
Belleek	013656
Bellingham (Northumberland)	01434
Bellshill	01698
Belmont Village	01204
Belper	01773
Belsay	01661
Belton	
3 figure numbers	0157286
6 figure numbers	01572
Benbecula	01870
Benburb	01861
Benefield	
3 figure numbers	018325
6 figure numbers	01832
Benington	01438
Bentham (North Yorks)	015242
Bentley (Hants)	01420
Bentpath	
5 figure numbers	013873
6 figure numbers	01387
Benwick (Cambs)	01354
Beragh	016627
Bere Regis	01929
Berkhamsted	01442
Berkswell	01676
Berneray	01876
Berriedale	
3 figure numbers	015935
6 figure numbers	01593
Berriew	01686
Berwick-upon-Tweed	01289
Bessbrook	01693
Betchworth (Surrey)	01737
Bethersden	01233
Bethesda	01248
Bettisfield	
3 figure numbers	0194875
6 figure numbers	01948
Bettyhill	
3 figure numbers	0164 12
6 figure numbers	01641
Betws-y-Coed	01690
Bewdley	01299
Bexhill-on-Sea	01424
Beyton	01359
Bicester	01869
Bickington	01626
Bickleigh	01884
Biddenden	01580
Bideford (Devon)	01237
Bidford-on-Avon	01789
Bigbury-on-Sea	01548
Biggar	01899

Biggin Hill	01959
Biggleswade	01767
3 figure numbers	019502
6 figure numbers	01950
Bildeston (Suffolk)	01449
Billericay	01277
Billesdon (Leics)	01533
Billinge	01744
Billinghay	01526
Billingshurst	01403
Bilsdale	014396
3 figure numbers	01439
6 figure numbers	01902
Bilston	01472
Binbrook	01929
Bindon Abbey	01949
Bingham (Notts)	01328
Binham (Norfolk)	01243
Birdham	01890
Birgham	0121
Birmingham	

Birsay	0185672
3 figure numbers	01856
6 figure numbers	01684
Birtsmorton	
Bishampton (Worcs)	0138682
3 figure numbers	01386
6 figure numbers	01388
Bishop Auckland	01673
Bishop Norton	01588
Bishop's Castle	01963
Bishop's Caundle	01823
Bishop's Lydeard	01769
Bishop's Nympton	01279
Bishops Stortford	
Bishopston (West Glam)	01792
Bishop's Waltham	01489
Bishopton (Renfrew)	01505
Bishop Wilton	01759
Bixter	0159581
3 figure numbers	01595
6 figure numbers	

Blackawton	01803
Blackburn	01254
Blackford	01764
Blacklunans	01250
Blackmoor (Hants)	01420
Blackmore (Essex)	01277
Blackpool	01253
Blackshaw	01538
Black Torrington	
3 figure numbers	0140923
6 figure numbers	01409
Blackwood	01495
Blaenau Ffestiniog	01766
Blaenavon	01495
Blagdon Hill (Taunton)	01823
Blaina	01495
Blainslie	
3 figure numbers	0189686
6 figure numbers	01896
Blair Atholl	01796
Blairgowrie	01250
Blakesley	01327

Blandford	01258
Blanefield	01360
Blantyre	01698
Bleadon (Avon)	01934
Bledlow Ridge	01494
Bletchington	01869
Blewbury	01235
Blisworth	01604
Blockley	01386
Bloxwich	01922
Blubberhouses	01943
Blythburgh	01502
Blythe Bridge	01782
Blyth (Northumberland)	
Blyth (Notts)	01670
Boarhills	01909
3 figure numbers	0133488
6 figure numbers	01334
Boat of Garten	01479
Bobbington	01384

Bodenham
3/4 figure numbers	0156884
6 figure numbers	01568
Bodfari	01745
Bodmin	01208
Bodorgan	01407
Bognor Regis	01243
Bollington	01625
Bolney	01444
Bolton	01204
Bolton Abbey	01756
Bolton-by-Bowland	01200
Bomere Heath	01939

Bonawe
3 figure numbers	0163175
6 figure numbers	01631
Boncath	01239

Bonchester Bridge
3 figure numbers	0145086
6 figure numbers	01450
Bo'ness	01506
Bonnybridge	01324

Bontddu
3 figure numbers	0134149
6 figure numbers	01341
Bonvilston	01446
Bookham	01372
Bootle	01229
Bordon (Hants)	01420

Boreland
3 figure numbers	015766
6 figure numbers	01576

Borgue
3 figure numbers	015577
6 figure numbers	01557
Bornish	01878
Boroughbridge(Yorks)	01423
Borough Green	01732
Borrowdale	017687
Borth	01970

Borthwickbrae
3 figure numbers	0145088
6 figure numbers	01450

Borve
3 figure numbers	0185185
6 figure numbers	01851
Bosbury	01531
Boscastle	01840
Bosham (W. Sussex)	01243
Boston (Lincs)	01205
Boston Spa	01937
Bothwell	01698
Botley (Hants)	01489
Bottesford	01949

Botwnnog
3 figure numbers	0175883
6 figure numbers	01758
Bourne	01778
Bourne End (Bucks)	01628
Bournemouth	01202
Bourton (Dorset)	01747
Bovey Tracey	01626
Bow (Devon)	01363
Bowmansgreen	01727
Bowmore	01496

Boxford (Berks)
3/4 figure numbers	0148838
6 figure numbers	(see Kintbury
Boxford (Suffolk)	01787
Bracklesham Bay	01243
Brackley	01280
Bracknell	01344
Braco	01786
Bradenstoke	01249
Bradfield	01734
Bradford-on-Avon	01225
Bradford-on-Tone	01823
Bradford(W Yorks)	01274
Bradworthy	01409

Brae
3 figure numbers	0180622
6 figure numbers	01806

Braemar
5 figure numbers	013397
6 figure numbers	01339
Brailes	01608
Braintree	01376

Braishfield	01794
Braithwaite	017687
Bramdean	01962
Bramfield	
3 figure numbers	0198684
6 figure numbers	01986
Brampton (Cumbria)	016977
Brampton (Suffolk)	01502
Brancaster	01485
Brandon Creek	01353
Brandsby	01347
Branscombe	
3 figure numbers	0129780
6 figure numbers	01297
Bransgore	01425
Bratton Clovelly	
3 figure numbers	0183787
6 figure numbers	01837
Braunton	01271
Brayford	01598
Bready	01504
Brean Down	01278

Brechfa	01267
Brechin	01356
Brecon (Wales)	01874
Brede	01424
Brediland	01505
Bredon	01684
Brenchley	01892
Brendon (Devon)	
3 figure numbers	015987
6 figure numbers	01598
Brent Knoll	01278
Brent Pelham	01279
Brentwood	01277
Bressay	
3 figure numbers	0159582
6 figure numbers	01595
Bressingham	
3/4 figure numbers	0137988
6 figure numbers	01379
Brewood	01902
Bridestowe	
3 figure numbers	0183786

6 figure numbers	01837
Bridgemere	
3 figure numbers	019365
6 figure numbers	01270
Bridgend (Mid Glam)	01656
Bridge of Allan	01786
Bridge of Balgie	01887
Bridge of Cally	01250
Bridge of Dee	01556
Bridge of Dun	01674
Bridge of Earn	01738
Bridge of Gaur	01882
Bridge of Weir	01505
Bridge of Westfield	
3 figure numbers	0184787
6 figure numbers	01847
Bridgerule	
3 figure numbers	0128881
6 figure numbers	01288
Bridge Sollars	
3 figure numbers	0198122
6 figure numbers	01981

Bridgnorth	01746
Bridgwater	01278
Bridlington	01262
Bridport	01308
Brierley Hill	01384
Brigg	01652
Brighouse	01484
Brighting	
3 figure numbers	0142482
6 figure numbers	01424
Brightlingsea	01206
Brighton	01273
Brigstock	01536
Brill	01844
Brimfield	01584
Brinscall	01254
Bristol	0117
Briton Ferry	01639
Brixham	01803
Broadfield	01763
Broadford	01471
Broad Haven	01437

Place	Code
Broadhembury	
3 figure numbers	0140484
6 figure numbers	01404
Broadstone	01202
Broadway	01386
Broadwindsor	01308
Brock	01995
Brockton	
3 figure numbers	0174636
6 figure numbers	01746
Brodick	01770
Brodie	
3 figure numbers	013094
6 figure numbers	01309
Bromesberrow	01531
Bromfield	
3 figure numbers	0158477
6 figure numbers	01584
Brompton Regis	
3 figure numbers	013987
6 figure numbers	01398
Bromsgrove	01527
Bromyard	01885
Bronant	
3 figure numbers	0197421
6 figure numbers	01974
Brooke	01508
Brookeborough	013655
Brookland	01797
Brookwood	01483
Brora	01408
Brough (Cumbria)	017683
Broughshane	01266
Broughton-in-Furness	01229
Broughton (Peebles)	
3 figure numbers	018994
6 figure numbers	01899
Broughton (Preston)	01772
Brownhills	01543
Broxburn	01506
Broxton	01829
Bruton	01749
Bryneglwys	
3 figure numbers	0149085
6 figure numbers	01490
Brynmawr	01495
Brynsiencyn	01248
Buchlyvie	
3 figure numbers	0136085
6 figure numbers	01360
Buckfastleigh	01364
Buckhaven	01592
Buckie	01542
Buckingham	01280
Buckland Newton	01300
Buckland (Oxon)	
3 figure numbers	0136787
6 figure numbers	01367
Buckland St Mary	01460
Buckler's Hard	01590
Buckley	01244
Bucklow Hill	01565
Bucknell	
3 figure numbers	015474
6 figure numbers	01547
Bude	01288
Budleigh Salterton	01395
Builth Wells	01982
Bulls Green	01438
Bulwick	01780
Bunbury	01829
Bungay	01986
Bunwell	01953
Bures	01787
Burford	01993
Burgess Hill	01444
Burgh-by-Sands	01228
Burghclere	01635
Burghead	01343
Burghfield Common	01734
Burgh Heath	01737
Burgh-on-Bain	01507
Burleydam	01948
Burley (Hants)	01425
Burley-in-Wharfedale	01943
Burnham (Bucks)	01628
Burnham-on-Sea	01278
Burnley	01282

Burnopfield 01207
Burnsall 01756
Burnt Fen
3 figure numbers 0135375
6 figure numbers 01353
Burntisland 01592
Burntwood 01543
Burravoe 0195782
Burray 01957
3 figure numbers 0185673
6 figure numbers 01856
Burrelton
3 figure numbers 018287
6 figure numbers 01828
Burrowbridge (Somerset) 01823
Burry Port 01554
Burscough 01704
Bursledon 01703
Burton Agnes 01262

Burton Bradstock 01308
Burton (Cumbria) 01524
Burton Joyce 0115
Burton Latimer 01536
Burton-on-Trent 01283
Burwarton
3 figure numbers 0174633
6 figure numbers 01746
Burwash 01435
Bury 01798
Bury St Edmunds 01284
Burythorpe 01653
Bushmills (Co. Antrim) 012657
Buttermere 017687
Butterstone 01350
Buxted (East Sussex) 01825
Buxton (Derbys) 01298
Buxton (Norfolk) 01603
Bwlch 01874
Byfield 01327
Byfleet 01932

Bythorn 01832
C
Cabrach
3 figure numbers 0146689
6 figure numbers 01466
Caergwrle 01978
Caerleon 01633
Caernarfon 01286
Caerphilly 01222
Caersws (Powys) 01686
Caerwys (Clwyd) 01352
Cairndow
3 figure numbers 014996.
6 figure numbers 01499
Cairngorm 01479
Cairnie
3 figure numbers 0146687
6 figure numbers 01466
Cairnryan 01581
Caistor (Lincs) 01472
Caldbeck 016974
Caldercruix 01236

Caldicot 01291
Caledon 01861
Callander 01877
Callanish
3 figure numbers 0185172
6 figure numbers 01851
Calne (Wilts) 01249
Calthwaite 01768
Calverhall
3 figure numbers 0194876
6 figure numbers 01948
Calvine 01796
Camberley 01276
Camborne 01209
Cambridge 01223
Cambusnethan 01698
Cameford 01840
Campbeltown 01586
Campsie 01504
Camptown
3 figure numbers 018354
6 figure numbers 01835

Place	Code
Camrose	01437
Canford Cliffs	01202
Cannich	01456
Cannock	01543
Canonbie	
5 figure numbers	013873
6 figure numbers	01387
Canon Pyon	01432
Canterbury	01227
Canvey Island	01268
Canworthy Water	01566
Capel Bangor	
3 figure numbers	0197084
6 figure numbers	01970
Capel Curig	
3 figure numbers	016904
6 figure numbers	01690
Cappercleuch	01750
Caputh	
3 figure numbers	0173871
6 figure numbers	01738
Carbost	01478
Cardenden	01592
Cardiff	01222
Cardigan	01239
Cardinham	01208
Cardross	01389
Careston	01356
Carew	01646
Carey	01432
Carlisle	01228
Carloway	0185173
Carluke	
3 figure numbers	01851
6 figure numbers	01555
Carmarthen	01267
Carmyllie	01241
Carnan	01870
Carnforth	01524
Carnlough	01574
Carno (Mid Wales)	01686
Carnoustie	01241
Carnwath	01555
Carradale	
3 figure numbers	01533
6 figure numbers	01583
Carrbridge	01479
Carrickfergus	01960
Carrickmore	016627
Carron	01340
Carrutherstown	
3 figure numbers	0138784
6 figure numbers	01387
Carryduff	01232
Carsington (Derby)	
3 figure numbers	0162985
6 figure numbers	01629
Carsphairn	
3 figure numbers	016446
6 figure numbers	01644
Carstairs	01555
Carterton	01993
Cartmel	015395
Castlebay	01871
Castle Caereinion	
3 figure numbers	0193883
6 figure numbers	01938
Castle Cary	01963
Castle Combe	01249
Castledawson	01648
Castlederg	016626
Castle Douglas	01556
Castleford	01977
Castlemartin	01646
Castlereagh	01232
Castle Rising	01553
Castlerock	01265
Castleton (Gwent)	01633
Castletown (Caithness)	
3 figure numbers	0184782
6 figure numbers	10847
Castletown (Isle of Man)	01624
Castlewellan	013367
Caston	01953
Caterham	01883

Name	Code
Catforth	01772
Caton	01524
Catterline	01569
3 figure numbers	0163686
6 figure numbers	01636
Cawdor	01667
Caxton	01954
CELLNET	0802
CELLNET	0860
CELLNET	0850
Cemaes Bay	01407
Cemmaes Road	01650
Ceres	
3/4 figure numbers	0133482
6 figure numbers	01334
Cerne Abbas	01300
Cerrigydrudion	01490
Chaddesley Corbett	01562
Chaddleworth	01488
Chadlington	01608
Chagford	01647
Chalfont St Giles	01494
Challock	01233
Chandler's Ford	01703
Chapel End	01203
Chapel-en-le-Frith	01298
Chapelknowe	
5 figure numbers	013873
6 figure numbers	01387
Chapelton	
3 figure numbers	013573
6 figure numbers	01357
Chard	01460
Charing (Kent)	01233
Charlbury	01608
Charlton Mackrell	01458
Charlton Mires	
3 figure numbers	0166579
6 figure numbers	01665
Charlton-on-Otmoor	01865
Charmouth	01297
Charsfield	01608
Chart 3/4 figure numbers	0147337
6 figure numbers	01473
Chathill	
3 figure numbers	0166589
6 figure numbers	01665
Chatteris	01354
Chatton	
3 figure numbers	016685
6 figure numbers	01668
Cheadle	01538
Checkendon	01491
Cheddar	01934
Cheddington	01296
Chelford	01625
Chelmsford	01245
Cheltenham	01242
Chelwood Gate	01825
Chepstow	01291
Cheriton Bishop	01647
Cheriton Fitzpaine	01363
Chertsey	01932
Chesham (Bucks)	01494
Cheslyn Hay	01922
Chester	01244
Chesterfield	01246
Chestfield (Kent)	01227
Cheswardine	
3 figure numbers	0163086
6 figure numbers	01630
Chevington	01284
Chew Magna	01275
Chichester	01243
Chiddingly	01825
Chideock	01297
Chieveley	01635
Chilbolton	01264
Child Okeford	01258
Childrey	01235
Childs Ercall	
3 figure numbers	0195278
6 figure numbers	01952
Chillaton	
3 figure numbers	0182286
6 figure numbers	01822
Chilton Polden	01278

Chinley	01663
Chippenham	01249
Chipping	01995
Chipping Norton	01608
Chipping Sodbury	01454
Chipping Warden	01295
Chirbury	
3 figure numbers	0193872
6 figure numbers	01938
Chirk	01691
Chirnside	01890
Chiselborough	01935
Chislet	01227
Chittlehamholt	01769
Chivelstone	
3 figure numbers	0154851
6 figure numbers	01548
Chobham (Woking)	01276
Cholderton	
3 figure numbers	0198064
6 figure numbers	01980
Cholesbury	01494

Cholmondeley	01829
Cholsey (Wallingford)	01491
Chorley (Lancs)	01257
Chorleywood	01923
Christchurch (Cambs)	01354
Christchurch (Dorset)	01202
Christow	01647
Chudleigh	01626
Chulmleigh	01769
Churchill	01934
Church Minshull	01270
Churchstanton	01823
Churchstoke	01588
Church Stretton	01694
Churnet Side	01538
Churston	01803
Chute Standen	01264
Chwilog	01766
Cirencester	01285
Clachan	
3 figure numbers	018804
6 figure numbers	01880

Clacton-on-Sea	01255
Clanfield	
3 figure numbers	0136781
6 figure numbers	01367
Clapham (North Yorks)	015242
Clarbeston	01437
Clare	01787
Clarencefield	
3 figure numbers	0138787
6 figure numbers	01387
Claudy	01504
Claverdon	01926
Claverley	01746
Clawdd Newydd	01824
Clayhanger	
3 figure numbers	013986
6 figure numbers	01398
Cleator Moor	01946
Cleckheaton	01274
Cleethorpes	01472
Cleish Hills	01577

Cleland	01698
Cleobury Mortimer	01299
Clevedon	01275
Cleveleys	01253
Cley	01263
Clifford	01497
Clifton Campville	01827
Clifton Hampden	01865
Clipston	
3 figure numbers	0185886
6 figure numbers	01858
Clitheroe	01200
Clive	
3 figure numbers	0193928
6 figure numbers	01939
Clochan	01542
Clogher	0166 25
Clopton	01832
Cloughmills	0126 56
Clova	01575
Clovelly	01237

Place	Number
Clovenfords	0189685
3 figure numbers	
6 figure numbers	
Clows Top	01299
Clun	01588
Clunderwen	01437
Clydach	01792
Clynder	01436
Clynderwen (see Clunderwen)	
Clynnogfawr	01286
Coads Green	01566
Coagh	0164 87
Coalburn	01555
Coalisland	018687
5 figure numbers	
6 figure numbers	
Coalville	01530
Coatbridge	01236
Cobham (Surrey)	01932
Cockburnspath	01368
Cockermouth	01900
Cockfield Green	01284
Cockshutt	01939
Coddenham	
3 figure numbers	0144979
6 figure numbers	01449
Codsall	01902
Coggeshall	01376
Colaton Raleigh	01395
Colchester	01206
Coldingham	
5 figure numbers	018907
6 figure numbers	01890
Coldstream	01890
Coleraine	01265
Coleshill	01675
Colinsburgh	
3 figure numbers	0133334
6 figure numbers	01333
Colintraive	
3 figure numbers	0170084
6 figure numbers	01700
3 figure numbers	018793
6 figure numbers	01879
Collier Street	01892
Collieston	01358
Collin	
3 figure numbers	0138775
6 figure numbers	01387
Collingbourne Ducis	01264
Collingham Bridge	01937
Colmonell	
3 figure numbers	0146588
6 figure numbers	01465
Colmworth (Beds)	01234
Colne (Lancs)	01282
Colonsay	
3 figure numbers	019512
6 figure numbers	01951
Colpy	
3 figure numbers	014644
6 figure numbers	01464
Colwall	01684
Colwyn Bay	01492
Colyton	01297
Combe Martin	01271
Comber	01247
Comberbach	01606
Combwich	01278
Compton (Berks)	01635
Compton (W Sussex)	01705
Comrie	01764
Coneysthorpe	01653
Coney Weston	01359
Congleton	01260
Coningsby	01526
Coniston	015394
Connell	
3 figure numbers	0163171
6 figure numbers	01631
Consett	01207
Cooden (E Sussex)	01424
Cookstown	016487
Coolham	01403
Coombe Bissett	
3 figure numbers	0172277

6 figure numbers	01722	Corton Denham	01963
Copdock	01473	Corven	01490
Copplestone	01363	Cosham (Hants)	01705
Coppull	01257	Cotheridge	01905
Copthorne	01342	Cotswold	01451
Corby Glen	01476	Cottenham	01954
Corby (Northants)	01536	Cottered	01763
Corfe Castle	01929	Cotterstock	
Cornhill		*3 figure numbers*	018326
3 figure numbers	014666	*6 figure numbers*	01832
6 figure numbers	01466	Coulport	01436
Cornwood	01752	Coupar Angus	01828
Corpach	01397	Coventry	01203
Corrie	01770	Cowbridge	01446
Corringham (Lincs)	01427	Cowden	01342
Corris	01654	Cowdenbeath	01383
Corscombe	01935	Cowers Lane	01773
Corsham (Wilts)	01249	Cowfold	01403
Corsock		Coxtie Green	01277
3 figure numbers	016444	Coxwold	01347
6 figure numbers	01644	Cracoe	01756
Cortachy	01575	Craddock	01884

Cradley Heath	01384	Cranwell	01400
Crafts Hill	01954	Crathes	01330
Craigavon	01762	Crathie	
Craigie		*5 figure numbers*	013397
3 figure numbers	0156386	*6 figure numbers*	01339
6 figure numbers	01563	Craven Arms	01588
Craignure		Crawfordjohn	
3 figure numbers	016802	*3 figure numbers*	018644
6 figure numbers	01680	*6 figure numbers*	01864
Craigton	01575	Crawford (Lanark)	
Crail	01333	*3 figure numbers*	018642
Crailing		*6 figure numbers*	01864
3 figure numbers	018355	Crawley	01293
6 figure numbers	01835	Crayford	01322
Cramlington	01670	Creaton	
Cranborne	01725	*3 figure numbers*	0160124
Cranbrook	01580	*6 figure numbers*	01604
Cranford		Crediton	01363
3 figure numbers	0153678	Creetown	01671
6 figure numbers	01536	Cressage	01952
Cranleigh	01483	Crewe	01270
Crantock	01637	Crewkerne	01460

Place	Code
Crianlarich	01838
Criccieth	01766
Crick	01788
Crickhowell	01873
Crieff	01764
Crinan	
3 figure numbers	0154683
6 figure numbers	01546
Crocketford	01556
Croesgoch	01348
Croglin	01768
Cromarty	01381
Cromer	01263
Crookham	01890
Crooklands	015395
Crosby-on-Eden	01228
Cross	01504
Cross Ash	01873
Crossbost	
3 figure numbers	0185186
6 figure numbers	01851

Place	Code
Crossford	
3 figure numbers	0155586
6 figure numbers	01555
Crossgar	01396
Cross Hands	01269
Crosshill (Ayrshire)	
3 figure numbers	016554
6 figure numbers	01655
Cross Hills	01535
Cross Houses	01743
Cross Keys	01495
Crossmaglen	01693
Crossmichael	
3 figure numbers	0155667
6 figure numbers	01556
Crosswell	
3 figure numbers	0123979
6 figure numbers	01239
Crosswood	
3 figure numbers	019743
6 figure numbers	01974
Crosthwaite	015395

Place	Code
Croston (Lancs)	01772
Croughton	01869
Crowborough	01892
Crowcombe	
3 figure numbers	019848
6 figure numbers	01984
Crowhurst	01424
Crowthorne	01344
Croxton (Cambs)	01480
Croy	01667
Croyde	01271
Crucorney	01873
Cruden Bay	01779
Crumlin	01849
Crymych	01239
Crynant	01639
Cuffley	01707
Culbokie	
3 figure numbers	0134987
6 figure numbers	01349
Culcheth	01925
Culford	01284

Place	Code
Culgaith	01768
Cullen	01542
Cullingworth	01535
Cullompton	01884
Cullybackey	01266
Culverthorpe	
3 figure numbers	015295
6 figure numbers	01529
Cumbernauld	01236
Cuminestown	
3 figure numbers	018883
6 figure numbers	01888
Cummertrees	01461
Cumnock	01290
Cunningsburgh	
3 figure numbers	019503
6 figure numbers	01950
Cupar (Fife)	01334
Curdworth	01675
Cushendall	012667
Cushendun	012667
Cutnall Green	01299

Cwm	01495
Cwmbran	01633
Cwrtnewydd	01570
Cyffylliog	
3 figure numbers	018246
6 figure numbers	01824
Cymmer	01639
Cynghordy	
3 figure numbers	015505
6 figure numbers	01550
Cynwyl Elfed	01267
D	
Dailly	
3 figure numbers	0146581
6 figure numbers	01465
Dalbeattie	01556
Dalchreichart	
3 figure numbers	01320
6 figure numbers	01646
Dale	01383
Dalgety Bay	
Dallas	
3 figure numbers	0134389
6 figure numbers	01343

Dalleagles	
3 figure numbers	0129081
6 figure numbers	01290
Dalmally	01838
Dalmellington	01292
Dalnawillan (see Westerdale)	
Dalry (Ayrshire)	01294
Dalry (Kircuds)	
3 figure numbers	016443
6 figure numbers	01644
Dalrymple	
3 figure numbers	0129256
6 figure numbers	01292
Dalston (Cumbria)	01228
Dalton-in-Furness	01229
Dalwhinnie	
3 figure numbers	015282
6 figure numbers	01528
Danbury (Essex)	01245
Dane End	01920
Danehill	01825
Dapple Heath	01889

Darlington	01325
Dartford (Kent)	01322
Dartmouth	01803
Darvel	01560
Darwen	01254
Daventry	01327
Daviot	01463
Dawes Green	01306
Dawlish	01626
Deal	01304
Dean	01594
Debenham	01728
Dechmont	01506
Deddington	01869
Deepcut	01252
Deeping St Nicholas	
3 figure numbers	0177588
6 figure numbers	01775
Deerness	
3 figure numbers	0185674
6 figure numbers	01856
Deeside	01244

Denbigh	01745
Denham (Bucks)	01895
Denholm	
3 figure numbers	0145087
6 figure numbers	01450
Denny	01324
Dent	015396
Derby	01332
Dereham	01362
Derryadd	01762
Derrygonnelly	013656
Derrylin	013657
Dersingham	01485
Dervaig	
3 figure numbers	016884
6 figure numbers	01688
Dervock (Co Antrim)	012657
Desford	01455
Dethick	01629
Devizes	01380
Dewsbury	01924

Place	Code
Diabaig	
3 figure numbers	0144581
6 figure numbers	01445
Didcot	01235
Dinas Cross	
3 figure numbers	0134 86
6 figure numbers	01348
Dinas Mawddwy	01650
Dinas Powys	0222
Dingestow	
3 figure numbers	0160083
6 figure numbers	01600
Dingley	01858
Dingwall	01349
Dinnington	01909
Dinsdale	01325
Dipton	01207
Dirleton	
3 figure numbers	0162085
6 figure numbers	01620
Disley	01663
Diss	01379
Ditcheat	01749
Dittisham	01803
Ditton Priors	
3 figure numbers	0174 634
6 figure numbers	01746
Dochgarroch	
3 figure numbers	0146386
6 figure numbers	01463
Docking	01485
Doddington (Kent)	
3 figure numbers	0179586
6 figure numbers	01795
Dolgarrog	01492
Dolgellau	01341
Dollar	01259
Dolphinton	01968
Dolton	
3 figure numbers	018054
6 figure numbers	01805
Dolwen	
3 figure numbers	0149260
6 figure numbers	01492
Dolwyddelan	
3 figure numbers	016906
6 figure numbers	01690
Donaghadee	01247
Donaghmore	01868
Doncaster	01302
Donhead	01747
Dorchester	01305
Dores	
3 figure numbers	0146375
6 figure numbers	01463
Dorking	01306
Dormans Park	01342
Dornie (Kyle)	
3 figure numbers	0159985
6 figure numbers	01599
Dornoch	01862
Dorrington	01743
Douglas (Isle of Man)	01624
Douglas (Lanarks)	01555
Douglas Water	01555
Doune	01786
Dover	01304
Downderry	
3 figure numbers	015035
6 figure numbers	01503
Downham Market	01366
Downham	01737
Downpatrick	01396
Downton	01725
Draperstown	01648
Draycott	01332
Drewsteignton	01647
Driffield	01377
Drinnishadder	01859
Drochil Castle	01721
Droitwich	01905
Dromara	01238
Dromore (Co Down)	01846
Dromore (Co Tyrone)	01662
Dronfield	01246
Drongan	01292
Droxford	01489

Drumbeg	
3 figure numbers	015713
6 figure numbers	01571
Drumblade	
3 figure numbers	0146684
6 figure numbers	01466
Drumbo	01232
Drumchardine	01463
Drumclog	01357
Drumlithie	01569
Drummore	01776
Drummuir	01542
Drumnadrochit	01456
Drumoak	01330
Drumquin	01662
Drybridge	01563
Drymen	01360
Dryslwyn	01558
Duddington (Stamford)	
3 figure numbers	0178083
6 figure numbers	01780

Dudleston Heath	
3 figure numbers	0169175
6 figure numbers	01691
Dudley (Wt Midlands)	01384
Dufftown	01340
Dulnain Bridge	01479
Dulverton	01398
Dumbarton	01389
Dumfries	01387
Dummer	01256
Dunamanagh	01504
Dunbar	01368
Dunbeath	
3 figure numbers	015933
6 figure numbers	01593
Dunblane	01786
Dundee	01382
Dundonald	01232
Dundonnell	
3 figure numbers	0185483
6 figure numbers	01854
Dundrennan	01557

Dundrod	01232
Dundrum (Co Down)	013967
Dunecht	013306
3 figure numbers	01330
6 figure numbers	01383
Dunfermline	
Dungannon	
5 figure numbers	0186 87
6 figure numbers	01868
Dungiven	015047
Dunham-on-Trent	01777
Dunkeld	01350
Dunloy (Co. Antrim)	012656
Dunning	01764
Dunoon	01369
Dunphail	01309
Dunragit	01581
Duns	01361

Dunsop Bridge	01200
Dunstable	01582
Dunster	01643
Dunsyre	
3 figure numbers	0189981
6 figure numbers	01899
Duntocher	01389
Duntulm	
3 figure numbers	0147052
6 figure numbers	01470
Dunure	
3 figure numbers	0129250
6 figure numbers	01292
Dunvegan	
3 figure numbers	0147022
6 figure numbers	01470
Durham	0191
Durisdeer	
3 figure numbers	018485
6 figure numbers	01848
Durley (Hants)	01489
Durness	01971

Place	Code
Duror	
3 figure numbers	0163174
6 figure numbers	01631
Durrington Walls	01980
Dursley (Glos)	01453
Dyffryn	01341
Dymchurch	01303
Dymock	01531
Dyserth	01745
E	
Eaglescliffe	01642
Eaglesham	
4 figure numbers	013553
6 figure numbers	01355
Earby	01282
Eardisley	01544
Eardiston	
3 figure numbers	0158470
6 figure numbers	01584
Earls Colne	01787
Earl Shilton	01455
Earl Soham	01728
Earlston	
3/4 figure numbers	0189684
6 figure numbers	01896
Earlswood	01564
Easingwold	01347
East Allington	01548
Eastbourne	01323
East Bridgford	01949
Eastchurch	01795
East Dean	01323
East End	
3 figure numbers	0159065
6 figure numbers	01590
Eastergate	01243
East Grinstead	01342
East Harling	01953
East Harlsey	01609
East Horsley (Surrey)	01483
East Ilsley	01635
East Kilbride	
5 figure numbers	013552
6 figure numbers	01355
East Kirkby (Lincs)	01790
East Knoyle	01747
East Langton	
3 figure numbers	0185884
6 figure numbers	01858
East Leake	01509
Eastleigh	01703
Eastling	01795
East Linton	01620
East Marden	
3 figure numbers	0124359
6 figure numbers	01243
East Meon	01730
Eastoft	01724
East Peckham	01622
Eastriggs	01461
East Rudham	01485
East Stoke	01636
East Stour	01747
Eaton Bray	01525
Ebbw Vale	01495
Ebchester	01207
Ecclefechan	01576
Eccleshall	01785
Eccleston	01257
Eckington (Derbys)	01246
Eday	
3 figure numbers	018572
6 figure numbers	01857
Edderton	
3 figure numbers	0186282
6 figure numbers	01862
Eddleston	01721
Eden (Banff)	
3 figure numbers	012616
6 figure numbers	01261
Edenbridge	01732
Edenham	
3 figure numbers	0177832
6 figure numbers	01778
Edge Hill	01295
Edinbane	0147082
6 figure numbers	01470

Name	Code
Edinburgh	0131
Edmundbyers	01207
Edzell	01356
Egerton (Kent)	
3 figure numbers	0123376
6 figure numbers	01233
Egham	01784
Eglinton	01504
Embleton (Northumberland)	01665
Egremont	01946
Elgin	01343
Elham (Kent)	01303
Elie (Fife)	01333
Ellastone	01335
Ellesmere (Shrops)	01691
Ellon	01358
Elmham	01362
Elmley Castle	01386
Elmsted (Kent)	01233
Elmswell	01359
Elstead (Surrey)	01252
Elsworth	01954
Elvanfoot	
3 figure numbers	018645
6 figure numbers	01864
Elveden	01842
Elvington	01904
Ely (Cambs)	01353
Empingham	01780
Emsworth	01243
Enniskillen	01365
Epping	01992
Epsom	01372
Epworth	01427
Eriskay	01878
Erith (Kent)	01322
Errol	01821
Erwood	01982
Escrick	01904
Esher	01372
Eskdale	019467
Eskdalemuir	
5 figure numbers	013873
6 figure numbers	01387
Essendy	01250
Eston Grange	01642
Etchingham	01580
Ettrick Bridge	01750
Ettrick Valley	01750
Etwall	01283
Evanton	01349
Evercreech	01749
Evershot	01935
Eversley	01734
Evesham	01386
Evie	
3 figure numbers	185675
6 figure numbers	01856
Exbourne	
3 figure numbers	183785
6 figure numbers	01837
Exeter	01392
Exford	
3 figure numbers	0164383
6 figure numbers	01643
Exmouth	01395
Exning	01638
Eyemouth	
5 figure numbers	018907
6 figure numbers	01890
Eye (Suffolk)	01379
Eyke	01394
F	
Faddiley	
3 figure numbers	0127074
6 figure numbers	01270
Fairbourne	01341
Fair Isle	
3 figure numbers	013512
6 figure numbers	01595
Fairlie	01475
Fairseat	01732
Fakenham	01328
Falfield	01454

Falkirk	**01324**
Falkland (Fife)	**01337**
Falmouth	**01326**
Fareham (Hants)	**01329**
Faringdon	**01367**
Farley	
3 figure numbers	**0172272**
6 figure numbers	**01722**
Farnborough (Banbury)	
3 figure numbers	**0129 589**
6 figure numbers	**01295**
Farnborough (Hants)	**01252**
Farnborough (Kent)	**01689**
Farndon (Chester)	**01829**
Farnell	**01674**
Farnham Common (Bucks)	**01753**
Farnham (Surrey)	**01252**
Farningham	**01322**
Farnworth	**01204**
Farr	
3 figure numbers	**018083**
6 figure numbers	**01808**
Farway	
3 figure numbers	**0140487**
6 figure numbers	**01404**
Fauldhouse	**01501**
Faversham	**01795**
Fawley (Hants)	**01703**
Faygate	**01293**
Fearn (Ross-shire)	**01862**
Feeny	**015047**
Felixstowe	**01394**
Felton (Northumberland)	**0670**
Feltwell	**01842**
Fenny Compton	**01295**
Fenton Claypole	**01636**
Fenwick	**01560**
Fern (Angus)	**01356**
Ferndale	**01443**
Ferndown	**01202**
Ferryhill	**01740**
Ferryside	**01267**
Fetlar	
3 figure numbers	**0195783**
6 figure numbers	**01957**
Fettercairn	**01561**
Feughside	**01330**
Ffestiniog	
4 figure numbers	**0176676**
6 figure numbers	**01766**
Field	**01889**
Filleigh	**01598**
Fillongley	**01676**
Finavon	**01307**
Fincham	**01366**
Findhorn	**01309**
Findon	**01903**
Finmere	**01280**
Finstown	
3 figure numbers	**0185676**
6 figure numbers	**01856**
Fintona	**01662**
Fintry	
3 figure numbers	**0136086**
6 figure numbers	**01360**
Fionnphort	
3 figure numbers	**016817**
6 figure numbers	**01681**
Fishguard	**01348**
Fittleworth	
3 figure numbers	**0179882**
6 figure numbers	**01798**
Fivemiletown	**013655**
Fiveways	**01563**
Flax Bourton	**01275**
Flaxton Moor	**01904**
Fleet (Hants)	**01252**
Fleetwood	**01253**
Fleggburgh	**01493**
Flimwell	
3 figure numbers	**0158087**
6 figure numbers	**01580**
Flint	**01352**
Flitwick	**01525**
Flookburgh	**015395**
Florencecourt	**01365**

Place	Code
Fochabers	01343
Folkestone	01303
Folkingham	
3 figure numbers	015297
6 figure numbers	01529
Fontmell Magna	01747
Fordcombe	01892
Forden	01938
Fordingbridge	01425
Ford (Lochgilphead)	
3 figure numbers	0154681
6 figure numbers	01546
Ford (Midlothian)	01875
Foreside	01307
Forest Green	01306
Forest Row	01342
Forfar	01307
Forgue	
3 figure numbers	0146682
6 figure numbers	01466
Forkhill	01693
Formby	01704
Forres	01309
Forss	01847
Fort Augustus	01320
Forth	01555
Forton	01524
Fortrose	01381
Fort William	01397
Fosdyke	
3 figure numbers	0120585
6 figure numbers	01205
Fossoway	01577
Foula	
4 figure numbers	013933
6 figure numbers	01595
Foulsham	
3/4 figure numbers	0136284
6 figure numbers	01362
Fountainhall	01578
Four Elms	01732
Fovant	01722
Fowey	01726
Fowlmere	01763
Fownhope	01432
Framfield	01825
Framingham Earl	01508
Framingham	01728
Frant	01892
Fraserburgh	01346
Freckleton	01772
Freeland	01993
Frensham	01252
Fressingfield	
3/4 figure numbers	0137986
6 figure numbers	01379
Frilford Heath	01865
Frinton-on-Sea	01255
Friockheim	01241
Friskney	01754
Frittenden	
3 figure numbers	0158080
6 figure numbers	01580
Fritton	01493
Frodsham	01928
Frogmore	01548
Frome	01373
Fulmer	01753
Fulstow	01507
Fundenhall	01508
Furnace (Argyll)	
3 figure numbers	01495
6 figure numbers	01499
Furnace End	01675
Fyfield	01277
Fyvie	01651

G

Place	Code
Gaerwen	01248
Gainsborough	01427
Gairloch	01445
Galashiels	01896
Galgate	01524
Galston	01563
Gamlingay	01767
Gamston	01777
Ganllwyd	
3 figure numbers	0134140
6 figure numbers	01341

Gara Bridge — 01548
Garboldisham
- 3/4 figure numbers — 0195381
- 6 figure numbers — 01953

Gardenstown — 01261
Garelochhead — 01436
Gargunnock — 01786
Garlieston — 01988
Garn Dolbenmaen
- 3 figure numbers — 0176675
- 6 figure numbers — 01766

Garrabost — 01851
Garsington — 01865
Garstang — 01995
Garston — 01923
Gartly
- 3 figure numbers — 0146688
- 6 figure numbers — 01466

Gartocharn
- 3 figure numbers — 0138983
- 6 figure numbers — 01389

Garvagh — 012665

Garvald
- 3 figure numbers — 0162083
- 6 figure numbers — 01620

Garve — 01997
Gask
- 3 figure numbers — 0173873
- 6 figure numbers — 01738

Gatehouse — 01557
Gatwick — 01293
Gauldry
- 3 figure numbers — 0182624
- 6 figure numbers — 01382

Gayton — 01553
Gedney Drove End
- 3 figure numbers — 014408
- 6 figure numbers — 01406

Gerrards Cross — 01753
Gifford (East Lothian)
- 3 figure numbers — 0162081
- 6 figure numbers — 01620

Gigha
- 3 figure numbers — 015835
- 6 figure numbers — 01583

Gifford (Co. Armagh) — 01762
Gillingham (Dorset) — 01747
Gillock
- 3 figure numbers — 0195586
- 6 figure numbers — 01955

Gilsland — 016977
Gilwern — 01873
Girvan — 01465
Gisburn — 01200
Gladestry
- 3 figure numbers — 0154422
- 6 figure numbers — 01544

Glamis — 01307
Glandyfi — 01654
Glantawe — 01639
Glarryford — 01266
Glasbury — 01497
Glasgow — 0141
Glass
- 3 figure numbers — 0146685
- 6 figure numbers — 01466

Glastonbury — 01458
Glemsford — 01787
Glenalmond
- 3 figure numbers — 0173888
- 6 figure numbers — 01738

Glenanne — 01861
Glenarm — 01574
Glenbarr
- 3 figure numbers — 015832
- 6 figure numbers — 01583

Glenboig — 01236
Glenborrodale
- 3 figure numbers — 019724
- 6 figure numbers — 01972

Glencaple
- 3 figure numbers — 0138777
- 6 figure numbers — 01387

Glencarse
- 3 figure numbers — 0173886
- 6 figure numbers — 01738

Glendale
- 3 figure numbers — 0147081

Place	Code
6 figure numbers	01470
Glendaruel	
3 figure numbers	0136982
6 figure numbers	01369
Glenelg	
3 figure numbers	0159982
6 figure numbers	01599
Glenfarg	01577
Glenferness	01309
Glengormley	01232
Glenisla	01575
Glenkindie	
5 figure numbers	019756
6 figure numbers	01975
Glenlivet	
3 figure numbers	018073
6 figure numbers	01807
Glenluce	01581
Glenlyon	01887
Glenmazeran	
3 figure numbers	018084
6 figure numbers	01808
Glenmoriston	01320
Glenridding	017684
Glenrothes	01592
Glenshee	01250
Glenshiel	
3 figure numbers	059981
6 figure numbers	01599
Glenurquhart	01456
Glenwherry	
3 figure numbers	0126683
6 figure numbers	01266
Glossop	01457
Gloucester	01452
Glyn Ceiriog	01691
Glynde	01273
Glyndwr	
3 figure numbers	0149083
6 figure numbers	01490
Glyn Neath	01873
Gobion	01483
Godalming	01883
Godstone	01808
Golden Valley	01981
Golspie	01408
Good Easter	01245
Gooderstone	01366
Goole	01405
Gordon	01573
Gorebridge	01875
Goring-on-Thames	01491
Gorseinon	01792
Gorsley	
3 figure numbers	0198982
6 figure numbers	01989
Gorthleck	01456
Gortin	016626
Gosforth (Cumbria)	0194 67
Gosport (Hants)	01705
Gott	
3 figure numbers	0159584
6 figure numbers	01595
Goudhurst	01580
Gourock	01475
Gowanbank	01241
Gower	01792
Gowerton	01792
Graffham	
3 figure numbers	017986
6 figure numbers	01798
Grange	01542
Grangemouth	01324
Grange-over-Sands	015395
Grantham	01476
Grantown-on-Spey	01479
Grantshouse	
3 figure numbers	013615
6 figure numbers	01361
Grasmere	0153 94
Grassington	01756
Grateley	01264
Gravesend	01474
Gravir	
3 figure numbers	0185188
6 figure numbers	01851
Grayrigg	01539
Grays Thurrock	01375

Great Alne	01789
Great Ayton	01642
Great Barton	
3/4 figure numbers	0128487
6 figure numbers	01284
Great Bentley	01206
Great Bernera	
3 figure numbers	0185174
6 figure numbers	01851
Great Bolas	01952
Great Brickhill	01525
Great Chatwell	01952
Great Cressingham	01760
Great Cubley	01335
Great Dunmow	01371
Great Easton	01371
Great Eccleston	01995
Greatford	01778
Great Glen	01533
Great Gransden	01767
Great Harwood	01254
Great Hockham	01953

Great Hormead	01763
Great Longstone	01629
Great Massingham	01485
Great Milton	01844
Great Missenden	01494
Great Mollington	01244
Great Oakley	01536
Great Ponton	
3 figure numbers	0147683
6 figure numbers	01476
Great Ryburgh	
3 figure numbers	0132878
6 figure numbers	01328
Great Sampford	01799
Great Shefford	01488
Great Smeaton	01609
Great Tew	01608
Great Wenham	01473
Great Witley	01299
Great Yarmouth	01493
Great Yeldham	01787
Greengairs	01236

Greenham	01823
Greenhithe	01322
Greenlaw	
3 figure numbers	013616
6 figure numbers	01361
Greenock	01475
Greenodd	01229
Grendon Underwood	01296
Gresford	01978
Gretna	01461
Greyabbey	012477
Greystoke	017684
Grimsby	01472
Grogarry	01870
Grundisburgh	01473
Guernsey	01481
Guildford	01483
Guilsfield	
3 figure numbers	0193875
6 figure numbers	01938
Guisborough (Cleveland)	01287

Guiseley	01943
Gullane	01620
Gutcher	
3 figure numbers	0195784
6 figure numbers	01957
Guyhirn	01945
Gwalchmai	01407
Gwynfe	
3 figure numbers	015504
6 figure numbers	10550
H	
Hackthorpe	01931
Haddenham (Bucks)	01844
Haddington	
4 figure numbers	0162082
6 figure numbers	01620
Hadleigh	01473
Hadlow Down(East Sussex)	01825
Hadlow (Kent)	01732
Hadnall	01939
Hagley	01562

Haverfordwest	01437	Hazelbury Bryan	01258	Helmsley	01439	Hevingham	01603
Haverhill	01440	Heacham	01485	Helsby	01928	Hexham	01434
Havering	01708	Headcorn	01622	Helston	01326	Heysham	01524
Hawarden	01244	Headley Down (Hants)		Hemel Hempstead	01442	Heywood	01706
Hawick	01450	Headley (Newbury)	01428	Hempnall	01508	Hickling	01692
Hawkchurch	01297	Heath and Reach	01635	Hemswell	01427	Higham	
Hawkedon		Heathfield	01525	Hemsworth	01977	*3 figure numbers*	0120637
3 figure numbers	0128489	Heath Hayes	01435	Hemyock	01823	*6 figure numbers*	01206
6 figure numbers	01284	Hebden Bridge	01543	Henfield	01273	High Bickington	01769
Hawkhurst	01580	Hebron	01422	Hengoed	01443	Highclere	01635
Hawkinge	01303	Heckfield	01994	Henlade	01823	Highcliffe	01425
Hawkley	01730	Heckmondwike	01734	Henley-in-Arden	01564	High Ercall	01952
Hawkshead	0153 94	Hedingham	01924	Henley-on-Thames	01491	High Halden	01233
Haworth	01535	Hednesford	01535	Hereford	01432	Highley	01746
Haxey	01427	Helens Bay	01543	Heriot	01875	High Wycombe	01494
Hayle	01736	Helensburgh	01247	Hermitage	01635	Hildenborough	01732
Hayling Island	01705	Hellifield	01436	Herne Bay	01227	Hilderstone	01889
Haynes (Beds)	01234	Helmingham	01729	Herriard	01256	Hillington	01485
Hay-on-Wye	01497	Helmsdale	01473	Herstmonceux	01323	Hillsborough	01846
Hayton (Cumbria)	01228	*3 figure numbers*	014312	Hertford	01992	Hillside	01674
Haytor	01364	*6 figure numbers*	01431	Hesketh Bank	01772	Hillswick	
Haywards Heath	01444			Hest Bank	01524	*3 figure numbers*	0180623

33

6 figure numbers	01806
Hilmarton	01249
Himbleton	
3 figure numbers	0190569
Hinckley	01905
Hindhead (Surrey)	01455
	01428
Hindon	01747
Hintlesham	01473
Hirwaun	01685
Hitchin	01462
Hoar Cross	
3 figure numbers	0128375
6 figure numbers	01283
Hoddesdon	01992
Hodnet	01630
Hoghton	01254
Holbeach	01406
Holbeach St John	01406
Holbeach St Marks	
3 figure numbers	0140632
6 figure numbers	01406
Holbeton	01752
Holbrook	01473
Holford	01278
Hollington	
3 figure numbers	0188926
6 figure numbers	01889
Holm	
3 figure numbers	0185678
6 figure numbers	01856
Holme Hale	01760
Holme Lacy	01432
Holme (Norfolk)	
3 figure numbers	0148525
6 figure numbers	01485
Holmes Chapel	01477
Holmfirth	01484
Holmrook	019467
Holnest	01963
Holsworthy	01409
Holt (Norfolk)	01263
Holyhead	01407
Holytown	01698
Holywell	01352
Holywood	01232
Homersfield	
3/4 figure numbers	0198686
6 figure numbers	01986
Honington (Suffolk)	01359
Honiton	01404
Hook (Hants)	01256
Hook Norton	01608
Hopeman	01343
Hope Valley	01433
Horam Road	01435
Horley	01293
Hornby	015242
Horncastle	01507
Hornchurch	01708
Horndean	01705
Horning	01692
Horns Cross	01237
Hornsea	01964
Horringer	01284
Horsham (West Sussex)	01403
	01526
Horsington	
Horton-in-Ribblesdale	01729
Horwich (Lancs)	01204
Hovingham	01653
How Caple	
3 figure numbers	0198886
6 figure numbers	01989
Howden	01430
Hoxne	
3/4 figure numbers	0137975
6 figure numbers	01379
Hoy	
3 figure numbers	0185679
6 figure numbers	01856
Hubberts Bridge	01205
Huddersfield	01484
Hull	01482
Humbie	01875
Hundon (Suffolk)	01440
Hundred House	01982

Name	Code
Hungarton	01533
Hungerford	01488
Hunstanton	01485
Huntingdon	01480
Huntly	01466
Hunton (Kent)	01622
Hursley	01962
Hurstbourne Tarrant	
3 figure numbers	0126476
6 figure numbers	01264
Hurst Green	01580
Hurstpierpoint	01273
Huttoft	01507
Huxley	01829
Hythe (Hants)	01703
Hythe (Kent)	01303

I

Name	Code
Ibstock	01530
Ickford	01844
Ide Hill	01732
Iden	01797
Idmiston	01980
Ilchester	01935
Ilfracombe	01271
Ilkeston	01115
Ilketshall	01986
Ilkley	01943
Ilmington	01608
Ilminster	01460
Immingham	01469
Inchture	01828
Ingatestone	01277
Ingleton (North Yorks)	015242
Ingoldsby	01476
Ingrebourne	01708
Inkberrow	01386
Inkpen	01488
Innellan	
3 figure numbers	0136983
6 figure numbers	01369
Innerleithen	01896
Innerwick	01368
Insch	01464
Instow	01271
Inverallochy	01346
Inveraray	01499
Inverarity	01307
Inverbervie	01561
Invergarry	
3 figure numbers	018093
6 figure numbers	01809
Invergordon	01349
Inverkeilor	01241
Inverkeithing	01383
Inverness	01463
Invershin	01476
Inversnaid	
3 figure numbers	0154982
6 figure numbers	01549
Inveruglas	01877
Inverurie	
3 figure numbers	013014
6 figure numbers	01301
Iona	016817
Ipplepen	01803
Ipstones	01538
Ipswich	01473
Ironbridge	01952
Irvine	01294
Irvinestown	013656
Isfield	01825
Islandmagee	01960
Isle Brewers	01460
Isle of Man	01624
Isle of Wight	01983
Isle Ornsay	
3 figure numbers	014713
6 figure numbers	01471
Itchen Abbas	01962
Iver	01753
Ivington	
3 figure numbers	0156688
6 figure numbers	01568

J

Name	Code
Jedburgh	01835
Jerrettspass	01693

Jersey (5 & 6 fig nos)	01534
John O'Groats	
3 figure numbers	0195581
6 figure numbers	01955
Johnston (Dyfed)	01437
Johnstone Bridge	
3 figure numbers	015764
6 figure numbers	01576
Johnstone (Renfrew)	01505
Joppa	01292
Jura	
K	
3 figure numbers	0149682
6 figure numbers	01496
Katesbridge	018206
Keady	01861
Kegworth	01509
Keighley	01535
Keiss	
3 figure numbers	0195583
6 figure numbers	01955

Keith	01542
Kellas (Angus)	
3 figure numbers	0182625
6 figure numbers	01382
Kellaways	01249
Kells	01266
Kelsall (Chester)	01829
Kelshall (Herts)	01763
Kelso	01573
Kelty	01383
Kelvedon	01376
Kemnay	01467
Kendal	01539
Kenfig Hill	01656
Kenilworth	01926
Kenmore	01887
Kennethmont	
3 figure numbers	014643
6 figure numbers	01464
Kennoway	01333
Kentisbeare	
3 figure numbers	018846

6 figure numbers	01884
Keresley (Coventry)	01203
Kerry	01686
Kesh	013656
Kessock	
3 figure numbers	0146373
6 figure numbers	01463
Keswick	017687
Kettering	01536
Kettleholm	
6 figure numbers	015765
Kettlewell	01756
Kibworth	01533
Kidderminster	01562
Kidlington	01865
Kidmore End	01734
Kidwelly	01554
Kilbarchan	01505
Kilbirnie	01505
Kilchattan Bay	
3 figure numbers	0170083

6 figure numbers	01700
Kilchoan	
3 figure numbers	019723
6 figure numbers	01972
Kilchrennan	
3 figure numbers	018663
6 figure numbers	01866
Kilcreggan	
4 figure numbers	0143684
6 figure numbers	01436
Kildary	01862
Kildonan	01770
Kildrummy	
5 figure numbers	019755
6 figure numbers	01975
Kilfinan	
3 figure numbers	0170082
6 figure numbers	01700
Kilham	01262
Kilkeel	016937
Kilkenzie	
3 figure numbers	0158682

6 figure numbers	01586
Kilkhampton	0128882
3 figure numbers	01288
6 figure numbers	01360
Killearn	01360
Killeavy	01693
Killilan	
3 figure numbers	0159988
6 figure numbers	01599
Kilin	01567
Killinchy	01238
Killingholme	01469
Killyleagh	01396
Kilmacolm	01505
Kilmarnock	01563
Kilmartin	015465
3 figure numbers	01546
6 figure numbers	
Kilmelford	018522
3 figure numbers	01852
6 figure numbers	

Kilmore	0163177
3 figure numbers	01631
6 figure numbers	
Kilmun	0136984
3 figure numbers	01369
6 figure numbers	
Kilninver	
3 figure numbers	018526
6 figure numbers	01852
Kilrea	012665
Kilsyth	01236
Kiltarlity	
3 figure numbers	0146374
6 figure numbers	01463
Kilwinning	01294
Kimpton	01438
Kinbrace	
3 figure numbers	014313
6 figure numbers	01431
Kincardine	01259
Kincardine O'Neil	
5 figure numbers	013398

6 figure numbers	01339
Kincraig	01540
Kineton (Warwicks)	01926
Kingairloch	
3 figure numbers	0196783
6 figure numbers	01967
King Edward	01888
Kingham	01608
Kinghorn	01592
Kinglassie	01592
Kingsbridge	01548
Kingsclere	01635
Kings Cliffe	01780
Kingshouse	
3 figure numbers	018556
6 figure numbers	01855
Kingskerswell	01803
Kingsland	01568
Kings Langley(Herts)	01923
Kingsley	01928
Kings Lynn	01553
Kingston Blount	01844

Kingston St Mary	01823
Kingswear	01803
Kingswinford	01384
Kington	01544
Kingussie	01540
Kinlet	
3 figure numbers	0129924
6 figure numbers	01299
Kinlochard	01877
Kinlochbervie	01971
Kinlocheil	01397
Kinlochewe	
3 figure numbers	0144584
6 figure numbers	01445
Kinlochleven	
3 figure numbers	018554
6 figure numbers	01855
Kinloch Rannoch	01882
Kinlochspelve	
3 figure numbers	016804
6 figure numbers	01680
Kinnerton (Chester)	01244

Kinoulton	01949
Kinross	01577
Kinrossie	01821
Kintbury	01488
Kintore	01467
Kinver	01384
Kippen	01786
Kippford	
3 figure numbers	0155662
6 figure numbers	01556
Kirby Cane	01508
Kirby Misperton	01653
Kircubbin	012477
Kirdford	01403
Kirk Andreas (Isle of Man)	01624
Kirkbean	
3 figure numbers	0138788
6 figure numbers	01387
Kirkbride (Carlisle)	016973
Kirkby-in-Furness	01229
Kirkby Lonsdale	015242

Kirkby Malzeard	01765
Kirkbymoorside	01751
Kirkby Stephen	017683
Kirkby Thore	017683
Kirkcaldy	01592
Kirkcolm	01776
Kirkconnel	01659
Kirkcowan	01671
Kirkcudbright	01557
Kirkgunzeon	
3 figure numbers	0138776
6 figure numbers	01387
Kirkham	01772
Kirkinner	01988
Kirk Langley	01332
Kirklinton	01228
Kirkmichael (Ayrshire)	
3 figure numbers	016555
6 figure numbers	01655
Kirk Michael (Isle of Man)	01624

Kirkoswald	
3 figure numbers	016556
6 figure numbers	01655
Kirkpatrick Durham	
3 figure numbers	0155665
6 figure numbers	01556
Kirkpatrick Fleming	01461
Kirkton Manor	01721
Kirkwall	01856
Kirriemuir	01575
Kirtlebridge	01461
Kirton Lindsey	01652
Kirton (Suffolk)	
3 figure numbers	013948
6 figure numbers	01394
Kishorn	
3 figure numbers	015203
6 figure numbers	01520
Knarr Cross	0173128
3 figure numbers	01733
6 figure numbers	01547

Knightwick	01886
Knock	0146686
3 figure numbers	01466
6 figure numbers	01959
Knockholt	01691
Knockin	01253
Knott End	01564
Knowle	01565
Knutsford	01599
Kyle	01885
Kyre	
L	
Ladybank	01337
Laggan	
3 figure numbers	015284
6 figure numbers	01528
Lairg	01549
Lamberhurst	01892
Lambourn	01488
Lamington	
3 figure numbers	018995
6 figure numbers	01899
Knighton (Powys)	

Place	Code
Lamlash	01770
Lampeter	01570
Lamphey	01646
Lamplugh	01946
Lanark	01555
Lancaster	01524
Lanchester (Co Durham)	01207
Lancing	01903
Landrake	01752
Langbank	01475
Langdale	015394
Langholm	
5 figure numbers	013873
6 figure numbers	01387
Langley Mill	01773
Langport	01458
Langrick	01205
Langton	01892
Langtree	
3 figure numbers	018055
6 figure numbers	01805
Langwathby	01768
Lanivet	01208
Lanreath	01503
Lapford	01363
Lapworth	01564
Larbert	01324
Largs	01475
Larkhall	01698
Larne	01574
Lastingham	01751
Latheron	
3 figure numbers	015934
6 figure numbers	01593
Lauder	01578
Laugharne (Dyfed)	01994
Laughton	01427
Launceston	01566
Laurencekirk	01561
Laurieston	
3 figure numbers	016445
6 figure numbers	01644
Lavenham	01787
Laxey (Isle of Man)	01624
Layer-de-la-Haye	01206
Lazonby	01768
Leabrooks	01773
Leadhills	01659
Lea (Hereford)	01989
Leamington Spa	01926
Leatherhead	01372
Lea Valley	01992
Ledaig	
3 figure numbers	0163172
6 figure numbers	01631
Ledbury	01531
Leebotwood	01694
Lee Brockhurst	01939
Leeds	0113
Leedstown	01736
Leek	01538
Lee-on-the-Solent	01705
Leicester	01533
Leigh (Lancs)	01942
Leigh Sinton	01886
Leighton Buzzard	01525
Leintwardine	
3 figure numbers	015473
6 figure numbers	01547
Leire	01455
Leiston	01728
Leitholm	01890
Lempitlaw	01573
Lendalfoot	
3 figure numbers	0146589
6 figure numbers	01465
Lennoxtown	01360
Leominster	01568
Lerwick	01595
Lesmahagow	01555
Leswalt	01776
Letchworth	01462
Letham (Angus)	01307
Letham (Fife)	01337
Letterston	01348
Leuchars	01334
Leven (Fife)	01333

Place	Dialling code
Leverburgh	
3 figure numbers	0185992
6 figure numbers	01859
Lewdown	
3 figure numbers	0156683
6 figure numbers	01566
Lewes	01273
Leyland	01772
Leysdown-on-Sea	01795
Leysters	
3 figure numbers	0156887
6 figure numbers	01568
Lhanbryde	01343
Lichfield	01543
Liddesdale	
5 figure numbers	013873
6 figure numbers	01387
Lifton	01566
Lilliesleaf	
3 figure numbers	018357
6 figure numbers	01835
Lillingstone Dayrell	01280
Limavady	015047
Limekilns	01383
Lincoln	01522
Lindfield (West Sussex)	01444
Lingfield (Surrey)	01342
Linkenholt	
3 figure numbers	0126487
6 figure numbers	01264
Linley	
3 figure numbers	0158861
6 figure numbers	01588
Linlithgow	01506
Linstead	
3 figure numbers	0198685
6 figure numbers	01986
Linton-on-Ouse	01347
Lintrathen	01575
Liphook	01428
Lisbellaw	01365
Lisburn	01846
Liskeard	01579
Lismore	
3 figure numbers	0163176
6 figure numbers	01631
Lisnaskea	013657
Liss (Hants)	01730
Littleborough	01706
Little Brampton	
3 figure numbers	015887
6 figure numbers	01588
Little Budworth	01829
Little Chalfont	01494
Little Gaddesden	01442
Littlehampton	0903
Little Haywood	0889
Little Mill	01495
Little Steeping	01754
Littlewick Green	01628
Liverpool	0151
Livingston	01506
Llananno	
3 figure numbers	0159783
6 figure numbers	01597
Llanarmon Dyffryn-Ceiriog	0169176
3 figure numbers	01691
6 figure numbers	
Llanarmon-yn-Ial	
3 figure numbers	018243
6 figure numbers	01824
Llanarth	01545
Llanbedr	
3 figure numbers	0134123
6 figure numbers	01341
Llanbedrog	01758
Llanberis	01286
Llanboidy	01994
Llanbrynmair	01650
Llanddarog	01267
Llandderfel	
3 figure numbers	016783
6 figure numbers	01678
Llandegla	01978
Llandeilo	01558
Llandovery	01550

Place	3 figure numbers	6 figure numbers
Llandrillo	0149084	
Llandrindod Wells		01597
Llandudno		01492
Llandybie		01269
Llandyrnog		01824
Llandyssul		01559
Llanelli		01554
Llanerchymedd		01248
Llanfaethlu		01407
Llanfair Caereinion		01938
Llanfairfechan		01248
Llanfairpwll		01248
Llanfairtalhaiarn	0174584	01745
Llanferres	0135285	01352
Llanfrynach	0187486	

Place	3 figure numbers	6 figure numbers
		01874
Llanfyllin		01691
Llangadfan	0193888	01938
Llangadog		01550
Llangammarch Wells	015912	01591
Llangarron		01989
Llangefni		01248
Llangeitho		01974
Llangennech		01554
Llangennith (West Glam)		01792
Llangernyw	0174576	01745
Llangoed		01248
Llangollen		01978
Llangorse	0187484	

Place	3 figure numbers	6 figure numbers
		01874
Llangranog		01239
Llangunllo		01547
Llangurig	015515	01686
Llangybi	0157045	01570
Llanidloes		01686
Llanilar	019747	01974
Llannefydd	0174579	01745
Llanon		01974
Llanpumsaint		01267
Llanrhaeadr (Oswestry)		01691
Llanrwst		01492

Place	3 figure numbers	6 figure numbers
Llansannan	0174577	01745
Llansantffraid		01691
Llansilin (Clwyd)	0169170	01691
Llansteffan	0126783	01267
Llanteg	0183483	01834
Llantilio	0160085	01600
Llantrisant		01443
Llantwit Major		01446
Llanuwchllyn	016784	01678

Llanwddyn	
3 figure numbers	0169173
6 figure numbers	01691
Llanwern	01633
Llanwnda	01286
Llanwrtyd Wells	015913
6 figure numbers	01591
Llanybydder	01570
Llanymynech	01691
Llanynys	
3 figure numbers	0174578
6 figure numbers	01745
Llawhaden	01437
Llechryd	01239
Llithfaen	01758
Llwyndrain	
6 figure numbers	0123977
Lochgelly	01239
Llyswen	01874
Lochailort	
3 figure numbers	016877

6 figure numbers	01687
Lochans	01776
Lochavich	
3 figure numbers	018664
6 figure numbers	01866
Lochboisdale	01878
Lochbroom	
3 figure numbers	0185485
6 figure numbers	01854
Lochcarron	
6 figure numbers	015202
Lochearnhead	01520
Locheport	01567
Lochfoot	01876
3 figure numbers	0138773
6 figure numbers	01387
Lochgilphead	01592
Lochgoilhead	01546
3 figure numbers	013013
6 figure numbers	01301

Lochinver	015714
3 figure numbers	01571
6 figure numbers	01387
Lochmaben	01876
Lochmaddy	01971
Lochmore	01770
Lochranza	
Loch Scavaig	014716
3 figure numbers	01471
6 figure numbers	01505
Lochwinnoch	01576
Lockerbie	01672
Lockeridge (Wilts)	01794
Lockerley	01489
Locks Heath	01508
Loddon	01689
Lodge Hill	
Lodsworth	017985
3 figure numbers	01798
6 figure numbers	013555
Loganswell	
3 figure numbers	

6 figure numbers	01355
London	0171/0181
Londonderry	01504
Long Ashton	01275
Long Bredy	01308
Long Buckby	01327
Long Compton	01608
Long Crendon	01844
Longdown	01392
Long Eaton	0115
Longfield (Kent)	01474
Longforgan	
3 figure numbers	0182622
6 figure numbers	01382
Longformacus	
3 figure numbers	013617
6 figure numbers	01361
Longframlington	01665
Longhope (Orkney)	
3 figure numbers	0185670
6 figure numbers	01856
Longhorsley	01670

Longhoughton	01665
Longmorn	0134386
3 figure numbers	01343
6 figure numbers	
Longniddry	01875
Longnor	01298
Longparish	01264
Long Preston	01729
Longridge (Lancs)	01772
Longside	01779
Long Stratton	01508
Long Sutton (Somerset)	01458
Longton (Lancs)	01772
Longtown Castle	
3 figure numbers	0187387
6 figure numbers	01873
Longtown (Cumbria)	01228
Longville	01694
Longworth	01865
Lonmay	01346
Looe	01503

Lorton	01900
Lossiemouth	01343
Loughborough	01509
Loughgall	01762
Loughgiel	012656
Louth	01507
Loveden	01400
Lower Beeding	01403
Lower Peover	01565
Lower Withington	01477
Lowestoft	01502
Lowick Bridge	01229
Low Ireby	016973
Loxwood	01403
Ludlow	01584
Luing	018524
	01852
Lulsgate	01275
Lumphanan	
5 figure numbers	013398
6 figure numbers	01339

Lundin Links	01333
Luppitt	01404
Lurgan	01762
Luss	0143686
3 figure numbers	01436
6 figure numbers	
Lustleigh	016477
3 figure numbers	01647
6 figure numbers	01337
Luthrie	01582
Luton	01455
Lutterworth	
Lybster	015932
3 figure numbers	01593
6 figure numbers	
Lytbury North	015888
3 figure numbers	01588
6 figure numbers	
Lydd	
5 figure numbers	01679
6 figure numbers	01797

Lydeard St Lawrence	
3 figure numbers	019847
6 figure numbers	01984
Lydford	
3 figure numbers	0182282
6 figure numbers	01822
Lye	01384
Lyme Regis	01297
Lyminge	01303
Lymington (Hants)	01590
Lymm	01925
Lyndhurst	01703
Lynton	01598
Lyonshall	
3 figure numbers	015448
6 figure numbers	01544
Lytchett Minster	01202
Lytham	01253
Lyth	
3 figure numbers	0195584
6 figure numbers	01955

M		**Maesycrugiau**	0155935	**Manchester**	0161	**Marlborough**	01672
Mablethorpe	01507	*3 figure numbers*	01559	Manea	01354	Marlow	01628
Macclesfield	01625	*6 figure numbers*	01648	Manish		Marnhull	01258
Macduff	01261	Maghera	01648	*3 figure numbers*	0185983	Marown (Isle of Man)	01624
Machen	01633	Magherafelt	01633	*6 figure numbers*	01859	Marrburn	
Machrie	01770	Magor	01628	Manley	01928	*3 figure numbers*	018486
Machrihanish		Maidenhead	01628	Manorbier	01834	*6 figure numbers*	01848
3 figure numbers	0158681	Maiden Newton	01300	Mansfield	01623	Marshalls Cross	01744
6 figure numbers	01586	Maidstone	01622	Manton (Leics)		Marshbrook	01694
Machynlleth	01654	Maidwell		*3 figure numbers*	0157285	Marshchapel	01472
Madderty	01764	*3 figure numbers*	0160128	*6 figure numbers*	01572	Marshland Smeeth	01945
Madingley	01954	*6 figure numbers*	01604	March	01354	Marston Magna	01935
Madox	0994	Maldon (Essex)	01621	Mareham-le-Fen	01507	Martin	01526
Maenclochog	01437	Mallaig	01687	Market Bosworth	01455	Martin Cross	
Maentwrog		Malmesbury	01666	Market Deeping	01778	*3 figure numbers*	0172589
3 figure numbers	0176685	Malpas	01948	Market Drayton	01630	*6 figure numbers*	01725
6 figure numbers	01766	Malton	01653	Market Harborough	01858	Martinstown (Co Antrim)	
Maerdy		Malvern	01684	Markethill	01861		0126 67
3 figure numbers	0149081	Manaccan	01326	Market Rasen	01673	Martinstown (Dorset)	
6 figure numbers	01490	Manaton		Market Weighton	01430		01305
Maesteg	01656	*3 figure numbers*	0164722	Markfield	01530	Martletwy	01834
		6 figure numbers	01647	Mark Moor	01278	Martock	01935

Place	Code
Marton Heath	01260
Marton (Warwicks)	01926
Maryport	01900
Mary Tavy	01822
Matlaske	
3/4 figure numbers	0126377
6 figure numbers	01263
Matlock	01629
Mauchline	01290
Maud	01771
Mawgan (Helston)	01326
Maybole	01655
Mayfield	01435
Mayobridge	01693
Maze	01846
Meare Heath	01458
Measham	01530
Medbourne Green 3 figure numbers	0185883
6 figure numbers	01858
Medway	01634

Place	Code
Meifod	
3 figure numbers	0193884
6 figure numbers	01938
Meigle	
3 figure numbers	018284
6 figure numbers	01828
Meikleour	01250
Melbourne (Derby)	01332
Melbourne (Yorks)	01759
Melksham	01225
Mellis	01379
Mellor	01254
Melmerby	01765
Melrose	
4 figure numbers	0189682
6 figure numbers	01896
Melton Constable	01263
Melton Mowbray	01664
Melvich	
3 figure numbers	016413
6 figure numbers	01641
Memsie	01346

Place	Code
Menai Bridge	01248
Mendip	01761
Menmuir	01356
Menston	01943
Meopham	01474
Mereside	
3 figure numbers	0173129
6 figure numbers	01733
Mere (Wilts)	01747
Meriden	01676
Merkland	
3 figure numbers	0154983
6 figure numbers	01549
Merstham	01737
Merthyr Cynog	
3 figure numbers	0187489
6 figure numbers	01874
Merthyr Tydfil	01685
Metheringham	01526
Methlick	01651
Methven	01738
Methwold	01366

Place	Code
Mevagissey	01726
Mexborough	01709
Michaelchurch	
3 figure numbers	0198123
6 figure numbers	01981
Micheldever	01962
Mickleton	01386
Mickle Trafford	01244
Mid Calder	01506
Middlesbrough	01642
Middleton-on-Sea (West Sussex)	
Middleton-on-the-Wolds	01243
	01377
Middleton Scriven	
3 figure numbers	0174635
6 figure numbers	01746
Middleton Stoney	01869
Middlewich	01606
Middle Woodford	
3 figure numbers	0172273
6 figure numbers	01722

Place	Code
Midhurst	01730
Mid Yell	01957
Milborne Port	01963
Milborne St Andrew	01258
Mildenhall	01638
Milfield (Northumberland)	
3 figure numbers	016686
6 figure numbers	01668
Milford Haven	01646
Milland	01428
Millisle	01247
Millom	01229
Millport	01475
Milnthorpe	015395
Milstead	01795
Milton Abbas	
3 figure numbers	0182287
6 figure numbers	01822
Milton Damerel	01409
Milton Keynes	01908
Milverton	01823

Place	Code
Minard	01546
Mindrum	01890
Minehead	01643
Minster (Sheppey)	01795
Mintlaw	01771
Mirfield	01924
Mitchell	01872
Mobberley	01565
Moccas	01981
Mochrum	01988
Modbury	01548
Moelfre	01248
Moffat	01683
Mogador	01737
Moira	0846
Mold	01352
Moneymore	016487
Moniaive	
3 figure numbers	018482
6 figure numbers	01848
Monifieth	01382
Monmouth	01600

Place	Code
Montgomery	01686
Montrose	01674
Monymusk	01467
Moore	01925
Morchard Bishop	01363
Morcott	
3 figure numbers	0157287
6 figure numbers	01572
Morden	01929
Morebattle	01573
Morecambe	01524
Moreton	01277
Moretonhampstead	01647
Moreton-in-Marsh	01608
Morland	01931
Morpeth	01670
Mortimer	01734
Morton (Bourne)	01778
Morvern	01967
Morville	
3 figure numbers	0174631
6 figure numbers	01746

Place	Code
Morwenstow	01288
Moscow	01560
Mossley	01457
Mossyard	01557
Mostyn	01745
Motherwell	01698
Mottram	01457
Mountain Ash	01443
Mountfield	016627
Mouswald	
3 figure numbers	0138783
6 figure numbers	01387
Moy	
5 figure numbers	018687
6 figure numbers	01868
Moylegrove	
3 figure numbers	0123986
6 figure numbers	01239
Much Hadham	01279
Much Marcle	
3 figure numbers	0153184
6 figure numbers	01531

Name	Code
Much Wenlock	01952
Muckhart	01259
Muirhead	01382
Muirkirk	01290
Muir-of-Fowlis	
5 figure numbers	019755
6 figure numbers	01975
Muir-of-Ord	01463
Mulbarton	01508
Mulben	01542
Mullion	01326
Munderfield	01885
Mundesley	01263
Munlochy	
3 figure numbers	0146381
6 figure numbers	01463
Munslow	
3 figure numbers	0158476
6 figure numbers	01584
Mursley	01296
Muthill	01764

Name	Code
N	
Nacton	01473
Nailsea	01275
Nairn	01667
Nantgaredig	01267
Nantglyn	
3 figure numbers	0174570
6 figure numbers	01745
Nantwich	01270
Nantyderry	01873
Naphill	01494
Narberth	01834
Narborough	01760
Nayland (Suffolk)	01206
Nazeing	01992
Neath	01639
Nebo	01974
Needham Market	01449
Nefyn	01758
Nelson (Lancs)	01282
Nelson (Mid Glam)	01443

Name	Code
Nesscliffe	
3 figure numbers	0174381
6 figure numbers	01743
Netherbury	01308
Nether Stowey	01278
Nethybridge	01479
Nettlebed	01491
New Abbey	
3 figure numbers	0138785
6 figure numbers	01387
New Aberdour	01346
Newark	01636
Newbigging (Angus)	
3 figure numbers	0182623
6 figure numbers	01382
Newbiggin-on-Lune	015396
Newborough (Anglesey)	01248
Newbridge (Dumfries)	01387
Newbridge (Gwent)	01495

Name	Code
Newbridge-on-Wye	
3 figure numbers	0159789
6 figure numbers	01597
Newburgh (Aberdeen)	01358
Newburgh (Fife)	01337
Newbury (Berks)	01635
Newby Bridge	0153 95
Newcastle (Co Down)	0139 67
Newcastle Emlyn	01239
Newcastle-under-Lyme (Staffs)	01782
Newcastle upon Tyne (see Tyneside)	
New Cumnock	01290
New Deer	01771
Newdigate	01306
Newent	01531
New Galloway	
3 figure numbers	016442
6 figure numbers	01644

Newhaven	01273	Newquay (Cornwall)	01637
Newick	01825	New Quay (Dyfed)	01545
Newington	01795	New Radnor	
New Leake	0120584	3 figure numbers	0154421
3 figure numbers		6 figure numbers	01544
6 figure numbers	01205	New Romney	
New Luce	01581	5 figure numbers	01679
Newmachar	01651	6 figure numbers	01797
Newmarket	01638	Newry	01693
New Mills (Derbys)	01663	Newton Abbot	01626
Newmills (Fife)	01383	Newtonhill	01569
New Milton	01425	Newton-le-Willows	01925
Newnham Bridge		Newtonmore	01540
3 figure numbers	0158479	Newton Stewart	01671
6 figure numbers	01584	Newton Tracey	01271
New Oakley	01383	Newtownards	01247
New Pitsligo	01771	Newtownbutler	013657
Newport (Dyfed)	01239	Newtownhamilton	01693
Newport (Gwent)	01633	Newtown Llantwit	01443
Newport-on-Tay	01382	Newtown (Powys)	01686
Newport Pagnell	01908	Newtownstewart	
Newport (Shrops)	01952	(Co Tyrone)	016626

Newtyle		North Cadbury	01963
3 figure numbers	018285	Northchapel	01428
6 figure numbers	01828	North Crawley	01234
Neyland (Dyfed)	01646	North Curry	01823
Nicholforest	01228	North Erradale	
Nigg		3 figure numbers	0144585
3 figure numbers	0186285	6 figure numbers	01445
6 figure numbers	01862	North Grimston	01944
Nigg Station		Northiam	01797
3 figure numbers	0186286	Northill	01767
6 figure numbers	01862	North Kelsey	01652
Ninfield	01424	North Marston	01296
Nonington	01304	North Molton	
Norcott Brook	01925	3 figure numbers	015984
Nordelph		6 figure numbers	01598
3 figure numbers	013668	Northop	01352
6 figure numbers	01366	North Petherton	01278
Normanby-by-Spital	01673	North Petherwin	
Northallerton	01609	3 figure numbers	0156685
Northampton	01604	6 figure numbers	01566
Northbay	01871	North Rode	01260
North Berwick	01620		

Place	Number
North Roe	
3 figure numbers	018063
6 figure numbers	01806
North Ronaldsay	
3 figure numbers	018573
6 figure numbers	01857
North Somercotes	01507
North Tamerton	
3 figure numbers	0140927
6 figure numbers	01409
North Tawton	01837
North Tolsta	
3 figure numbers	0185189
6 figure numbers	01851
North Walsham	01692
Northwaterbridge	01674
North Weald	01992
Northwich	01606
Northwood	01923
Norton	
3 figure numbers	0195271
6 figure numbers	01952
Norwich	01603
Norwood Hill	01293
Nottingham	0115
Nuneaton	01203
Nuneham Courtenay	0186738
Nunnington	
3 figure numbers	014395
6 figure numbers	01439
Nutfield Ridge	01737
Nutley	01825
O	
Oakamoor	01538
Oakford	013985
Oakham	
3 figure numbers	01398
6 figure numbers	01572
Oakhill	01749
Oakley (Beds)	01234
Oakwood Hill	01306
Oban	01631
Occold	01379
Ochiltree	
3 figure numbers	012907
6 figure numbers	01290
Odiham	01256
Offley	01462
Offshore	01224
Offton	01473
Ogbourne St George	01672
Ogmore Valley	01656
Okehampton	01837
Old Dailly	
3 figure numbers	0146587
6 figure numbers	01465
Oldmeldrum	01651
Old Rayne	
3 figure numbers	014645
6 figure numbers	01464
Ollaberry	018064
Omagh	
3 figure numbers	01806
6 figure numbers	011662
Onecote	01538
Ongar	01277
Onich	
3 figure numbers	018553
6 figure numbers	01855
Orford (Suffolk)	01394
Ormsary	
3 figure numbers	018803
6 figure numbers	01880
Ormskirk	01695
Orphir	
3 figure numbers	0185681
6 figure numbers	01856
Orpington	01689
Orton (Cumbria)	015396
Orton (Moray)	
3 figure numbers	0134388
6 figure numbers	01343
Osmotherley	01609
Oswestry	01691
Otford (Kent)	01959
Otley	01943
Otterburn	01830

Place	Code		Place	Code
Otterham Station			Oxford	01865
3 figure numbers	018406		Oxshott	01372
6 figure numbers	01840		Oxted	01883
Ottershaw	01932		Oxton	01578
Ottery St Mary	01404		**P**	
Oundle	01832		Paddock Wood	01892
Ousden	01638		Padgate	01925
Out Skerries			Padiham	01282
3 figure numbers	018065		Padstow	01841
6 figure numbers	01806		Pagham	01243
Overbury	01386		Paignton	01803
Overstrand			Painscastle	01497
3/4 figure numbers	0126378		Painswick	01452
6 figure numbers	01263		Pakenham	01359
Overton (Lancs)	01524		Palnackie	
Overton-on-Dee	01978		3 figure numbers	0155660
Owersby Moor	01673		6 figure numbers	01556
Owslebury	01962		Pangbourne	01734
Owston Ferry	01427		Pantydwr	
Oxenwood			3 figure numbers	0159788
3 figure numbers	0126489		6 figure numbers	01597
6 figure numbers	01264		Papa Stour	01595

Place	Code		Place	Code
Papa Westray			Patching	
3 figure numbers	018574		3 figure numbers	0190674
6 figure numbers	01857		6 figure numbers	01903
Par	01726		Patna	01292
Parbold	01257		Pattingham	01902
Parkgate			Pattishall	01327
3 figure numbers	0138786		Paulerspury	
6 figure numbers	01387		3 figure numbers	0132733
Parkstone	01202		6 figure numbers	01327
Park Street	01727		Paxford	
Parracombe			3 figure numbers	0138678
3 figure numbers	015983		6 figure numbers	01386
6 figure numbers	01598		Peacehaven	01273
Parton	016447		Peasenhall	
Partridge Green	01644		3 figure numbers	0172879
Parwich	01403		6 figure numbers	01728
Parwich			Peasmarsh	01797
3 figure numbers	0133525		Peat Inn	
6 figure numbers	01335		3 figure numbers	0133484
Passfield	01428		6 figure numbers	01334
			Peebles	01721
			Peel (Isle of Man)	01624

Place	Number	Place	Number
Peldon	01206	Penmaenmawr	01492
Pelsall	01922	Pennal	01654
Pembridge		Pennant	
3/4 figure numbers	015447	3 figure numbers	0169174
6 figure numbers	01544	6 figure numbers	01691
Pembroke	01646	Penn (Bucks)	01494
Pembury	01892	Pennyghael	01892
Penarth	01222	3 figure numbers	016814
Pencader	01559	6 figure numbers	01681
Pencaitland	01875	Penrhyndeudraeth	01766
Penclawdd	01792	Penrith	01792
Pencoed	01656	Penshurst	01892
Pencombe	01885	Pentraeth	01248
Pendine		Pentrefoelas	
3 figure numbers	019945	3 figure numbers	016905
6 figure numbers	01994	6 figure numbers	01690
Penhow	01633	Pentyrch	01222
Penicuik	01968	Penybont	01597
Penketh	01925	Penygroes	01286
Penkridge	01785	Penzance	01736
Penmachno	01690	Pershore	01386
Penmaen	01792	Perth	01738

Place	Number	Place	Number
Peterborough	01733	Pitcaple	01467
Peterchurch	01981	Pitlochry	01796
Peterhead	01779	Plaistow	01403
Petersfield	01730	Plaxtol	01732
Peterston-super-Ely	01446	Pleshey	01245
Petham	01227	Plockton	
Petworth	01798	3 figure numbers	0159984
Philpstoun	01506	6 figure numbers	01599
Pickering	01751	Pluckley	01233
Pickmere	01565	Plumpton (East Sussex)	01273
Piddletrenthide	01300	Plumpton (Penrith)	01768
Pill	01275	Plumtree	0115
Pilling	01253	Plymouth	01752
Pilning	01454	Plymtree	01884
Pilton	01749	Pocklington	01759
Pinchbeck Bars	01775	Polegate	01323
Pinwherry		Polmont	01324
3 figure numbers	0146584	Polperro	01503
6 figure numbers	01465	Polruan	01726
Pipe Gate	01630	Pomeroy	01868
Pipers Pool	01566	Pontardawe	01792
Pirnmill	01770		

Place	Code	Place	Code
Pontardulais	01792	Porlock	01643
Pontefract	01977	Portadown	01762
Ponteland	01661	Portaferry	012477
Ponterwyd		Port Askaig	01496
3 figure numbers	0197085	Portavogie	012477
6 figure numbers	01970	Port Charlotte	
Pontrhydfendigaid	01974	*3 figure numbers*	0149685
Pontrhydygroes	01974	*6 figure numbers*	01496
Pontshaen		Port Dinorwic	01248
3 figure numbers	0154555	Port Ellen	01496
6 figure numbers	01545	Port Erin (Isle of Man)	01624
Pontyates	01269	Port Glasgow	01475
Pontyberem	01269	Portglenone	01266
Pontybodkin	01352	Porth	01443
Pontycymmer	01656	Porthcawl	01656
Pontypool	01495	Porthmadog	01766
Pontypridd	01443	Porthtowan	01209
Poole	01202	Portishead	01275
Poolewe		Portland	01305
3 figure numbers	0144586	Portmahomack	
6 figure numbers	01445	*3 figure numbers*	0186287
Pooley Bridge	0176 84		

Place	Code	Place	Code
6 figure numbers	01862	Poulton-le-Fylde	01253
Portnahaven	01496	Poundsgate	
Port-of-Menteith	01877	*3 figure numbers*	013643
Port-of-Ness		*6 figure numbers*	01364
3 figure numbers	0185181	Powburn	01665
6 figure numbers	01851	Powerstock	01308
Portpatrick	01776	Poynings	01273
Portreath	01209	Poynton	01625
Portree	01478	Poyntzfield	01381
Portrush	01265	Poyntzpass	01762
Port St Mary (Isle of Man)		Praze	01209
Portscatho	01872	Prestatyn	01745
Port Seton	01875	Prestbury	01625
Portsmouth	01705	Presteigne	01544
Portsoy	01261	Preston Candover	01256
Portstewart	01265	Preston Capes	
Port Talbot	01639	*3 figure numbers*	0132736
Port William	01988	*6 figure numbers*	01327
Potter Heigham	01692	Preston (Dorset)	01305
Potters Bar	01707	Preston (Lancs)	01772
Potton	01767	Prestonpans	01875
		Prestwick	01292

Place	Code
Prickwillow	0135388
3 figure numbers	01353
6 figure numbers	
Princes Risborough	01844
Princetown	01822
Privett	01730
Prudhoe	01661
Puddletown	01305
Pulborough (West Sussex)	01798
Pulham Market	01379
Pumpsaint	01558
Puncheston	01348
Purfleet	01708
Puriton	01278
Pwllheli	01758
Pymore	01353
Q	
Quatt	01746
Queens Head	01691
Quidenham	01953
Quorn	01509
R	
Raasay	01478
Rackenford	
3 figure numbers	0188488
6 figure numbers	01884
Radcliffe-on-Trent	0115
Radlett	01923
Radwinter	01799
Radyr (South Glam)	01222
Raglan	01291
Rainford	01744
Rainham (Essex)	01708
Rait	01821
Rampton	01777
Ramsbottom	01706
Ramsden	01993
Ramsey (Cambs)	01487
Ramsey (Essex)	01255
Ramsey (Isle of Man)	01624
Randalstown	01849
Rangeworthy	01454
Rasharkin	012665
Rathfriland	0182 06
Rathlin (Co Antrim)	012657
Rattlesden	01449
Raughton Head	016974
Ravenglass	01229
Raveningham	01508
Ravensworth	01931
Rayleigh	01268
Reading	01734
Rearsby	01664
Reawick	
3 figure numbers	0159586
6 figure numbers	01595
Reay	0184781
3 figure numbers	01847
6 figure numbers	01582
Redbrook Maelor	
3 figure numbers	0194873
6 figure numbers	01948
Redcar	01642
Redditch	01527
Redhill	01737
Redruth	01209
Reedness	01405
Reigate	01737
Rendham	01728
Resolven	01639
Reston	
5 figure numbers	018907
6 figure numbers	01890
Retford	01777
Rhandirmwyn	
3 figure numbers	015506
6 figure numbers	01550
Rhayader	01597
Rhiw	
3 figure numbers	0175888
6 figure numbers	01758
Rhoose	01446
Rhos (Dyfed)	01437
Rhosllanerchrugog	01978
Rhosneigr	01407
Rhu	01436

Place	Code
Rhuddlan	01745
Rhydlewis	01239
Rhydymain	
3 figure numbers	0134141
6 figure numbers	01341
Rhyl	01745
Rhymney	01685
Rhynie	
3 figure numbers	014646
6 figure numbers	01464
Ribchester	01254
Richards Castle	
3 figure numbers	0158474
6 figure numbers	01584
Richhill	01762
Richmond (North Yorks)	
3 figure numbers	017483
6 figure numbers	01748
Rickmansworth	01923
Ridgeway Cross	01886
Ridgewell	01440
Ridgmont	01525
Rillington	01944

Place	Code
Ringford	
3 figure numbers	0155722
6 figure numbers	01557
Ringmer	01273
Ringwood	01425
Ripe	01323
Ripley (Derbys)	01773
Ripon	01765
Risca	01633
Roade	01604
Roadhead	016977
Robertsbridge	01580
Rocester	0889
Rochdale	01706
Rockbourne	01725
Rockcliffe (Cumbria)	
3 figure numbers	017253
6 figure numbers	01228
Rockcliffe (Cumbria)	01228
Rockcliffe (Kirkcudbright)	01556
Rockingham	01536
Rock (Kidderminster)	01299

Place	Code
Rogart	01408
Rogate (West Sussex)	
3 figure numbers	01730
6 figure numbers	01708
Romford (Essex)	01708
Romsey (Hants)	01794
Romsley	01562
Ropley	01962
Rosehall	
3 figure numbers	0154984
6 figure numbers	01549
Rosehearty	01346
Roslea	013657
Rossendale	01706
Rossett	01244
Ross-on-Wye	01989
Rostrevor	016937
Rothbury	01669
Rotherby	01664
Rotherfield (East Sussex)	01892
Rotherfield Greys	01491
Rotherham	01709

Place	Code
Rothesay	01700
Rothes	01340
Rothiemay	01466
Rothienorman	01651
Rousay	
3 figure numbers	0185682
6 figure numbers	01856
Rowlands Castle	01705
Rowlands Gill	01207
Roxburgh	01573
Roxton (South Humberside)	01469
Roxwell	01245
Royal Bath & West	01749
Royal Show	01203
Roydon (Essex)	01279
Royston (Herts)	01763
Ruabon	01978
Rudgwick	01403
Rudyard	
3 figure numbers	0153833
6 figure numbers	01538

Rufford (Lancs)	01704
Rufforth (York)	01904
Rugby	01788
Rugeley	01889
Ruislip (Middlesex)	01895
Rumford (Bodmin)	01841
Runcorn	01928
Runfold	01252
Rushden	01933
Rushlake Green	01435
Rushton Spencer	01260
Ruskington (Lincs)	01526
Rusper	01293
Rustington (West Sussex)	
3 figure numbers	01903
6 figure numbers	01824
Ruthin	01824
Rye (East Sussex)	01797
Ryton (Shrops)	
3 figure numbers	0195287
6 figure numbers	01952
S	
Saddleworth	01457

Saffron Walden	01799
St Agnes	01872
St Albans	01727
St Andrews	01334
St Annes	01253
St Asaph	01745
St Athan	01446
St Austell	01726
St Benets	01692
St Boswells	01835
St Buryan	01736
St Clears	01994
St Columb	01637
St Cross	
3 figure numbers	0198682
6 figure numbers	01986
St Cyrus	01674
St Davids	01437
St Day	01209
St Fergus	01779
Saintfield	01238
St Field (see Saintfield)	

St Fillans	01764
St Gennys	01840
St Germans (Cornwall)	01503
St Germans (Norfolk)	01553
St Helens	01744
St Ives (Cambs)	01480
St Ives (Cornwall)	01736
St Johns (Isle of Man)	01624
St Keverne	01326
St Mabyn	01208
3 figure numbers	0120884
6 figure numbers	01208
St Margaret's Hope	
3 figure numbers	0185683
6 figure numbers	01856
St Marybourne	01264
St Mawes	01326
St Mawgan (Newquay)	01637
St Michaels	01995

St Monans	01333
St Nicholas (Dyfed)	
3 figure numbers	013485
6 figure numbers	01348
St Osyth	01255
St Weonards	
3 figure numbers	019818
6 figure numbers	01981
Salcombe	01548
Salen	
3 figure numbers	0196785
6 figure numbers	01967
Salisbury	01722
Salsburgh	01698
Saltash	01752
Saltcoats	01294
Saltfleetby	01507
Sambrook	01952
Samlesbury	01772
Sanday (Orkney)	
3 figure numbers	018575
6 figure numbers	01857

Place	Number
Sandhead	01776
Sandhurst (Kent)	01580
Sandiacre	0115
Sandiway	01606
Sandness	
3 figure numbers	0159587
6 figure numbers	01595
Sandon (Staffs)	01889
Sandwich (Deal)	01304
Sandwich (Orkney)	
3 figure numbers	0185684
6 figure numbers	01856
Sandwick (Shetland)	
3 figure numbers	019505
6 figure numbers	01950
Sandy (Beds)	01767
Sanquhar	01659
Sapcote	01455
Sark	01481
Satterthwaite	01229
Sauchen	01330
Saughall	01244
Saundby	01427
Saundersfoot	01834
Sawley	01765
Saxby-all-Saints	01652
Saxmundham	01728
Saxthorpe	
3/4 figure numbers	026387
6 figure numbers	01263
Scalford	
3 figure numbers	0166476
6 figure numbers	01664
Scalloway	
3 figure numbers	0159588
6 figure numbers	01595
Scalpay	
3 figure numbers	0185984
6 figure numbers	01859
Scarborough	01723
Scarinish	
3 figure numbers	018792
6 figure numbers	01879
Scarisbrick	01704
Scarista	
3 figure numbers	0185985
6 figure numbers	01859
Scarp	
3 figure numbers	0185986
6 figure numbers	01859
Scatwell	019976
Scawby	01997
Scaynes Hill	01444
Schivas	01358
Scillonia	01720
Scone	01738
Scotby	01228
Scotlandwell	01592
Scots Gap	
3 figure numbers	0167074
6 figure numbers	01670
Scourie	01971
Scremby	
3 figure numbers	0175485
6 figure numbers	01754
Scunthorpe	01724
Seaford (East Sussex)	01323
Seaforde (Co Down)	01396
Seagry	01249
Seahouses	01665
Seal Sands	01642
Searby	01652
Seascale	019467
Seaton (Devon)	01297
Sedbergh	015396
Sedgefield	01740
Sedgley	01902
Sedgwick	015395
Sedlescombe (Hastings)	01424
Seifton	
3 figure numbers	0158473
6 figure numbers	01584
Seighford	01785
Selborne	01420
Selby (North Yorks)	01757

Place	Number
Selkirk	01750
Sellindge (Kent)	01303
Selsey	01243
Selside	01539
Selsted	0130383
3 figure numbers	01303
6 figure numbers	01303
Senghenydd	01222
Sennen	01736
Sennybridge	01874
Settle	01729
Sevenoaks	01732
Seven Sisters	01639
Severn Stoke	01905
Shaftesbury	01747
Shaldon (Devon)	01626
Shap	01931
Sharpthorne	01342
Shaugh Prior	
3 figure numbers	0175539
6 figure numbers	01752
Shawbost	0185171
3 figure numbers	01851
6 figure numbers	01939
Shawbury	01706
Shaw (Lancs)	01409
Shebbear	01279
Sheering	01795
Sheerness	0114
Sheffield	
Shelsley Beauchamp	01886
Shenstone	01543
Shephall	01438
Shepherdswell	01304
Shepshed	01509
Shepton Mallet	01749
Sherborne (Dorset)	01935
Sherburn (North Yorks)	01944
Shere	01483
Sheriff Hutton	01347
Sheringham	01263
Shieldaig	015205
3 figure numbers	01520
6 figure numbers	01665
Shilbottle	01608
Shipston-on-Stour	
Shipton-under-Wychwood	01993
Shirenewton	01291
Shirwell	01271
Shiskine	01770
Shoreham-by-Sea	01273
Shorne	01474
Shotley	01473
Shottisham	01394
Shotts	01501
Shrewsbury	01743
Shrewton	01980
Sicklesmere	01284
Sidbury	01395
Sidlesham (West Sussex)	01243
Sidmouth	01395
Silchester	01734
Sileby	01509
Silloth	016973
Silsoe	01525
Silverdale	01524
Silver End	01376
Silverstone	01327
Singleton	01243
Sion Mills	016626
Sittingbourne	01795
Six Mile Bottom	01638
Skeabost Bridge	
3 figure numbers	0147032
6 figure numbers	01470
Skegness	01754
Skellister	
3 figure numbers	0159589
6 figure numbers	01595
Skelmersdale	01695
Skelton	017684
Skenfrith	
3 figure numbers	0160084

Stalham	01692
Stamford	01780
Stamford Bridge	01759
Stamfordham	01661
Standeford	01902
Standish	01257
Standon Rock	01782
Stanford-in-the-Vale	01367
Stanford-le-Hope	01375
Stanley (Co Durham)	01207
Stanley (Perths)	01738
Stannington (Northumberland)	01670
Stansted Airport	01279
Stanton (Glos)	
3 figure numbers	0138673
6 figure numbers	01386
Stanton St John	01865
Stanton (Suffolk)	01359
Staplecross	01580
Stapleford (Essex)	01708
Staplehurst	01580

Starcross	01626
Staveley (Cumbria)	01539
Staverton	01803
Stebbing	01371
Steele Road	01387
Steens Bridge	
3 figure numbers	0156882
6 figure numbers	01568
Steeple Aston	01869
Steeple Bumpstead	01440
Steeple Morden	01763
Steeton	01535
Stelling Minnis	
3 figure numbers	0122787
6 figure numbers	01227
Stenigot	01507
Stenton	01368
Stetchworth	01638
Stevenage	01438
Stevenston (Ayrshire)	01294
Stewarton	01560

Stewartstown	01868
Steyning	01903
Stichill	01573
Stirling	01786
Stithians	01209
Stobo	
3 figure numbers	017216
6 figure numbers	01721
Stock	01277
Stockland	01404
Stocksfield	01661
Stockton-on-Tees	01642
Stoer	
3 figure numbers	015715
6 figure numbers	01571
Stogumber	01984
Stoke Climsland	01579
Stoke Ferry	01366
Stoke Fleming	01803
Stoke Gabriel	01803
Stoke Goldington	
3 figure numbers	0190855

6 figure numbers	01908
Stoke-on-Trent	01782
Stoke St Milborough	
3 figure numbers	0158475
6 figure numbers	01584
Stokesley	01642
Stonehaven	01569
Stonehenge	01980
Stonehouse (Lanarks)	01698
Stonesfield	01993
Stone (Staffs)	01785
Stoneyburn	01501
Stoneyford	01846
Stonyhurst	01254
Stornoway	01851
Storrington	01903
Stottesdon	
3 figure numbers	0174632
6 figure numbers	01746
Stourbridge	01384
Stourport	01299
Stow	01578

Place	Number
Stowmarket	01449
Strabane	01504
Strachur	
3 figure numbers	0136986
6 figure numbers	01369
Stradbroke	01379
Straiton	
3 figure numbers	016557
6 figure numbers	01655
Strangford	01396
Stranraer	01776
Stratford-upon-Avon	01789
Strathardle	01250
Strathaven	01357
Strathconon	
3 figure numbers	019977
6 figure numbers	01997
Strathdon	
5 figure numbers	019756
6 figure numbers	01975
Strathkanaird	
3 figure numbers	0185486
6 figure numbers	01854
Strathkinness	
3 figure numbers	0133485
6 figure numbers	01334
Strathmiglo	01337
Strathnaver	
3 figure numbers	016416
6 figure numbers	01641
Strathpeffer	01997
Strathtay	01887
Strathy	
3 figure numbers	016414
6 figure numbers	01641
Strathyre	01877
Stratton Audley	01869
Street	01458
Strichen	01771
Stromeferry	
3 figure numbers	019756
6 figure numbers	01997
Stromness	01856
Stronsay	
3 figure numbers	018576
6 figure numbers	01857
Strontian	01967
Stroud (Glos)	01453
Struan	
3 figure numbers	0147072
6 figure numbers	01470
Struy	
3 figure numbers	0146376
6 figure numbers	01463
Stubbington	01329
Studland	
3 figure numbers	0192944
6 figure numbers	01929
Studley	01527
Sturminster Marshall	01258
Sturminster Newton	
5 figure numbers	0159987
6 figure numbers	01258
Suckley	01886
Sudbury (Derby)	01283
Sudbury (Suffolk)	01787
Sulby (Isle of Man)	01624
Sulgrave	01295
Sullom Voe	01806
Sully	01222
Sumburgh	01950
Sunbury-on-Thames	01932
Sunderland (see Wearside)	
Surfleet	01775
Surlingham	01508
Sutton Elms	01455
Sutton (Macclesfield)	01260
Sutton-on-Sea	01507
Sutton St James	
3 figure numbers	0194585
6 figure numbers	01945
Sutton St Nicholas	01432
Sutton (West Sussex)	
3 figure numbers	017987
6 figure numbers	01798
Swaby	01507
Swaffham	01760
Swainsthorpe	01508

Place	Code
Swalcliffe	01295
Swallow	01472
Swanage	01929
Swanley	01322
Swansea	01792
Swanton Abbott	01692
Swanton Morley	01362
Swaton	01529
Swatragh	01648
Swavesey	01954
Swimbridge	01271
Swinderby	01522
Swindon	01793
Swinton (Berwicks)	01890
Swynnerton	01782
Syderstone	
3 figure numbers	0148523
6 figure numbers	01485
Symbister	018066
3 figure numbers	0187487
6 figure numbers	01874
Symington	01563

Place	Code
Symonds Yat	01600
Syresham	01280
T	
Tackley	01869
Tadcaster	01937
Taddington	01298
Tadley	01734
Tadworth	01737
Taffs Well	01222
Tain	01862
Talgarth	01874
Talley	01558
Talmine	
3 figure numbers	0184756
6 figure numbers	01847
Talybont (Aberystwyth)	01970
Talybont-on-Usk	
3 figure numbers	0187487
6 figure numbers	01874
Talywain	01495
Tamworth	01827

Place	Code
Tandragee	01762
Tankerness	
3 figure numbers	0185686
6 figure numbers	01856
Tanworth-in-Arden	01564
Tarbert (Argyll)	01880
Tarbolton	01292
Tarfside	01356
Tarland	
5 figure numbers	013398
6 figure numbers	01339
Tarporley	01829
Tarrant Hinton	01258
Tarrington	01432
Tarskavaig	
3 figure numbers	014715
6 figure numbers	01471
Tarves	01651
Tarvin	01829
Tatsfield	01959
Tattenhall (Chester)	01829
Taunton	01823

Place	Code
Tavistock	01822
Tayinloan	
3 figure numbers	015834
6 figure numbers	01583
Taynuilt	
3 figure numbers	018662
6 figure numbers	01866
Tayport	01382
Tayvallich	
3 figure numbers	015467
6 figure numbers	01546
Tealby	01673
Tealing	
3 figure numbers	0182621
6 figure numbers	01382
Tean	01538
Tedburn St Mary	01647
Teesdale	01833
Teffont	01722
Teignmouth	01626
Telford	01952
Templecombe	01963

62

Name	Code		Name	Code
Twinstead	01787		6 figure numbers	01470
Twyford (Berks)	01734		Ullapool	01854
Twyford (Hants)	01962		Ulva Ferry	01962
Twynholm	015576		3 figure numbers	016885
3 figure numbers	01557		6 figure numbers	01688
Tydd	0194576		Ulverston	01229
3 figure numbers	01945		Up Holland	01695
6 figure numbers	01838		Uplawmoor	01505
Tyndrum	0191		Upminster	01708
Tyneside	01248		Upottery	
Tynygongl	01492		3 figure numbers	0140486
Tynygroes	01295		6 figure numbers	01404
Tysoe	01654		Upper Basildon	01491
Tywyn			Upper Cwmtwrch	01639
U				
Ubbeston	01986		Upper Largo	
Uckfield	01825		3 figure numbers	0133336
Uddingston	01698		6 figure numbers	01333
Udny	01651		Upper Sapey	01886
Uig			Upper Warlingham	01883
3 figure numbers	0147042		Uppingham	01572

Name	Code		Name	Code
Uppington			Velindre	01559
3 figure numbers	0195286		Verwood	01202
6 figure numbers	01952		Vidlin	
Upton Bishop			3 figure numbers	018067
3 figure numbers	0198985		6 figure numbers	01806
6 figure numbers	01989		VODAFONE	0370
Upton Magna	01743		VODAFONE	0374
Upton Noble	01749		VODAFONE	0385
Upton Snodsbury	01905		VODAFONE	0831
Upton-upon-Severn	01684		VODAFONE	0836
Upwey	01305		Voe	
Urray			3 figure numbers	018068
3 figure numbers	019973		6 figure numbers	01806
6 figure numbers	01997		W	
Usk	01291		Wadebridge	01208
Uttoxeter	01889		Wadhurst	01892
Uxbridge	01895		Wakefield	01924
Uyeasound			Walcott	01692
3 figure numbers	0195785		Waldringfield	01473
6 figure numbers	01957		Walkerburn	
V			3 figure numbers	0189687
Valley	01407		6 figure numbers	01896

Place	Code
Walkern	01438
Wallingford	01491
Walls	
3 figure numbers	0159571
6 figure numbers	01595
Walsall	01922
Walsham-le-Willows	01359
Walsingham (Norfolk)	01328
Waltham Cross	01992
Waltham-on-the-Wolds	
3 figure numbers	0166478
6 figure numbers	01664
Walton-on-Thames	01932
Wangford	01502
Wantage	01235
Warborough	01865
Ware	01920
Wareham	01929
Wargrave	01734
Waringstown	01762
Warmingham	
3 figure numbers	0127077
6 figure numbers	01270
Warminster	01985
Warmwell	01305
Warninglid	01444
Warrenpoint	016937
Warrington	01925
Wartle	01467
Warwick	01926
Wasdale	019467
Washford	01984
Washington	0191
Watchet	01984
Waterbeck	01461
Waterhouses	01538
Waterlooville	01705
Waternish	
3 figure numbers	0147083
6 figure numbers	01470
Watford	01923
Watlington	01491
Watten (Caithness)	
3 figure numbers	0195582
6 figure numbers	01955
Watton (Norfolk)	01953
Waunfawr	01286
Weardale	01388
Wearside	0191
Weasenham St Peter	
3/4 figure numbers	0132874
6 figure numbers	01328
Weaverham	01606
Wedmore	01934
Weedon	01327
Week St Mary	
3 figure numbers	0128884
6 figure numbers	01288
Weeley	01255
Weeton (Lancs)	01253
Weisdale	
3 figure numbers	0159572
6 figure numbers	01595
Welford	01858
Welfield	01429
Wellingborough	01933
Wellington (Somerset)	01823
Wells (Somerset)	01749
Welney	
3 figure numbers	0135471
6 figure numbers	01354
Welshpool	01938
Welton	01673
Welwyn	01438
Welwyn Garden	01707
Wem	01939
Wemyss Bay	01475
Wendling	01362
Wendover	01296
Wensleydale	01969
Wentworth	01344
Weobley	01544
Westbury (Wilts)	01373
3 figure numbers	0159572
6 figure numbers	01595
West Calder	01506
West Chiltington	01798

West Coker 01935
West Drayton 01895
Westerdale
3 figure numbers 0184784
6 figure numbers
Westerham 01847
West Haddon 01959
West Heslerton 01788
Westhoughton 01944
West Kilbride 01942
West Kingsdown 01294
Westleton 01474
3 figure numbers 0172873
6 figure numbers
West Linton 01728
West Lulworth 01968
3 figure numbers 0192941
6 figure numbers
West Lutton 01929
West Malling 01944
West Meon 01732
West Mersea 01730
3 figure numbers 01206

West Monkton 01823
Weston (Herts) 01462
Weston (Staffs) 01889
Weston-super-Mare 01934
Weston-under-Lizard
3 figure numbers 0195276
6 figure numbers
Weston Zoyland 01952
Westray 01278
3 figure numbers 018577
West Runton 01263
3 figure numbers 01857
6 figure numbers
Westruther 01578
West Sandwick
3 figure numbers 0195786
6 figure numbers
West Wellow 01957
Wetheral 01794
Wetherby 01228
Wetley Rocks 01937
Wettenhall 01782
3 figure numbers 0127073

6 figure numbers 01270
Wetwood
3 figure numbers 0163082
6 figure numbers 01630
Weybourne
3/4 figure numbers 0126370
6 figure numbers
Weybridge 01932
Weyhill 01264
Weymouth 01305
Whaley Bridge 01663
Whalley 01254
Whatton (Morpeth) 01670
Whatton (Notts) 01949
Wheathampstead 01582
Wheathill 01963
Wheatley (Oxon) 01865
Wheaton Aston 01785
Wheldrake 01904
Whiddon Down 01647
Whimple 01404
Whipsnade 01582

Whissendine
3 figure numbers 0166479
6 figure numbers 01664
Whitburn (West Lothian) 01501
Whitby 01947
Whitchurch (Avon) 01275
Whitchurch (Hants) 01256
Whitchurch (Shrops) 01948
Whiteabbey 01232
Whiteface
3 figure numbers 0186288
6 figure numbers 01862
Whitehaven 01946
Whitehead 01960
Whitehills 01261
Whitehouse (Argyll)
3 figure numbers 0188073
6 figure numbers 01880
Whitekirk
3 figure numbers 0162087
6 figure numbers 01620

67

Place	Code	Place	Code
Withernsea	01964	Woodchurch	01233
Witherslack	015395	Woodhall Spa	01526
Witnesham	01473	Woodhouse Eaves	01509
Witney	01993	Woodseaves	01785
Wittersham	01797	Woodstock	01993
Witton-le-Wear	01388	Wootton	
Wiveliscombe	01984	*3 figure numbers*	0150844
Wivelsfield Green	01444	*6 figure numbers*	01508
Wivenhoe	01206	Woolacombe	01271
Woburn (Beds)	01525	Wooler	01668
Woking	01483	Woolhampton (Berks)	01734
Wokingham	01734	Woolverstone (Suffolk)	01473
Woldingham (Surrey)	01883	Wooperton	
Wolston	01203	*3 figure numbers*	016687
Wolverhampton	01902	*6 figure numbers*	01668
Wolvesnewton	01291	Wootton (Humberside)	01469
Wolviston	01740	Worcester	01905
Wombourne (West Midlands)	01902	Worfield	0174 64
Woodborough (Wilts)	01672	*3 figure numbers*	
Woodbridge	01394	*6 figure numbers*	01746
Woodbury	01395		

Place	Code	Place	Code
Workington	01900	Wroxham	01603
Worksop	01909	Wychbold	01527
Worlingworth	01728	Wye (Kent)	01233
Wormbridge		Wylam	01661
3 figure numbers	0198121	Wylye	
6 figure numbers	01981	*3 figure numbers*	019856
Wormley (Surrey)	01428	*6 figure numbers*	01985
Wormshill		Wymeswold	01509
3 figure numbers	0162784	Wymondham (Leics)	
6 figure numbers	01622	*3 figure numbers*	0157284
Worplesdon	01483	*6 figure numbers*	01572
Worthen	01743	Wymondham (Norfolk)	
Worthing	01903		01953
Worth Matravers	01929	Wythall	01564
Wragby	01673		
Wraysbury	01784	**Y**	
Wrentham		Yapton	01243
3 figure numbers	0150275	Yardley Gobion	01908
6 figure numbers	01502	Yardley Hastings	01604
Wrestlingworth	01767	Yarpole	01568
Wrexham	01978	Yarrow	01750
Wrington	01934	Yarrowford	01750
		Yateley	01252

Yatton	01934
Yelverton	01822
Yeovil	01935
Yetholm	01573
Yetminster	01935
Ynysddu	01495
Ynysowen	01443
Ynysybwl	01443
Yockleton	01743
York	01904
Youlgrave	01629
Yoxall	01543
Yoxford	01728
Ythanwells	
3 figure numbers	014647
6 figure numbers	01464

Z

Zelah	01872

Section 2
National dialling codes decoder

This section gives the new national dialling codes listed numerically and followed by place name.

Most BT telephone numbers in the UK consist of either an area code followed by a personal number, or a city code followed by a district code and a personal number.

Here you will find lists of all these codes in numerical order, along with the approximate geographical location such as the exchange name and/or nearest postal town for area codes, and the city and district names for city codes.

Please note the locations shown for area codes refer to the postal address of the exchange – not of the customer, who may be a few miles away from the exchange and have a different address.

If a number does not begin with a 0, it will not be included in the decoder.

Other licensed operators

Abbrev	*Operator's full name*
ACC	Anglia Cable Communications Ltd
AT	Atlantic Telecom
BCL	Birmingham Cable Ltd
BCCL	Bradford Cable Communications Ltd
CBTL	Cabeltel (UK) Ltd
CLP	Cable London plc
CNW	Cable Northwest
CCL	Cambridge Cable Ltd
DCL	Diamond Cable Ltd
ECTL	Encom Cable TV & Telecommunications Ltd
ECL	Energis Communications Ltd
EL	Eurobell Ltd
H	Hutchison Paging
JCGL	Jones Cable Group Ltd
LCL	Leicester Communications Ltd
LBCL	Liberty Communications Ltd
MCL	Mercury Communications Ltd
MCCL	Midlands Cable Commuications Ltd
NCL	Nynex Cablecomms Ltd
O	Orange Personal Communication Services Ltd
SBC	SBC Cablecomms
TC	Telecential Communications
TCC	The Cable Corporation
UACL	United Artists Communications Ltd
VGP	Vodafone Group plc

As from April 16, 1995, the code for **Leeds** has changed to 0113 from 0532 and customers' numbers are prefixed by 2

0133 2300 **Adel Leeds, 2301** Adel, **2302** Headingley, **2303** Adel, **2304** Headingley, **2305** Headingley, **2306** Headingley, **2307** Headingley, **2309** Rothwell, **2310** Armley, **2311** Armley, **2319** Armley, **2320** Garforth, **2321** Crossgates, **2323** Seacroft, **2325** Seacroft, **2326** Crossgates, **2328** Crossgates, **2329** Crossgates, **2350** Harehills, **2351** Harehills, **2354** Harehills, **2359** Harehills, **2360** Pudsey, **2361** Pudsey, **2362** Pudsey, **2363** Pudsey, **2365** Harehills, **369** Moortown, **2370** Moortown, **2371** Moortown, **2374** Chapeltown, **2376** Pudsey, **2378** Armley, **2379** Chapeltown, **2380** Morley, **2381** Morley, **2382** Morley, **2383** Morley, **2386** Rawdon, **2387** Rawdon, **2390** Horsforth, **2391** Rawdon, **2392** Pudsey, **2393** Pudsey, **2394** Pudsey, **2395** Horsforth, **2396** Pudsey, **2397** Rawdon, **2398** Horsforth, **240** Harehills, **2415** Armley, **248** Harehills, **249** Harehills, **250** Rawdon, **252** Morley, **253** Morley, **254** MCL Leeds, **255** Pudsey, **256** Pudsey, **257** Pudsey, **258** Horsforth, **2590** Horsforth, **2591** Horsforth, **2592** Horsforth, **2596** Horsforth, **260**, Crossgates, **261** Adel, **262** Chapeltown, **263** Armley, **264** Crossgates, **265** Seacroft, **266** Moortown, **267** Adel, **268** Moortown, **269** Moortown, **270** Hunslet, **271** Hunslet, **272** Seacroft, **273** Seacroft, **274** Headingley, **275** Headingley, **2760** Hunslet, **2761** Hunslet, **2762** Hunslet, **2763** Hunslet, **2764** Hunslet, **2765** Hunslet, **2766** Hunslet, **2768** Hunslet, **277** Hunslet, **278** Headingley, **279** Armley, **280** MCL Leeds, **281** Barwick-in-Elmet, **282** Rothwell, **283** MCL Leeds, **2841** Arthington, **2842** Arthington, **2843** Arthington, **2852** Drighlington, **2853** Drighlington, **2854** Drighlington, **286** Garforth, **287** Garforth, **2880** Rothwell, **2883** Headingley, **2886** Harewood, **2889** Rothwell, **289** Thorner, **293** JCGL, **other numbers** Leeds

As from April 16, 1995, the code for **Sheffield** has changed to 0114 from 0742 and customers' numbers are prefixed by 2

0114 230 Beauchief, **231** Wadsley Bridge, **232** Wadsley Bridge, **233** Wadsley Bridge, **234** Wadsley Bridge, **235** Beauchief, **236** Beauchief, **237** Greenhill, **239** Intake, **240** Ecclesfield, **242** Attercliffe, **243** Attercliffe, **244** Attercliffe, **245** Ecclesfield, Ecclesfield, **247** Mosborough, **248** Mosborough, **250**Sharrow, **251** Mosborough, **2530** Intake, **2531** Intake, **254** Woodhouse, **255**Sharrow, **2560** Attercliffe, **256**Attercliffe, **2562**Attercliffe, **2563** Attercliffe, **2564** Attercliffe, **2565** Attercliffe, **2566** Attercliffe, **2567** Attercliffe, **2568** Meadowhall, **2569** Meadowhall, **257** Ecclesfield, **258** Sharrow, **261** Attercliffe, **262** Beauchief **263** Ranmoor, **264** Intake, **265** Intake, **266** Broomhill, **267** Broomhill, **268** Broomhill, **269** Woodhouse, **271** MCL, **2740** Woodseats,

73

2745 Woodseats, 2746 Woodseats, 2747 Woodseats, 2748 Woodseats, 2749 Woodseats, 282 MCL Sheffield, 2830 Stocksbridge, 2831 Stocksbridge, 2839 Greenhill, 284 High Green, 2851 Bradfield, 2852 Wadsley Bridge, 2853 Wadsley Bridge, 2854 Wadsley Bridge, 2855 Wadsley Bridge, 2856 Wadsley Bridge, 2861 Oughtibridge, 2862 Oughtibridge, 2863 Oughtibridge, 2864 Oughtibridge, 2869 High Green, 287 Aston Common, 288 Stocksbridge, 2890 Holmsfield, 2891 Holmsfield, 2899 Holmsfield, **other numbers Sheffield**

As from April 16, 1995, the code for **Nottingham** has changed to **0115** from **0602** and customers' numbers are prefixed by **9**
0115 920 Arnold Nottingham, 9211 Clifton/Ruddington, **9212** Clifton/Ruddington, **9213** Clifton/Ruddington, **9214** Clifton/Ruddington, **9215** Clifton/Ruddington, **9216** Clifton/Ruddington, **9217** Clifton/Ruddington, **9218** Sandiacre, **922** Beeston, **923** Edwalton, **9240** City Centre Nottingham, **9241** City Centre Nottingham, **9242** City Centre Nottingham, **9243** City Centre Nottingham, **9244** Basford, **9245** Sherwood, **9249** Basford, **925** Beeston, **926** Arnold, **927** Bulwell, **928** Wollaton, **929** Billborough, **930** Ilkeston, **9311** Burton Joyce, **9312** Burton Joyce, **9313** Burton Joyce, **932** Ilkeston, **9332** Radcliffe-on-Trent, **9333** Radcliffe-on-Trent, **9334** Radcliffe-on-Trent, **9335** Radcliffe-on-Trent, **9336** Radcliffe-on-Trent, **934** City Centre Nottingham, **935** MCL, **936** MCL, **937** Plumtree, **938** Kimberley, **939** Sandiacre, **9400** Gedling, **9401** Gedling, **9402** Gedling, **9403** Gedling, **9404** Gedling, **9405** Clifton/Ruddington, **9406** Clifton/Ruddington, **9407** Gedling, **941** City Centre, **9420** Basford, **9421** Basford, **9422** Basford, **9423** Basford, **9424** Basford, **9425** Billborough Nottingham, **9426** Billborough, **9427** Basford, **9428** Billborough, **9430** Beeston, **9431** Beeston, **9432** Beeston, **9433** Beeston, **9434** Beeston, **9435** Meadows Area, **9436** Beeston, **437** City Centre, **9438** Meadows Area, **944** Ilkeston, **9452** Edwalton, **9453** City Centre, **9454** City Centre, **9455** West Bridgford, **9456** Clifton/Ruddington, **9457** Clifton/Ruddington, **9458** Kimberley, **9459** Kimberley, **946** Long Eaton, **947** City Centre, **948** City Centre, **9490** Sandiacre, **9491** Sandiacre, **9492** City Centre, **9493** City Centre, **9494** City Centre, **9495** City Centre, **9496** Sandiacre, **9497** Sandiacre, **9498** City Centre, **9499** Sandiacre, **950** City Centre, **9510** City Centre, **9512** Ilkeston, **9513** Beeston, **9514** Beeston, **9515** Beeston, **9516** Beeston, **9518** Beeston, **952** DCL, **953** DCL, **954** ECL, **955** DCL, **956** DCL, **9571** Beeston, **9572** Beeston, **9573** Beeston, **9574** Beeston, **9575** Beeston, **958** City Centre, **959** City Centre, **960** Sherwood, **961** Gedling, **962** Sherwood, **963** Hucknall, **9640**

Hucknall, **9641** Hucknall, **9642** Hucknall, **9643** Meadows Area, **9645** Meadows Area, **9652** Woodborough, **9653** Woodborough, **9654** Woodborough, **9655** Woodborough, **9656** Woodborough, **9657** Woodborough, **9658** Gedling, **9662** Arnold, **9663** Lowdham, **9664** Lowdham, **9670** Arnold, **9671** Arnold, **9672** Arnold, **9673**Arnold, **9674** Arnold, **9675** Arnold, **9676** Arnold, **9677** Beeston, **9678** Beeston, **9679** Arnold, **9680** Hucknall, **9681** Hucknall, **9682** Meadows Area, **9683** Beeston, **9686** Beeston, **9687** Beeston, **9688** Meadows Area/City Centre, **9691** Sherwood, **9692** Sherwood, **9693** Sherwood, **9694** West Bridgford, **9695** Sherwood, **970** Basford, **972** Long Eaton, **973** Long Eaton, **975** Bulwell, **976** Bulwell, **9770** Bulwell, **9771** Bulwell, **9772** West Bridgford, **9773** West Bridgford, **9774** West Bridgford, **978** Basford, **9790** Basford, **9791** Basford, **9792** Basford, **9793** City Centre, **9794** Bulwell, **9795** Bulwell, **9796** West Bridgford, **9797** Bulwell, **9798** Bulwell, **9799** City Centre, **980** Nottingham, **981** West Bridgford, **982** West Bridgford, **9830** Gotham, **9831** Gotham, **9834** Hucknall, **984** Clifton/Ruddington, **9850** Meadows Area, **9851** Meadows Area, **9852** Meadows Area, **9854** Wollaton, **9855** Wollaton, **9856** Sherwood, **9857** Sherwood, **9858** Sherwood, **9859** City Centre, **986** Meadows Area, **987** Gedling, **988** City Centre, **989** Cotgrave, **other numbers** Nottingham

As from April 16, 1995, the code for Leicester has changed to **0116** from **0533** and customers' numbers are prefixed by 2
0116 230 Rothley Leics, **231** Glenfield/Groby, **2320** Glenfield/Groby, **2321** Glenfield/Groby, **2322** Glenfield/Groby, **2323** Anstey/Beaumont, **2324** Glenfield/Groby, **233** LCL, **234** Anstey/Beaumont, **235**. Anstey/Beaumont, **236** Anstey/Beaumont, **238** Kirby Muxloe, **239** Kirby Muxloe, **240** Fleckney, **241** Thurnby/Evington, **242** City Centre, **243** Thurnby/Evington, **2440** Aylestone, **2448** Stoneygate/Knighton, **246** Humberstone, **470** City Centre/Western Park, **2471** City Centre/Western Park, **2472** City Centre/Western Park, **2473** City Centre/Western Park, **2474** City Centre/Western Park, **2477** West Wigston/Blaby, **2478** Peatling Magna, **248** City Centre, **249** Evington, **251** City Centre, **252** City Centre/Western Park, **253** City Centre, **254** City Centre/Western Park, **255** City Centre/Western Park, **256** MCL, **2570** East Wigston/South Knighton, **2571** East Wigston/South Knighton, **2572** East Wigston/South Knighton, **2574** City Centre/Western Park, **2575** City Centre/Western Park, **2576** City Centre/Western Park, **577** City Centre/Western Park, **2583** Evington Leicester, **2584** Evington, **2585** City Centre/Western Park, **2586** City Centre/Western Park, **2588** Evington, **2592** Great Glen, **2593** Great Glen, **2595** Hungarton, **2596** Billesdon, **2597** Tilton, **2598**Tugby, **260** Syston/Goscote, **261** Belgrave, **262**

75

City Centre, **263** Braunstone/Westcotes, **264** Syston/Goscote, **265** MCL, **266** Belgrave , **267** Birstall, **268** Belgrave, **269** Syston/Goscote, **270** Stoneygate/Knighton, **271** Oadby, **2720** Oadby, **27210**Oadby Leics, **2722** Oadby, **2723** Oadby, **2724** Narborough, **2725** Narborough, **2726** Narborough, **2727** Narborough, **2728** Oadby, **273** Evington, **274** Humberstone, **2750** Narborough, **2751** Narborough, **2752** Narborough, **2753** Narborough, **2755** City Centre/Western Park, **2756** City Centre/Western Park, **2757** City Centre/Western Park, **2758** City Centre/Western Park, **2759** West Wigston/Blaby, **276** Humberstone, **277** West Wigston/Blaby, **278** West Wigston/Blaby, **279** Kibworth, **280** Leicester, **2810** East Wigston/South Knighton, **2811** East Wigston/South Knighton, **2812** East Wigston/South Knighton, **2813** East Wigston/South Knighton, **2814** Braunstone/Westcotes, **282** Braunstone/Westcotes, **283** Aylestone, **284** Narborough, **285** City Centre/Western Park, **286** Narborough , **287** Glenfield/Groby, **288** East Wigston/South Knighton, **289** Braunstone/Westcotes, **290** ECL, **291** LCL, *other numbers Leicester*

As from April 16, 1995, the code for **Bristol** has changed to 0117 from 0272 and customers' numbers are prefixed by **9**
0117 932 Bitton Bristol, **9371** Abson Wick, **9372** Abson Wick, **9373** Abson Wick, **9374** Abson Wick, **940** MCL Bristol, **949** MCL Bristol, **949** UACL Bristol, **975, 9**75, MCL Bristol, **976** MCL Bristol, **983** UACL Bristol, **984** MCL Bristol, **986** Keynsham, **987** UACL Bristol, **988** MCL Bristol, *other numbers Bristol*

01200 43 MCL Clitheroe Lancs, **445** Gisburn, **446** Slaidburn, **447**Bolton-by-Bowland, **448** Dunsop Bridge, *other numbers* Clitheroe
01202 20 Bournemouth Dorset, **29** Bournemouth, **30** Boscombe, **31** Bournemouth, **34** MCL, **39** Boscombe, **40** Bournemouth, **41** Bournemouth, **42** Southbourne, **43** Southbourne, **44** Bournemouth, **47** Christchurch, **48** Christchurch, **49** Christchurch, **50** MCL Bournemouth, **51** Winton, **52** Winton, **53** Winton, **54** Winton, **55** Bournemouth, **57** Northbourne, **58** Northbourne, **59** Bournemouth, **60** Broadstone, **63** Lytchett Minster, **64** Broadstone, **65** Broadstone, **66** Poole, **67** Poole, **68** Poole, **69** Broadstone, **70** Canford Cliffs, **71** Parkstone, **72** Parkstone, **73** Parkstone, **74** Parkstone, **75** Westbourne, **76** Westbourne, **78** Bournemouth, **81** Verwood, **82** Verwood, **84** Wimborne, **85** Ferndown, **86** Ferndown, **87** Ferndown, **88** Wimborne, **89** Ferndown
01203 202 Allesley Coventry, **West Midlands, 203** Allesley, **204** Allesley, **214** Tollbar End, **215** Tollbar End, **216** Tollbar End, **233** Binley, **28** Energis, **29** MCL, **30** Tollbar End, **31** Bedworth, **32** Nuneaton, **33** Keresley, **34** Nuneaton, **35** Nuneaton, **36** Exhall, **37**

Nuneaton, **38** Nuneaton, **39** Chapel End, **40** Allesley Coventry, **41** Gibbet Hill/Finham, **42** Tile Hill, **43** Binley, **44** Binley, **45** Binley, **46** Tile Hill, **47** Tile Hill, **49** Bedworth, **50** Cheylesmore, **51** Tollbar End, **53** MCL, **54** Wolston, **56** Binley, **58** Foleshill, **59** Radford, **601** Radford, **602** Walsgrave-on-Sowe, **603** Walsgrave-on-Sowe, **604** Walsgrave-on-Sowe, **61** Walsgrave-on-Sowe Coventry, West Midlands, **62** Walsgrave-on-Sowe, **635** Binley, **636** Binley, **637** Foleshill, **638** Foleshill, **639** Tollbar End, **640** Bedworth, **641** Nuneaton, **642** Nuneaton, **643** Bedworth, **644** Exhall, **645** Binley, **65** Binley, **66** Foleshill, **67** Earlsdon, **68** Foleshill, **690** Gibbet Hill/Finham, **691** Earlsdon, **692** Gibbet Hill, **693** Gibbet Hill, **694** Tile Hill, **695** Tile Hill, **696** Royal Show, **697** Gibbet Hill/Finham, **698** Gibbet Hill/Finham, **70** Foleshill, **71** Earlsdon, **81** Coventry, **835** Foleshill, **841** Walsgrave-on-Sowe, **842** Walsgrave-on-Sowe, **845** Gibbet Hill/Finham, **847** Gibbet Hill/Finham, **852** Tile Hill, **853** Gibbet Hill/Finham, **854** Earlsdon, **855** Tile Hill, **856** Tile Hill, **86** MCL, **87** Earlsdon, **882** Tollbar End, **883** Tollbar End/Tile Hill, **884** Binley, **886** Tollbar End, **other numbers** Coventry

01204 30 Astley Bridge, **47** Horwich, **49** Doffcocker, **51** Bolton, **59** Astley Bridge, **61** Daubhill, **62** Daubhill, **63** Daubhill, **64** Daubhill, **65** Daubhill, **66** Daubhill, **661** Daubhill, **665** Daubhill, **667** Horwich, **668** Horwich, **669** Horwich, **67** Horwich, **68** Horwich, **69** Horwich, **7** Farnworth, **8** Belmont Village, **84** Doffcocker, **85** Turton, **86** Farnworth, **87** MCL Bolton, **88** Tottington, **other numbers** Bolton

01205 26 Fosdyke, **27** New Leake, **28** Langrick, **29** Hubbert's Bridge, **46** Sutterton, **48** Stickney, **72** Kirton, **75** Sibsey, **76** Butterwick, **82** Swineshead, **84** New Leake, **85** Fosdyke, **87** Old Leake, **88** Boston, **other numbers** Boston

01206 21 Marks Tey Colchester Essex, **3** Ardleigh, **24** Fordham, **25** Great Bentley, **26** Nayland, **27** Great Horkesley, **29** East Bergholt, **30** Brightlingsea, **32** Dedham, **330** Birch, **331** Birch, **337** Higham, **38** West Mersea, **39** Manningtree, **72** Rowhedge, **734** Layer de la Haye, **735** Peldon, **738** Layer de la Haye, **82** Wivenhoe, **other numbers** Colchester

01207 23 Stanley Co Durham, **255** Edmundbyers, **27** Burnopfield, **28** Stanley, **29** Stanley, **50** Consett, **52** Lanchester, **54** Rowlands Gill, **55** Edmundbyers, **56** Ebchester, **57** Dipton, **58** Consett, **59** Consett, **60** MCL Consett, **7** Burnopfield

01208 81 Wadebridge, **82** Cardinham, **83** Lanivet, **84** St Mabyn, **85** St Tudy, **86** Trebetherick, **87** Lostwithiel, **88** Port Isaac, **89** Wadebridge, **other numbers** Bodmin

01209 21 Redruth, **31** Redruth, **61** Camborne, **71** Camborne, **82** St Day, **83** Praze, **84** Portreath, **85** Camborne, **86** Stithians, **89** Porthtowan

77

0121 Birmingham Area Code, 200 City Centre and Hockley, **212** City Centre and Hockley, **214** City Centre, **230** City Centre, **232** City Centre and Hockley, **233** City Centre and Hockley, **234** City Centre and Hockley, **235** City Centre and Hockley, **236** City Centre and Hockley, **237** City Centre and Hockley, **252** Birmingham, **262** City Centre, **265** City Centre, **275** ECL, **276** O, **306** Erdington, **308** Four Oaks, **311** Whitehouse Common, **313** Walmley, **321** Sutton Coldfield and Kingstanding, **322** Washwood Heath and Witton, **323** Four Oaks, **325** Great Barr, **326** Washwood Heath and Witton, **327** Washwood Heath and Witton, **328** Washwood Heath and Witton, **329** Whitehouse Common, **331** Birchfield and Perry Barr, **332** Birchfield and Perry Barr, **333** Aston, **344** Birchfield and Perry Barr, **350** Erdington and Kingstanding, **351** Walmley, **352** Kingstanding and Streetly, **353** Kingstanding and Streetly, **354** Sutton Coldfield and Kingstanding, **355** Sutton Coldfield and Kingstanding, **356** Birchfield and Perry Barr, **357** Perry Barr and Hampstead, **358** Perry Barr and Hampstead, **359** Aston, **360** Great Barr, **362** Sutton Coldfield, **366** Great Barr, **373** Erdington and Kingstanding, **377** Erdington, **378** Whitehouse Common, **380** Aston, **382** Erdington and Kingstanding, **384** Erdington and Kingstanding, **386** Erdington and Kingstanding, **411** Northfield, **414** Selly Oak, **415** Selly Oak, **420** Bearwood, **421** Woodgate and Quinton, **422** Woodgate and Quinton, **423** Woodgate and Quinton, **427** Harborne, **428** Harborne, **429** Bearwood, **430** Druids Heath, **432** Selly Oak, **433** Kings Norton, **434** Bearwood, **436** Druids Heath, **440** Calthorpe and Balsall Heath, **441** Kings Heath, **442** Moseley, **443** Kings Heath, **444** Kings Heath, **445** Barnt Green and Alvechurch, **446** Calthorpe and Balsall Heath, **447** Barnt Green and Alvechurch, **449** Moseley, **451** Kings Norton, **452** Edgbaston, **453** Rubery, **454** Edgbaston, **455** Edgbaston, **456** Edgbaston, **457** Rubery, **458** Kings Norton, **459** Kings Norton, **460** Rubery, **471** Selly Oak, **472** Selly Oak, **474** Druids Heath, **475** Northfield, **476** Northfield, **477** Northfield, **478** Northfield, **482** Northfield, **483** Northfield, **486** Kings Norton, **500** West Bromwich, **501** Halesowen, **502** Wednesbury, **503** Halesowen, **504** Halesowen, **505** Wednesbury, **507** Handsworth, **511** Oldbury, **515** Handsworth, **520** Tipton, **521** Tipton, **522** Tipton, **523** Handsworth, **524** West Bromwich, **525** West Bromwich, **526** Darlaston, **530** Midland Cable, **541** Oldbury, **543** Oldbury, **544** Oldbury, **545** Tipton, **550** Halesowen, **551** Handsworth, **552** Oldbury, **553** West Bromwich, **554** Handsworth, **555** Smethwick, **556** Wednesbury, **557** Tipton, **558** Smethwick, **559** Blackheath, **561** Blackheath, **565** Smethwick, **567** West Bromwich, **568** Darlaston, **569** West Bromwich, **580** West Bromwich, **585** Halesowen, **588** West Bromwich, **600** City Centre, **602** MCCL, **603** BCL.

78

604 BCL, 605 BCL, 606 MCL, 607 MCL, 608 BCL, 609 MCL, 616 City Centre, 622 Smallbrook, 623 MCL, 624 BCL, 625 MCL, 626 MCL, 627 MCL, 628 BCL, 629 MCL, 631 City Centre, 632 City Centre, 633 City Centre, 634 City Centre, 643 City Centre, 644 City Centre, 652 Birmingham, 654 City Centre, 665 City Centre, 666 Smallbrook, 680 BCL, 681 BCL, 692 Smallbrook, 693 BCL, 694 BCL, 695 MCL, 696 MCL, 700 Acocks Green and Sparkbrook, 701 Shirley, 702 Hall Green, 703 Solihull, 704 Solihull, 705 Solihull, 706 Acocks Green, 707 Acocks Green, 708 Acocks Green, 709 Solihull, 711 Solihull, 712 Solihull, 713 Solihull, 717 Chelmsley Business Park, 722 Sheldon, 730 Castle Bromwich, 733 Shirley, 742 Sheldon, 743 Shirley, 744 Shirley, 745 Shirley, 747 Castle Bromwich, 748 Castle Bromwich, 749 Castle Bromwich, 753 Small Heath and Sparkbrook, 764 Acocks Green, 765 Acocks Green, 766 Small Heath and Sparkbrook, 767 Elmdon, 770 Chelmsley Wood, 771 Small Heath and Sparkbrook, 772 Small Heath and Sparkbrook, 773 Small Heath and Sparkbrook, 776 Castle Bromwich, 777 Hall Green, 778 Hall Green, 779 Marston Green and Chelmsley Wood, 780 Elmdon (NEC), 781 Elmdon, 782 Elmdon, 783 Stechford, 784 Stechford, 785 Stechford, 786 Stechford, 787 Elmdon, 788 Chelmsley Wood, 789 Stechford.

01222 26 MCL Cardiff, 35 Penarth, 50 MCL Cardiff, 51 Dinas, 53 Sully, 58 MCL Cardiff, 70 Penarth, 71 Penarth, 81 Taffs Well, 83 Senghenydd, 84 Radyr, 85 Caerphilly, 86 Caerphilly, 88 Caerphilly, 89 Pentyrch, other numbers Cardiff
01223 202 Histon Cambridge, 203 Waterbeach, 204 Waterbeach, 205 Waterbeach, 207 Arrington, 208 Arrington, 21 Cherry Hinton, 23 Histon, 24 Cherry Hinton, 25 MCL Cambridge, 26 Comberton, 27 Girton, 290 West Wratting, 292 Teversham, 293 Teversham, 294 Teversham, 295 Teversham, 40 Cherry Hinton, 410 Cherry Hinton, 411 Cherry Hinton, 412 Cherry Hinton, 413 Cherry Hinton, 414 Cherry Hinton, 415 Cherry Hinton, 416 Cherry Hinton, 440 Waterbeach, 441 Waterbeach, 49 Sawston, 50 CCL Cambridge, 51 CCL Cambridge, 551 Trumpington, 56 CCL, 57 CCL, 58 MCL Cambridge, 81 Bottisham, 822 Sawston, 83 Sawston, 84 Trumpington, 86 Waterbeach, 87 Harston, 88 Fulbourn, 89 Linton, other numbers Cambridge
01224 Aberdeen and Offshore, 20 West Aberdeen, 21 Lochnagar, 24 Kincorth, 27 North Aberdeen, 280 Lochnagar, 281 Lochnagar, 282 Lochnagar, 3 West Aberdeen, 40 MCL Aberdeen, 41 MCL Aberdeen, 48 North Aberdeen, 49 North Aberdeen, 57 Lochnagar, 58 Lochnagar, 59 Lochnagar, 62 Denburn, 63 Denburn, 64 Denburn, 66 Ashgrove, 68 Ashgrove, 69 Ashgrove, 70 Balgownie, 71 Lochnagar,

Bucksburn, 72 Dyce, 73 Cutter, 74 Kingswell, 77 Dyce, 78 Portlethen, 79 Kinellar, 80 Lochnagar, 82 Balgownie, 84 MCL Aberdeen, 86 Bieldside, 87 Kincorth, 89 Kincorth

01225 40 UACL Bath, 70 Melksham, 71 Trowbridge, 72 Limpley Stoke, 73 MCL Bath, 74 Box Corsham, 75 Trowbridge, 76 Trowbridge, 77 Trowbridge, 78 North Trowbridge, 79 Melksham, 81 Hawthorn, 83 Combe Down, 840 Combe Down, 85 Batheaston, 86 Bradford-on-Avon, 87 Saltford, 89 Marshfield, **other numbers Bath**

01226 30 MCL, 34 Wombwell South Yorkshire, 35 Hoyland, 36 Hoyland, 37 Penistone, 38 Darton, 39 Darton, 70 Royston, 71 Cudworth, 72 Royston, 74 Hoyland, 75 Wombwell 76 Penistone, 78 Cudworth, 79 Silkstone, **other numbers Barnsley**

01227 2 Whitstable Kent, 3 Herne Bay, 4 Canterbury, 700 Petham, 709 Stelling Minnis, 71 Sturry, 72 Wingham, 73 Chartham, 74 Herne Bay, 75 Boughton, 76 Canterbury, 77 Whitstable, 78 Canterbury, 79 Chestfield, 83 Bridge, 86 Chisle, **other numbers Canterbury**

01228 513 Scotby Carlisle, Cumbria, 56 Wetheral, 573 Crosby-on-Eden, 576 Burgh-by-Sands, 577 Nicholforest, 70 Hayton, 71 Dalston, 74 Rockcliffe, 75 Kirklinton, 79 Longtown, 89 MCL Carlisle, **other numbers Carlisle**

01229 46 Dalton-in-Furness, 47 Walney Island, 48 Ulverston, 58 Ulverston, 715 Broughton-in-Furness, 716 Broughton-in-Furness, 717 Ravenglass, 718 Bootle, 77 Millom, 860 Satterthwaite, 861 Greenodd, 862 Greenodd, 863 Greenodd, 869 Bardsea, 885 Lowick Bridge, 889 Kirkby-in-Furness, **other numbers Barrow-in-Furness**

01232 42 Holywood Co Down, 48 Dundonald Belfast, 448 Castlereagh Belfast, 52 MCL Belfast, 53 MCL Belfast, 54 MCL Belfast, 55 MCL Belfast, 56 MCL Belfast, 81 Carryduff Belfast, 825 Dundrod Crumlin, Co Antrim, 826 Drumbo Belfast, 83 Glengormley Belfast, 84 Glengormley Belfast, 85 Whiteabbey Belfast, 86 Whiteabbey Belfast, **other numbers Belfast**

01233 21 MCL, 50 Sevington Ashford Kent, 6 Ashford, 71 Charing, 72 Aldington, 73 Ham Street, 74 Challock, 750 Elmsted, 756 Egerton, 758 Appledore, 77 Smarden, 81 Wye, 82 Bethersden, 84 Pluckley, 85 High Halden, 86 Woodchurch, **other numbers Ashford**

01234 21 Bedford Beds, 22 Bedford, 24 Olney, 26 Bedford, 27 Bedford, 32 Bedford, 33 Bedford, 34 Bedford, 35 Bedford, 36 Bedford, 37 Colmworth, 38 Haynes, 39 North Crawley, 70 Riseley, 71 Olney, 72 Harrold, 73 MCL Bedford, 74 Wilstead, 75 Cranfield.

76 Lowe, Shelton, 77 Ravensden, 78 Sharnbrook, 79 MCL Bedford, 82 Oakley, 83 Cardington, 84 Kempston, 85 Kempston, 87 Great Barford, 88 Turvey, other numbers Bedford

01235 40 MCL Abingdon, Oxon, 43 Rowstock, 44 Rowstock, 46 Abingdon, 50 Didcot, 51 Didcot, 52 Abingdon, 53 Abingdon, 54 Abingdon, 55 Abingdon, 75 Childrey, 76 Wantage, 77 Wantage, 81 Didcot, 82 Rowstock, 83 Rowstock, 84 Sutton Courteney, 85 Blewbury Didcot, 861 Rowstock, 862 Rowstock, 863 Rowstock, 864 Rowstock, 865 Rowstock, 868 West Hanney, 869 West Hanney, other numbers Abingdon

01236 42 Coatbridge Lanarkshire, 43 Coatbridge, 44 Coatbridge, 45 Cumbernauld, 72 Cumbernauld, 73 Cumbernauld, 74 Airdrie, 75 Airdrie, 76 Airdrie, 77 Cumbernauld, 78 Cumbernauld, 81 MCL Glasgow, 82 Kilsyth, 83 Greengairs, 84 Caldercruix, 87 Glenboig,

01237 42 Bideford Devon, 43 Clovelly, 44 Hartland, 45 Horns Cross, 47 Bideford

01238 51 Saintfield Ballynahinch, Co Down, 52 Ballygowan, 53 Dromara, 54 Killinchy, 56 Ballynahinch, 61 Cardigan

01239 62 Cardigan Dyfed, 65 Llangranog, 68 Llechryd, 69 Llwyndrain, 71 Newcastle, 77 Llwyndrain, 79 Crosswell, 81 Aberporth, 82 Newport, 83 Crymych, 84 Boncath, 85 Rhydlewis, 86 Moylegrove, 88 Moylegrove, 89 Crosswell,

01241 4 Arbroath Angus, 82 Friockheim, 83 Inverkeilor, 84 MCL Arbroath, 85 Carnoustie, 86 Carmyllie, 87 Arbroath, 89 Gowanbank, 60 Winchcombe

01242 62 Alderton Tewkesbury, Glos, 63 MCL Cheltenham, 66 Bishops Cleeve, 67 Bishops Cleeve, 68 Coombe Hill, 82 Andoversford Chelt, 86 Shurdington, 87 Coberley, 89 Withington, other numbers Cheltenham

01243 26 Pagham Chichester West Sussex, 37 Emsworth, 38 Emsworth, 51 Birdham, 54 Eastergate, 55 Yapton, 57 Bosham, 58 Middleton-on-Sea, 59 East Marden, 60 Selsey, 62 MCL Chichester, 64 Sidlesham, 81 Singleton Chichester, 812 Chichester, 814 Slindon, 82 Bognor Regis, 83 Bognor Regis, 84 Bognor Regis, 85 Bognor Regis, 86 Bognor Regis, other numbers Chichester

01244 28 Deeside Clwyd, 30 Mickle Trafford Chester, 33 Christleton, 52 Hawarden, 53 Hawarden, 54 Buckley, 55 Buckley, 57 Rossett Clwyd, 62 Aldford, 66 Kinnerton, 81 Deeside, 82 Deeside, 83 Deeside, 84 Deeside, 851 Great Mollington, 853 Deeside, 88

81

Saughall, **89** MCL Chester, *other numbers Chester*

01245 22 Danbury Chelmsford, **Essex, 231** Good Easter, **233** Terling, **237** Pleshey, **243** Great Baddow, **248** Roxwell, **32** Woodham Ferrers, **36** Little Waltham, **38** Hatfield Peverel, **40** Hanningfield, **42** Writtle Chelmsford, **44** Broomfield, **45** Boreham, **451** Boreham, **4565** Boreham, **46** Boreham, **47** Great Baddow, **51** Broomfield, **70** MCL Chelmsford, *other numbers Chelmsford*

01246 24 Bolsover Derbys, **25** Clay Cross, **26** Old Whittington, **28** Staveley, **29** Dronfield, **41** Dronfield, **43** Ecklington, **45** Old Whittington, **47** Staveley, **50** MCL Chesterfield, **561** Staveley, **566** Holymoorside, **567** Holymoorside, **568** Holymoorside, **569** Holymoorside, **57** Clowne, **58** Baslow Bakewell, **59** Ashover, **81** Clowne, **82** Bolsover, **85** Holmewood, **86** Clay Cross, *other numbers Chesterfield*

01247 51 MCL Bangor, **72** Portaferry Newtownards Co Down, **73** Kircubbin Newtownards Co Down, **758** Ballywalter **77** Portavogie, **78** Greyabbey, **80** Newtownards, **81** Newtownards, **82** Newtownards, **85** Helens Bay, **86** Millisle, **87** Comber, **88** Donaghadee, *other numbers Bangor*

01248 41 Moelfre Gwynedd, **42** Gaerwen, **3** Brynsiencyn, **44** Newborough, **45** Pentraeth, **47** Llanerchymedd, **49** Llangoed, **60** Bethesda, **67** Port Dinorwic, **68** Llanfairfechan, **71** Menai Bridge, **72** Llangefni, **75** Llangefni, **81** Beaumaris, **85** Tynygongl, *other numbers Bangor*

01249 70 Corsham Witts, **71** Corsham, **72** Seagry, **73** Lacock, **74** Kellaways, **75** Kington Langley, **76** Hilmarton, **78** Castle Combe, **81** Caln, **82** Calne, **85** MCL Chippenham, **89** Bradenstoke, *other numbers Chippenham*

01250 87 Blairgowrie Perthshire, **881** Strathardle, **882** Blacklunans, **883** Meikleour, **884** Essendy, **885** Glenshee, **886** Bridge-of-Cally

01252 2 Aldershot **Hants30** MCL Aldershot, **31** Aldershot, **33** Aldershot, **34** Aldershot, **35** Aldershot, **362** Farnborough, **363** Farnborough, **364** Fleet, **366** Aldershot, **37** Farnborough, **38** Farnborough International Airshow, **381** Farnborough International Airshow, **382** Farnborough, **383** Farnborough, **384** Farnborough, **385** Farnborough, **386** Farnborough, **387** Farnborough, **388** Farnborough, **39** Farnborough, **5** Farnborough, **6** Fleet, **70** Elstead, **71** Farnham, **72** Farnham, **73** Farnham, **74** Farnham, **76** MCL

82

Aldershot, **77** Fleet, **78** Runfold, **79** Frensham, **81** Fleet, **83** Deepcut, **84** Hartley Wintney, **85** Crondall, **86** Yateley, **87** Yateley, **89** Yateley, **other numbers** Aldershot

01253 61 Blackpool Lancs, **70** Hambleton, **71** St Annes, **72** St Annes, **73** Lytham, **74** Lytham, **77** Fleetwood, **78** St Annes, **790** Pilling, **794** Lytham, **795** Lytham, **796** Lytham, **81** Knott End, **82** Cleveleys, **836** Weeton, **84** MCL Blackpool, **85** Cleveleys, **86** Cleveleys, **87** Fleetwood, **88** Poulton-le-Fylde, **89** Poulton-le-Fylde, **other numbers** Blackpool

01254 23 Accrington Lancs, **30** Accrington, **35** Accrington, **39** Accrington, **70** Darwen, **72** MCL, **760** Darwen, **761** Darwen, **762** Darwen, **763** Darwen, **764** Mellor, **765** Mellor, **766** Mellor, **767** Mellor, **768** Mellor, **769** Mellor, **77** Darwen, **781** Mellor, **821** Whalley, **822** Whalley, **823** Whalley, **824** Whalley, **826** Stoneyhurst, **827** Stoneyhurst, **83** Brinscall, **85** Hoghton, **870** Darwen, **871** Accrington, **872** Accrington, **873** Darwen, **874** Darwen, **875** Great Harwood, **876** Great Harwood, **877** Great Harwood, **878** Ribchester, **88** Great Harwood, **89** CL Blackburn, **other numbers** Blackburn.

01255 24 Harwich Essex, **5** Harwich, **6** Frinton-on-Sea, **81** Holland-on-Sea Clacton-on-Sea, **82** St Osyth, **83** Weeley, **85** Frinton-on-Sea, **86** Little Clacton, **87** Wix Manningtree, **88** Ramsey, **other numbers** Clacton-on-Sea

01256 2 Basingstoke Hants, **30** Basingstoke, **31** Basingstoke, **33** Basingstoke, **34** Basingstoke, **37** Basingstoke, **381** Herriard and Lasham, **384** Herriard and Lasham, **389** Preston Candover, **39** Dummer, **4** Basingstoke, **5** Basingstoke, **60** MCL Basingstoke, **63** Basingstoke, **64** Basingstoke, **68** MCL Basingstoke, **69** MCL Basingstoke, **700** Odiham, **701** Odiham, **702** Odiham, **703** Odiham, **704** Odiham, **705** Chineham, **706** Chineham, **707** Chineham, **709** Chineham, **74** Hook, **76** Hook, **77** Overton, **78** Oakley, **79** Basingstoke, **81** Basingstoke, **84** Basingstoke, **85** Monk, **86** Long Sutton, **88** Turgis Green, **89** Whitchurch, **other numbers** Basingstoke

01257 22 Chorley Lancs, **23** Chorley, **24** Chorley, **25** Appley Bridge, **26** Chorley, **27** Chorley, **40** SBC Coppull, **41** MCL Coppull, **42** Standish, **45** Eccleston, **46** Parbold, **470** Coppull, **471** Coppull, **472** Standish, **473** Standish, **474** Adlington, **475** Adlington, **48** Adlington, **49** MCL Coppull, **79** Coppull

01258 39 MCL Blandford Dorset, **45** Blandford, **47** Sturminster Newton, **48** Blandford, **7** Sturminster Newton, **81** Hazelbury Bryan,

82 Marnhull, 84 Witchampton, 85 Sturminster Marshall, 86 Child Okeford, 87 Milborne St Andrew, 88 Milton Abbas, 89 Tarrant Hinton

01259 21 Alloa Clackmannanshire, 72 Alloa, 73 Kincardine, 74 Dollar, 75 Tillicoultry, 76 Alva, 78 Muckhart, 223 North Rode, 224 Marton Heath, 226 Rushton Spencer, 227 Wincle, 25 Sutton, 26 MCL Congleton, 27 Congleton, 28 Congleton, 29 Congleton

01261 81 Banff, 821 Eden Banff, 832 Macduff, 842 Portsoy, 851 Gardenstown, 861 Whitehills

01262 420 Kilham Driffield North Humberside, 468 Skipsea, 470 Thwing, 488 Beeford, 490 Burton Agnes, 85 Flamborough.
other numbers Bridlington

01263 51 Cromer Norfolk, 577 Matlaske, 578 Overstrand, 579 Matlaske, 584 Saxthorpe, 587 Saxthorpe, 588 Weybourne, 71 Holt, 72 Mundesley, 73 Aylsham, 74 Cley, 76 Hanworth, 82 Sheringha, 833 Southrepps, 834 Southrepps, 837 West Runton, 838 West Runton. 86 Melton Constable, 87 Saxthorpe.

01264 32 Andover Hants, 33 Andover, 34 Andover, 35 Andover, 36 Andover, 38 Andover, 70 Chute Standen, 71 Abbotts Ann, 72 Longparish, 73 St Marybourne, 75 Hatherden, 76 Hurstbourne, 77 Weyhill, 78 Wallop, 79 Ludgershall, 81 Stockbridge, 85 Collingbourne Ducis, 86 Chilbolton, 87 Linkenholt, 88 Grateley, 89 Oxenwood

01265 63 Cloughmills, 641 Loughgiel, 65 Dunloy, 66 Ballymoney, 73 Bushmills, 762 Ballycastle, 7630 Ballycastle, 7631 Ballycastle, 7632 Ballycastle, 7633 Ballycastle, 7634 Ballycastle, 7635 Ballycastle, 7636 Ballycastle, 7637 Ballycastle, 7638 Ballycastle, 7639 Rathlin, 769 Ballycastle, 74 Dervock, 751 Armoy, 82 Portrush, 83 Portstewart, 84 Castlerock, 868 Aghadowey.
other numbers Coleraine

01266 4 Ballymena, 54 Kilrea, 55 Garvagh, 571 Rasharkin, 63 Ballymena, 65 Ballymena, 66 Ballymena, 684 Aughafatten, 685 Glarryford, 74 Cushendun, 75 Cushendun, 76 Cushendun, 77 Cushendall, 82 Portglenone, 83 Glenwherry, 84 Aughafatten, 86 Broughshane, 87 Ahoghill, 88 Cullybackey, 89 Kells

01267 20 Brechfa Carmarthen Dyfed, 21 Bancyfelin, 22 Carmarthen, 23 Carmarthen, 24 Llansteffan, 25 Llanpumsaint 26 Ferryside, 27 Llandarog, 28 Cynwyl Elfed, 29 Nantgaredig, 83 Llansteffan

84

01268 4 Laindon Basildon Essex, **50** MCL Basildon, **51** Canvey Island, **54** Laindon, **55** Vange, **560** Wickford, **561** Wickford, **562** Wickford, **565** South Benfleet, **566** South Benfleet, **57** Wickford, **58** Vange, **590** North Benfleet, **591** North Benfleet, **642** Rayleigh, **65** Rayleigh, **66** Canvey Island, **68** Canvey Island, **69** Canvey Island, **7062** Laindon, **71** Ramsden Heath, **72** North Benfleet, **73** Wickford, **74** Rayleigh, **75** South Benfleet, **76** Wickford, **77** Rayleigh, **78** Rayleigh, **79** South Benfleet, **88** Laindon, *other numbers Basildon*

01269 59 Ammanford Llanelli Dyfed, **82** Amman Valley, **83** Cross Hands, **84** Cross Hands, **85** Llandybie, **86** Pontyates, **87** Pontyberem, **41** MCL

01270 45 Crewe Cheshire, **520** Bridgemere, **522** Church Minshull, **524** Faddiley, **526** Warmingham, **528** Wettenhall, **60** Willaston, **610** Nantwich, **611** Nantwich, **613** Nantwich, **62** Nantwich, **65** Willaston, **66** Willaston, **67** Willaston, **68** Willaston, **69** Willaston, **73** Wettenhall, **74** Faddiley, **75** Sandbach, **76** Sandbach, **77** Warmingham, **78** Aston, **81** Audlem, **82** Betley, **84** Wybunbury, **87** Alsager, **88** Alsager, *other numbers Crewe Cheshire*

01271 81 Braunton Devon,**850** Shirwell, **858** Newton Tracey, **860** Instow, **861** Instow, **862** Ilfracombe, **863** Ilfracombe, **864** Ilfracombe, **865** Ilfracombe, **866** Ilfracombe, **867** Ilfracombe, **87** Woolacombe, **88** Combe Martin, **89** Croyde, *other numbers Barnstaple, Devon*

01273 2 Hove East Sussex, **30** Rottingdean, **32** Hove, **33** Withdean, **36** Withdean, **38** NCL, **400** Barcombe, **401** Barcombe, **404** Lewes, **406** Lewes, **41** Portslade, **42** Portslade, **43** Portslade, **44** Shoreham-by-Sea, **45** Shoreham-by-Sea, **46** Shoreham-by-Sea, **47** Lewes East Sussex, **48** Lewes, **49** Henfield, **50** Withdean, **51** Newhaven, **52** Newhaven, **54** Withdean, **56** Withdean, **57** Kemptown, **58** Peacehaven, **59** Southwick, **60** Kemptown, **61** Newhaven, **62** Kemptown, **64** Kemptown, **66** Kemptown, **67** Kemptown, **68** Kemptown, **69** Kemptown, **70** Nynex, **71** Hove, **72** Hove, **73** Hove, **74** Hove, **75** Hove, **76** Hove, **77** Hove, **79** MCL Brighton, **812** Ringmer, **813** Ringmer, **814** Ringmer, **815** Ringmer, **818** Brighton Marina, **819** Brighton Marina, **82** Hove, **83** Hurstpierpoint, **84** Hassocks, **857** Poynings, **858** Glynde, **86** MCL Brighton, **87** Southwick, **88** MCL Brighton, **89** Plumpton, *other numbers Brighton*

01274 363 Manningham West Yorkshire, 364 Manningham, 365 Manningham, 366 Manningham, 48 Manningham, 49 Manningham, 50 Horton Bank, 51 Bingley, 52 Horton Bank, 53 Shipley, 54 Manningham, 55 Bingley, 56 Bingley, 57 Horton Bank, 58 Shipley, 59 Shipley, 60 Low Moor, 61 Idle, 620 Idle, 621 Idle, 622 Idle, 624 Horton Bank, 625 Horton Bank, 626 Undercliffe, 627 Undercliffe, 63 Undercliffe, 64 Undercliffe, 651 Dudley Hill, 652 Dudley Hill, 653 Dudley Hill, 654 Dudley Hill, 655 Dudley Hill, 656 Laisterdyke, 657 Laisterdyke, 66 Laisterdyke, 67 Low Moor, 68 Dudley Hill, 69 Low Moor, 77 BCCL, 81 Queensbury, 82 MCL, 83 Thornton, 84 MCL Bradford, 85 Cleckheaton, 86 Cleckheaton, 87 Cleckheaton, 88 Queensbury, other numbers Bradford

01275 33 Chew Magna Bristol, 34 Clevedon, 37 Pill, 39 Long Ashton, 46 Flax Bourton, 472 Lulsgate, 473 Lulsgate, 474 Lulsgate, 54 MCL Bristol, 55 MCL Bristol, 76 MCL Bristol, 79 UACL Bristol, 810 Nailsea, 816 Portishead, 817 Portishead, 818 Portishead, 819 Nailsea, 83 Whitchurch, 84 Portishead, 85 Nailsea, 87 Clevedon, 89 Whitchurch, other numbers Bristol Area (South)

01276 2 Camberley Surrey, 3 Blackwater, 41 Camberley, 45 Bagshot, 47 Bagshot, 60 Blackwater, 61 Camberley, 62 Camberley, 63 Camberley, 64 Camberley, 65 Camberley, 66 Camberley, 67 Camberley, 68 Camberley, 69 Camberley, 80 MCL Camberley, 853 Bagshot, 855 Chobham, 856 Chobham, 857 Chobham, 858 Chobham, 87 TC Camberley, 88 MCL Camberley, other numbers Camberley

01277 2 Brentwood, 35 Ingatestone, 36 Ongar, 37 Coxtie Green, 62 Billericay, 63 Billericay, 65 Billericay, 69 Brentwood, 72 MCL Brentwood, 81 Herongate, 82 Blackmore, 84 Stock Ingatestone, 890 Moreton, 896 Willingale, 899 Fyfield

01278 64 Mark Moor Bridgwater Somerset, 65 Combwich, 66 North Petherton, 67 Spaxton, 68 Puriton, 69 Weston Zoyland, 72 Chilton Polden, 73 Nether Stowey, 74 Holford, 75 Brean Down, 76 Brent Knoll, 77 Burnham-on-Sea, 78 Burnham-on-Sea, 79 Burnham-on-Sea, other numbers Bridgwater

01279 40 Harlow Essex, 41 Harlow, 42 Harlow, 43 Harlow, 44 Harlow, 45 Harlow, 46 Harlow, 463 Harlow, 60 Sawbridgeworth, 62 Harlow, 63 Harlow, 64 Stansted, 66 Stansted Airport, 68 Stansted Airport, 69 Stansted Airport, 718 Hatfield, 72 Sawbridgeworth, 73 Sheering, 771 Albury, 775 Harlow, 777 Brent, 79 Roydon, 81 Stansted, 82 MCL Bishops Stortford, 83 ACC Bishops Stortford, 84 Much Hadham, 85 Henham, 86 ACC Bishops Stortford, 870 Takeley, 871 Takeley, 876 White Roding, other Bishops Stortford, other

numbers Bishops Stortford

01280 40 MCL Buckingham, 70 Brackley, 71 Brackley, 81 Buckingham, 82 Buckingham, 84 Finmere, 85 Syresham, 86 Lillingstone Dayrell, other numbers Buckingham

01282 44 Earby Colne Lancs, 60 Nelson, 61 Nelson, 69 Nelson, 77 Padiham, 81 Barnoldswick, 84 Earby, 85 Barnoldswick, 86 Colne, 87 Colne, other numbers Burnley

01283 21 Swadlincote Derbys, 22 Swadlincote, 520 Tutbury, 55 Swadlincote, 57 HoarCross, 58 Sudbury, 59 MCL,70 Repton, 71 Barton-under-Needwood, 72 Barton-under-Needwood, 73 Etwall, 75 Hoar Cross, 76 Overseal, 79 Alrewas, 81 Tutbury, 82 Marchington, 84 Abbots Bromley, other numbers Burton-upon-Trent

01284 30 MCL Bury St Edmunds Suffolk, 38 Sicklesmere, 520 Tutbury, 55 Swadlincote, 728 Culford, 73 Horringer, 787 Gt Barton, 788 Gt Barton, 789 Hawkedon, 81 Barrow, 82 Cockfield, 83 Hartest, 85 Chevington, 87 Great Barton, 89 Hawkedon, other numbers Bury St Edmunds

01285 71 Fairford, 72 Fossebridge, 74 Bibury, 75 Coln-St-Aldwyn, 76 Frampton Mansell, 77 Kemble, 81 Kempsford, 82 Miserden, 83 North Cerney, 84 Rodmarton, 85 Poulton, 86 South Cerney, other numbers Cirencester Glos

01286 65 Waunfawr Caernarfon Gwynedd, 66 Clynnogfawr, 67 Caernarfon, 68 Caernarfon, 83 Llanrwnda, 87 Llanberis, 88 Penygroes, 59 MCL Guisborough, 61 Guisborough, 62 Saltburn-by-the-Sea, 63 Guisborough, 64 Loftus, 65 Skelton

01287 66 Castleton Whitby, 676 Brotton, 76 Brotton

01288 32 Kilkhampton Bude Cornwall, 33 Morwenstow, 34 Week, 35 Bude, 36 Widemouth Bay, 38 Bridgerule, 81 Bridgerule, 84 Week

01289 30 Berwick-on-Tweed Northumberland, 33 Berwick-on-Tweed, 381 Beal, 382 Norham, 386 Paxton, 387 Ancroft, 388 Lowick, 389 Holy Island 88 Lowick, 89 Holy Island

01290 3 New Cumnock Cumnock, 41 MCL 42 Cumnock, 5 Mauchline, 6 Muirkirk, 7 Ochiltree, 81 Dalleagles

01291 42 Caldicot, 43 Caldicot, 61 MCL Shirenewton, 62 Chepstow, 63 Chepstow, 64 Shirenewton, 65 Wolvesnewton, 67 Usk, 68 Tintern, 69 Raglan

87

01292 26 Ayr, 8 Ayr, 31 Troon, 4 Alloway, 47 Prestwick, 50 Dunure, 51 MCL, 52 Annbank, 53 Patna, 54 Tarbolton Mauchline, 55 Dalmellington, 56 Dalrymple, 57 Joppa, 59 Drongan, 61 Ayr, 67 Prestwick, 7 Prestwick

01293 40 EL Crawley, West Sussex, 76 MCL Crawley, 77 Horley, 81 Horley, 82 Horley, 85 Faygate, 86 Norwood Hill, 87 Rusper, 88 Pound Hill, 89 MCL Crawley, other numbers Crawley/Gatwick

01294 2 Irvine Ayrshire, 31 Irvine, 46 Ardrossan, 460 Saltcoats, 460 Stevenston, 461 Saltcoats, 461 Stevenston, 469 Saltcoats, 469 Stevenston, 5 Kilwinning, 60 Ardrossan, 82 West Kilbride, 83 Dalry, 85 Torranyard

01295 20 MCL Banbury Oxon, 22 Banbury, 25 Banbury, 26 Banbury, 27 Banbury, 28 Banbury, 29 Banbury, 66 Chipping Warden, 67 Edge Hill, 68 Tysoe, 69 Farnborough, 71 Middleton Cheney, 72 Bloxham, 73 Wroxton St Mary, 75 Cropredy, 77 Fenny Compton, 78 Swalcliffe, 81 Adderbury, 89 Farnborough, other numbers Banbury

01296 2 Aylesbury Bucks, 3 Aylesbury, 4 Aylesbury, 50 MCL Aylesbury, 51 MCL Aylesbury, 58 JCGL Aylesbury, 61 Stoke Mandeville, 62 Wendover, 63 Aston Clinton, 64 Whitchurch, 650 Waddesdon, 651 Waddesdon, 655 Quainton, 658 Waddesdon, 66 Cheddington, 67 North Marston, 68 Wing, 69 Wendover, 71 Winslow, 72 Mursley, 73 Steeple Claydon, 74 Stone, 77 Grendon Underwood, 8 Aylesbury, other numbers Aylesbury

01297 2 Seaton Devon, 3 Axminster, 44 Lyme Regis, 48 Chideock, 55 Colyton, 56 Charmouth, 62 Seaton, 67 Hawkchurch, 68 Branscombe, 80 Branscombe, 89 Chideock.

01298 81 Chapel-en-le-Frith Stockport Cheshire, 83 Longnor, 84 Hartington, 85 Taddington, 87 Tideswell, other numbers Buxton

01299 25 Hartlebury Kidderminster Worcs, 26 Rock, 27 Cleobury Mortimer, 40 Bewdley, 82 Stourport, 83 Clows Top, 84 Kinlet, 85 Cutnall Green, 86 Arley, 87 Stourport, 89 Great Witley.

01300 2 Maiden Newton Dorchester Dorset, 34 Cerne Abbas, 4 Piddletrenthide, 5 Buckland Newton

01301 2 Arrochar Dunbartonshire, 3 Lochgoilhead, 4 Inveruglass, 702 Arrochar, 703 Lochgoilhead, 704 Inveruglass

01302 Doncaster South Yorkshire, 30 Armthorpe, 31 Balby, 33 Adwick-le-Street, 35 Hatfield, 37 Cantley, 53 Cantley, 70 Askern.

88

71 Bawtry, 72 Adwick-le-Street, 74 Tickhill, 75 Tickhill, 77 Finningley, 79 MCL, 82 Bentley, 83 Armthorpe, 84 Hatfield, 85 Balby, 86 Rossington, 87 Bentley, 88 Barnby, 89 Barnby, other numbers Doncaster

01303 20 MCL, 23 Hythe Kent, 26 Hythe, 27 Cheriton, 29 Cheriton, 81 Sellindge, 840 Elham, 844 Selsted, 86 Lyminge, 87 Dymchurch, 89 Hawkinge, other numbers Folkestone

01304 2 Dover Kent, 3 Deal, 50 MCL 6 Sandwich, 81 Ash, 82 Archers Court, 83 Shepherdswell, 84 Nonington, 85 St Margarets Bay, other numbers Dover

01305 20 Dorchester Dorset, 21 Dorchester, 22 Dorchester, 25 Dorchester, 26 Dorchester, 76 Weymouth, 77 Weymouth, 78 Weymouth, 81 Upwey, 82 Portland, 83 Preston, 84 Puddletown, 85 Warmwell, 86 Portland, 87 Abbotsbury, 88 Martinstown

01306 50 NCL, 51 MCL Dorking Surrey, 61 Dawes Green, 621 Forest Green, 627 Oakwood Hill, 628 Oakwood Hill, 63 Newdigate, 71 Capel, 73 Abinger, other numbers Dorking

01307 4 Forfar Angus, 81 Letham, 82 Inverarity, 83 Aberlemno, 84 Glamis, 85 Finavon, 86 Foreside,

01308 2 Bridport Dorset, 42 Bridport, 48 Bridport, 5 Bridport, 6 Broadwindsor, 85 Powerstock, 862 Beaminster, 863 Beaminster, 867 Beaminster, 868 Beaminster, 88 Netherbury, 89 Burton Bradstock

01309 611 Dunphail Morayshire,641 Brodie Forres, Morayshire651 Glenferness Morayshire67 Forres Morayshire69 Findhorn Forres, Morayshire

0131 Edinburgh, 220 West Central Edinburgh, 221 Fountainbridge, 225 West Central Edinburgh, 226 West Central Edinburgh and Bruntsfield, 228 Fountainbridge, 229 Tollcross,229 Viewforth, 312 Barnton (part), Cramond, Davidsons Mains & Silverknowes, 313 Dalry, Gorgie, Murrayfield & Roseburn, 315 Blackhall, Comely Bank, Dean, Drylaw, Muirhouse & Stockbridge, 316 Clermiston (part) & Corstophine (part), 317 Barnton (part), Clermiston (part). Corstophine (part). & Maybury, 319 Abercorn, Dalmeny & South Queensferry, 331 Abercorn, Dalmeny & South Queensferry, 332 Blackhall, Comely Bank, Dean, Drylaw, Muirhouse & Stockbridge, 333 Kirkliston, Ratho, Ratho Station & Newbridge, 334 Clermiston (part) & Corstophine (part), 335 Newbridge, 336 Barnton (part), Cramond, Davidsons Mains & Silverknowes, 337 Dalry, Gorgie, Murrayfield & Roseburn, 339 Barnton (part), Clermiston (part),

Airth, **84** Banknock, **85** Slamannan, **86** Avonbridge

01325 28 Darlington Co. Durham, **30** Aycliffe, **31** Aycliffe, **32** Aycliffe, **33** Dinsdale, **34** Darlington, **35** Darlington, **36** Darlington, **374** Piercebridge, **377** Barton, **378** North Cowton, **38** Darlington, **39** Darlington, **46** Darlington, **48** Darlington, **50** MCL Darlington, **71** East Layton, **72** Croft Darlington, **73** Gainford, **74** Darlington

01326 22 Mawgan Helston Cornwall, **23** Manaccan, **24** Mullion, **25** Mawnan Smith, **27** St Mawes, **28** St Keverne, **29** The Lizard, **34** Constantine, **37** Penryn, **4** Constantine, **5** Helston, other numbers Falmouth Cornwall

01327 26 Byfield Northants, **30** Daventry, **31** Daventry, **32** Silverstone, **34** Weedon, **35** Towcester, **36** Preston Capes, **6** Byfield, **7** Daventry, **81** Paulerspury, **83** Pattishall, **84** Long Buckby, **85** Silverstone, **86** Blakesley, **88** Daventry, **89** MCL

01328 70 Tittleshall Fakenham Norfolk, **71** Wells, **73** Burnham Market, **74** Weasenham St Peter, **78** Great Ryburgh, **820** Walsingham, **821** Walsingham, **823** South Creake, **829** Gt Ryburgh, **830** Binham, **838** Weasenham St Peter, **85** Fakenham, **86** Fakenham, **87** Thursford, **88** MCL Fakenham

01329 31 NCL Fareham Hants, **44** Titchfield, **51** NCL Fareham, **66** Stubbington, **81** MCL Fareham, **83** Wickham, **84** Titchfield, **85** Titchfield, other numbers Fareham

01330 50 MCL Banchory Kincardineshire, **82** Banchory, **83** Sauchen, **844** Crathes, **845** Feughside, **86** Dunecht, **88** Drumoak,

01332 27 Peartree, **280** Spondon, **281** Spondon, **288** Spondon, **51** Mickleover, **52** Mickleover, **54** Allestree, **55** Allestree, **57**, Alvaston, **60** MCL, **62** MCL, **66** Spondon, **67** Spondon, **68** Spondon, **69** Chellaston, **70** Chellaston, **71** Derby, **75** Alvaston, **76** Peartree, **77** Peartree, **78** Horsley, **79** Shardlow, **81** Castle Donington, **82** Kirk Langley, **83** Breadsall, **84** Duffield, **85** Castle Donington, **86** Melbourne, **87** Draycott, **88** Horsley, other numbers Central Derby

01333 31 Anstruther Fife, **32** Lundin Links, **33** Elie Leven, **34** Colinsburgh, **35** Kennoway, **36** Upper Largo, **42** Leven, **45** Crail, **72** Arncroach, **73** St Monans

01334 4 St Andrews Fife, **45** MCL, **6** Cupar, **82** Ceres, **83** Leuchars, **84** Peat Inn, **85** Strathkinness, **87** Balmullo, **88** Boarhills

01335 27 Alstonefield Staffs, **28** MCL, **29** Thorpe, **31** Alstonefield, **32** Ellastone, **33** Great Cubley, **35** Thorpe Cloud, **36** Brailsford.

37 Hulland Ward, 39 Parwich, other numbers Ashbourne

0336 Premium Rate Services

0337 *81 Letham Cupar Fife, 82 Auchtermuchty, 83 Ladybank, 84 Newburgh, 85 Falkland, 86 Strathmiglo, 87 Luthrie*

0338 Premium Rate Services

01339 *41 Braemar Aboyne, Aberdeenshire, 42 Crathie, 5 Ballater, 81 Tarland, 82 Torphins, 83 Lumphanan, 85 Aboyne, 86 Aboyne, 87 Aboyne, 884 Kincardine O'Neil, 82 Dufftown,*

01340 *83 Rothes, 871 Aberlour, 881 Aberlour*

01341 *Dyffryn, Gwynedd, 241 Llanbedr, 242 Dyffryn, 247 Dyffryn, 25 Fairbourne, 28 Barmouth Gwynedd, 40 Ganllwyd, 41 Rhydymain, 42 Dolgellau, 43 Bontddu, 44 Ganllwyd, 45 Rhydymain, 49 Bontddu, 3 East Grinstead, 41 East Grinstead, 71 Copthorne, 81 Sharpthorne, 82 Forest Row, 83 Lingfield, 84 Smallfield, 85 Cowden*

01342 *87 Dormans Park East Grinstead West Sussex, 89 South Godstone, other numbers East Grinstead*

01343 *54 Elgin Morayshire, 55 Elgin, 81 Lossiemouth, 82 Fochabers, 83 Hopeman, 83 Burghead, 84 Lhanbryde, 85 Alves, 86 Longmorn, 87 Spey Bay, 88 Orton Fochabers, 89 Dallas*

01344 *2 Ascot Berks, 3 Bracknell, 4 Bracknell, 5 Bracknell, 63 Ascot, 64 TC Thames Valley, 70 MCL, 71 MCL, 72 MCL, 73 MCL, 74 MCL, 75 Crowthorne, 76 Crowthorne, 77 Crowthorne, 78 Crowthorne, 81 MCL, 82 Bracknell , 84 Wentworth, 85 Bracknell, 86 Bracknell, 87 Ascot, 8 Winkfield Row, 89 Winkfield Row, other numbers Bracknell*

0345 BT Lo-call

01346 *51 Fraserburgh, 53 Lonmay, 54 Memsie, 56 New Aberdour, 57 Rosehearty, 58 Inverallochy*

01347 *Easingwold York, 81 Stillington, 82 Easingwold, 83 Tollerton, 84 Linton-on-Ouse, 85 MCL Easingwold, 86 Coxwold, 87 Sheriff Hutton, 88 Brandsby*

01348 *5 St Nicholas Goodwick Dyfed, 6 Dinas Cross, 81 Dinas Cross, 83 Croesgoch, 84 Letterston, 87 Fishguard, 88 Puncheston, 89 St Nicholas*

01349 6 Dingwall Ross-shire, *83* Evanton, *85* Invergordon, *87* Culbokie, *88* Alness

01350 6 MCL Dunkeld, *723* Trochry, *724* Butterstone, *725* Amulree, *727* Dunkeld, *728* Dunkeld

01351 2 Fair Isle Shetland

01352 71 Holywell Clwyd, *72* Caerwys, *73* Flint, *76* Flint, *77* Pontybodkin, *78* Halkyn Holywell, *79* Flint, *81* Llanferres, *84* Northop, *85* Llanferres, **other numbers Mold**

01353 61 CCL Ely Cambs, *62* Soham, *63* MCL Ely, *64* Stretham, *675* Burnt Fen, *676* Brandon Creek, *68* Prickwillow, *69* Pymore, *72* Soham, *74* Haddenham, *75* Burnt Fen, *76* Brandon Creek, *77* Sutton, *86* Littleport, *88* Prickwillow, **other numbers Ely**

01354 61 Welney Norfolk, *63* Christchurch, *67* Benwick, *68* Manea, *69* Chatteris, *71* Welney, *74* Doddington, *76* Benwick, **other numbers March**

01355 2 East Kilbride Glasgow, *3* Eaglesham, *4* East Kilbride, *5* Loganswell, *6* East Kilbride, *84* MCL East Kilbride, **other numbers East Kilbride**

01356 62 Brechin Angus, *63* Careston, *64* Edzell, *65* Fern Angus, *66* Menmuir, *67* Tarfside

01357 Strathaven Lanarkshire, *3* Chapelton, *4* Drumclog

01358 70 Auchnagatt Ellon Aberdeenshire, *71* Auchleuchries, *72* Ellon, *74* Balmedie, *75* Collieston, *76* Schivas, *78* Newburgh, *86* MCL Ellon

01359 22 Coney Weston Bury St Edmunds Suffolk, *23* Pakenham, *24* Elmswell, *250* Stanton, *251* Stanton, *252* Stanton, *258* Walsham-le-Willows, *259* Walsham-le-Willows, *26* Honington, *27* Beyton Bury St Edmunds, Suffolk

01360 31 Lennoxtown Glasgow, *44* Balfron, *50* Killearn, *60* Drymen, *62* Balmore Torrance, *77* Blanefield, *84* MCL Killearn, *85* Buchlyvie, *86* Fintry, *87* Balmaha

01361 81 Greenlaw Duns, *84* Abbey St Bathans, *85* Grantshouse, *88* Duns, *89* Longformacus

01362 62 Swanton Morley Dereham Norfolk, *63* Swanton, *65* Dereham, *66* Elmham, *683* Foulsham, *684* Foulsham, *687* Wendling, *688* Bawdeswell, *69* Dereham, *82* Shipdham, *84* Foulsham, *85* Mattishall, *86* Gressenhall

01363 7 Crediton Devon, 82 Bow, 83 Lapford, 84 Copplestone, 85 Copplestone, 86 Cheriton Fitzpaine, 87 Morchard Bishop

01364 2 Widecombe-in-the-Moor, 3 Poundsgate, 4 Buckfastleigh, 62 Widecombe-in-the-Moor, 63 Poundsgate, 64 Buckfastleigh, 65 Ashburton, 66 Haytor, 7 South Brent

01365 32 Enniskillen Co. Fermanagh, 341 Springfield, 348 Florencecourt, 385 Lisbellaw, 386 Belcoo, 387 Lisbellaw, 388 Ballinamallard, 52 Fivemiletown, 53 Brookeborough, 54 Tempo, 56 Trillick, 62 Irvinestown, 63 Kesh, 64 Derrygonnelly, 65 Belleek, 72 Lisnaskea, 73 Newtownbutler, 74 Derrylin, 75 Roslea, 87 Lisbellaw

01366 324 Nordelph, 328 Gooderstone, 34 Fincham, 37 Southery, 38 Downham Market, 5 Stoke Ferry, 6 Southery, 7 Methwold

01367 24 Faringdon Oxon, 25 Lechlade, 71 Stanford-in-the-Vale, 81 Clanfield, 82 Uffington, 85 Southrop, 86 Filkins, 87 Buckland, 89 MCL, other numbers Faringdon

01368 83 Cockburnspath Berwickshire, 84 Innerwick, 85 Stenton, 86 Dunbar

01369 Dunoon Argyll, 81 Ardentinny, 82 Glendaruel, 83 Innellan, 84 Kilmun, 86 Strachur, 87 Toward

0370 VGP

01371 79 ACC Gt Dunmow Essex, 81 Great Bardfield, 82 Felsted, 83 Thaxted, 850 Shalford Green, 851 Shalford Green, 854 Shalford Green, 856 Stebbing, 870 Great Easton, other numbers Great Dunmow

01372 222 Ashtead Surrey, 223 Leatherhead, 27 Ashtead, 3 Leatherhead, 45 Bookham, 46 Esher, 47 Esher, 7 Epsom, 81 MCL, 84 Oxshott

01373 81 Mells Frome Somerset, 82 Westbury, 830 Beckington, 831 Beckington, 832 Chapmanslade, 834 Faulkland, 836 Nunney, 85 Westbury, 86 Westbury, other numbers Frome

01374 VGP

01375 30 MCL Grays Thurrock Essex, 360 Stanford-le-Hope, 361 Stanford-le-Hope, 363 Tilbury, 653 Stanford-le-Hope, 654 Stanford-le-Hope, 67 Stanford-le-Hope, 84 Tilbury, 85 Tilbury, 89 Orsett, other numbers Grays

01376 3 Braintree Essex, 50 Witham, 51 Witham, 52 Witham, 53 Witham, 55 Braintree, 56 Coggeshall, 57 Kelvedon, 58 Silver End

94

01377 217 Middleton-on-the-Wolds Driffield North Humberside, 22 Tibthorpe, 23 Wetwang, 26 Langtoft, 27 Watton, 28 Huggate, **other numbers Driffield**

01379 38 Stradbroke, 58 Fressingfield, 60 Pulham Market, 64 Diss, 65 Diss, 66 Hoxne, 672 Diss, 674 Tivetshall, 676 Pulham Market, **677 Tivetshall, 678 Occold, 68 Bressingham,** 74 Dickleburgh, 78 Mellis, 85 Harleston, 86 Fressingfield, **87 Eye, 88 Bressingham, 89 Botesdale**

01380 60 MCL Devizes, 81 Lavington, **82 Seend,** 83 Bratton, 84 Chirton, 85 Bromham, 86 Cannings, 87 Keevil, **other numbers Devizes**

01381 60 Cromarty Ross-shire, 61 Pontryfield, 62 Fortrose

01382 2 Steeple Dundee, 22 Steeple, **32 Auchterhouse, 322 Steeple,** 33 Gauldry, **35 Kellas, 36 Longforgan, 37 Newbigging, 38 Tealing, 400 Lochee,** 45 Baxter, **46 Baxter, 477 Broughty Ferry,** 48 Broughty Ferry, 5 Claverhouse, 53 Monifieth, **54 Newport-on-Tay, 55 Tayport, 566 Park, 58 Muirhead, 59 MCL Dundee,** 60 Park, 61 Lochee, 62 Lochee, 64 Park, 65 Park, 66 Park, 67 Park, 68 Park, **69 Park, 7 Broughty Ferry,** 73 Broughty Ferry, 77 Broughty Ferry, **8 Fairmuir,** 81 Fairmuir, **82 Fairmuir, 858 Fairmuir, 88 Fairmuir**

01383 4 Inverkeithing, 51 Cowdenbeath, 61 Cowdenbeath, 62 Dunfermline, **64 MCL, 72 Dunfermline, 73 Dunfermline, 74 Dunfermline, 82 Dalgety Bay, 83 Kelty,** 85 New Oakley, 86 Aberdour, **87 Limekilns, 88 Newmills**

01384 22 Bobbington, 26 Brierley Hill, 27 Kingswinford, **28 Kingswinford, 29 Kingswinford, 37 Stourbridge, 39 Stourbridge, 40 Kingswinford,** 41 Cradley Heath, **42 Lye,** 44 Stourbridge, **47 Brierley Hill,** 48 Brierley Hill, **55 Dudley, 56 Cradley Heath, 57 Brierley Hill, 6 Cradley Heath,** 63 Cradley Heath, 7 Brierley Hill, **82 MCCL, 83 MCCL,** 84 MCL **85 MCCL, 87 Kinver, 89 Lye, other numbers Dudley**

0385 VGP

01386 43 Mickleton Glos, 46 Bishampton, **50 Evesham,** 55 Pershore, 56 Pershore, **58 Stanton, 59 Paxford,** 70 Blockley, **710 Elmley Castle, 716 Badsey, 72 Overbury, 75 Eckington,** 78 Paxford, **79 Inkberrow, 83 Badsey, 84 Chipping Campden, 85 Broadway,**

86 Cropthorne, 87 Harvington, 88 Ashton-under-Hill, **other numbers** Evesham

01387 300 Chapelknowe Dumfries, 370 Bentpath, 371 Canonbie, 373 Eskdalemuir, 380 Langholm, 381 Langholm, 375 Liddesdale, 376 Steele Road, 4 Dumfries, 5 Dumfries, 6 Dumfries, 71 Amisfield, 72 Newbridge, 73 Lochfoot, 74 Auldgirth, 75 Collin, 76 Kirkunzeon, 77 Glencaple, 78 Southwick, 81 Lochmaben, 82 Dunscore, 83 Mouswald, 84 Carrutherstown, 85 New Abbey, 86 Parkgate, 87 Clarencefield, 88 Kirkbean

01388 42 Spennymoor Co Durham, 45Bishop Auckland, 488 Witton-le-Wear, 51 Eastgate, 52 Frosterley, 53 Wearhead, 60 Bishop Auckland, 66 Bishop Auckland, 71 Cockfield, 72 Rushyford, 73 Tow Law, 74 Willington, 76 Crook, 77 Shildon, 81 Spennymoor, 82 Spennymoor, 83 West Auckland

01389 3 Dumbarton, 4 Dumbarton, 6 Dumbarton, 7 Dumbarton, 71 Alexandria, 81 MCL, 83 Gartocharn, 84 Cardross, 85 Arden, 87 Duntocher, 89 Duntocher

01392 31 MCL Exeter Devon, 81 Longdown, 82 Exminster, 83 Kennford, 84 Stoke Canon, 85 Newton St Cyres, 86 Silverton, 87 Topsham, 88 Hele, **other numbers** Exeter Devon

01393 3 Foula Shetland, 6 Foula

01394 2 Felixstowe, 30 MCL Woodbridge, 38 Woodbridge, 41 Shottisham, 42 Eyke, 444 Woodbridge, 448 Kirton, 45 Orford, 46 Eyke, 60 Felixstowe, 61 Felixstowe, 67 Felixstowe, 69 Felixstowe

01395 22 Exmouth, 23 Woodbury, 25 Exmouth, 26 Exmouth, 27 Exmouth, 4 Budleigh Salterton, 51 Sidmouth, 56 Colaton Raleigh, 57 Sidmouth, 59 Sidbury

01396 61 Downpatrick Co Down, 72 Newcastle, 75 Dundrum, 76 Annalong, 77 Castlewellan, 81 Seaforde, 82 Killyleagh, 83 Crossgar, 84 Ardglass, 85 Ballykinler, 88 Strangford

01397 70 Fort William Inverness-shire, 71 Spean Bridge, 72 Kinlocheil, 73 Tulloch, 772 Corpach

01398 2 Dulverton Somerset, 32 Dulverton, 33 Bampton, 34 Anstey Mills, 35 Oakford, 36 Clayhanger, 37 Brompton Regis, 4 Anstey Mills, 5 Oakford, 6 Clayhanger, 7 Brompton Regis

96

01400 23 Ancaster Lincs, 25 Honington, 26 Cranwell, 27 Fulbeck, 28 Long Bennington, 5 Honington, 7 Fulbeck, *other numbers Loveden*

01403 70 Wisborough Green Billingshurst West Sussex, 11 Partridge Green, 73 Southwater, 74 Coolham, 75 Loxwood, 78 Billingshurst, 79 Slinfold, 820 Kirdford, 822 Rudgwick, 823 Rudgwick, 83 MCL Horsham, 86 Cowfold, 87 Plaistow, 89 Lower Beeding, *other numbers Horsham West Sussex*

01404 81 Ottery St Mary Devon, 82 Whimple, 83 Wilmington, 84 Broadhembury, 85 Feniton, 86 Upottery, 87 Farway, 88 Stockland, 9 Luppitt, *other numbers Honiton*

01405 70 Reedness, 74 Thorne Goole, 78 Sykehouse, 81 Thorne Goole, 83 Rawcliffe, 84 Reedness, 85 Sykehouse, 86 Snaith, *other numbers Goole*

01406 32 Holbeach St Marks Lincs, 33 Whaplode Drove, 35 Sutton Bridge, 36 Long Sutton, 37 Moulton, 38 Moulton Chapel, 54 Holbeach St John, 55 Gedney, 70 Holbeach St Marks, 8 Gedney, *other numbers Holbeach*

01407 71 Cemaes Bay Gwynedd, 72 Gwalchmai, 73 Llanfaethlu, 74 Valley, 76 Holyhead, 81 Rhosneigr, 83 Amlwch, 84 Bodorgan, 86 Trearddur Bay

01408 62 Brora, 63 Golspie, 64 Rogart

01409 21 Ashwater, 22 Beaworthy, 23 Black Torrington, 24 Bradworthy, 25 Holsworthy, 26 Milton Damerel, 27 North Tamerton, 28 Shebbear

0141 Glasgow, *204 City Centre, 220 City Centre, 221 City Centre, 225 City Centre, 226 City Centre, 227 City Centre, 242 City Centre, 248 City Centre, 303 MCL, 304 MCL, 305 MCL, 306 MCL, 307 MCL, 308 MCL, 309 MCL, 331 City Centre (North), 332 City Centre (North), 333 City Centre (North), 334 Hillhead, 336 Hamitonhill, 337 Hillhead, 347 Possil, 357 Hillhead, 414 Bridgeton, 420 Gorbals & Kingston, 422 Govanhill & Strathbungo, 423 Govanhill & Strathbungo, 424 Govanhill & Strathbungo, 425 Govan, 427 Bellahouston & Ibrox, 429 Gorbals & Kingston, 440 Govan, 445 Govan, 550 Bridgeton, 551 Bridgeton, 552 City Centre*

(East), 553 City Centre (East), 554 Bridgeton, Dennistoun & Parkhead, 556 Parkhead, 557 Balornock & Springburn, 558 Balornock & Springburn, 613 Rutherglen & Torglen, 616 Newton Mearns, 620 Carnwadric, 621 Giffnock, 630 Croftfoot, 631 Castlemick, Fernhill & Croftfoot, 632 Langside, Pollockshaws & Shawlands, 633 Cathcart & Netherlee, 634 Castlemilk, Fernhill & Croftfoot, 636 Langside, Pollockshaws & Shawlands, 637 Cathcart & Netherlee, 638 Carnwadric, Giffnock & Thornliebank, 639 Newton Mearns, 641 Cambuslang, 643 Rutherglen & Torglen, 644 Busby & Clarkston, 646 Cambuslang, 647 Rutherglen & Torglen, 649 Langside, Pollockshaws & Shawlands, 762 Auchinairn, Bishopbriggs, Cadder & Colston, 763 Sandyhills, Shettleston & Tollcross, 764 Shettleston, 770 Provanmill & Riddrie, 771 Baillieston & Easterhouse, 772 Auchinairn, 773 Baillieston & Easterhouse, 774 Craigend, 775 Kirkintilloch & Lenzie, 776 Kirkintilloch & Lenzie, 777 Kirkintilloch & Lenzie, 778 Sandyhills, Shettleston & Tollcross, 779 Muirhead & Stepps, 781 Baillieston, 810 Cardonald, Hillington & Penilee, 812 Erskine, 840 Paisley, 842 Paisley, 848 Paisley, 879 Barrhead, 880 Barrhead, Neilston & Nitshill, 881 Barrhead, Neilston & Nitshill, 882 Cardonald, Hillington & Penilee, 883 Cardonald, Hillington & Penilee, 884 Glenburn, 885 Renfrew, 886 Renfrew, 887 Paisley, 889 Paisley, 941 Clydebank, Dalmuir & Yoker, 942 Bearsden, 943 Bearsden, 944 Drumchapel, 945 Lambhill, Maryhill & Ruchill, 946 Lambhill, Maryhill & Ruchill, 949 Drumchapel, 950 Jordanhill, Knightswood, Scotstoun & Whiteinch, 951 Clydebank, Dalmuir & Yoker, 952 Clydebank, Dalmuir & Yoker, 954 Jordanhill, Knightswood, Scotstoun & Whiteinch, 955 Milngavie, 956 Milngavie, 958 Jordanhill, Knightswood, Scotstoun & Whiteinch, 959 Jordanhill, Knightswood, Scotstoun & Whiteinch

01420 2 Bentley Hants. 40 MCL Alton, 47 Bordon, 48 Bordon, 51 Selbourn, 53 Blackmoor, 54 Alton, 56 Four Marks & Medstead, 58 Tisted, 59 Alton, 8 Alton, other numbers Alton

01422 20 Hipperholme West Yorkshire, 24 Illingworth, 310 Elland, 311 Elland, 312 Elland, 313 Elland, 316 Sowerby Bridge, 318 Sowerby Bridge, 37 Elland, 82 Ripponden, 83 Sowerby Bridge, 84 Hebden Bridge, 88 Calder Valley, other numbers Halifax

01423 32 Boroughbridge York, 33 Green Hammerton, 34 Copgrove, 35 Tockwith, 36 Helperby, 71 Pateley Bridge, 73 Huby, 75 Ramsgill Dale, 77 Birstwith, 78 Darley, 84 MCL, 86 Knaresbrough, 87 Oatlands Mount, 88 Starbeck, other numbers Harrogate

01424 2 Bexhill-on-Sea East Sussex, 4 Hastings, 71 Hastings, 72 Hastings, 73 Bexhill-on-Sea, 75 Baldslow, 77 Battle, 81

Guesting, 82 Brightling, 830 Crowhurst, 838 Brightling, 84 Cooden, 85 Castleham, 87 Sedlescombe, 88 Brede, 89 Ninfield, *other numbers* Hastings

01425 27 Highcliffe Hants, 28 Highcliffe, 40 Burley, 46 Ringwood, 47 Ringwood, 48 Ringwood, 61 New Milton, 62 New Milton, 63 New Milton, 65 Fordingbridge, 7 Bransgore, 89 MCL Burley

0426 BT Mobile Communications (Radio Paging)

01427 62 Laughton Gainsborough Lincs, 66 Hemswell, 71 Torksey, 72 Owston Ferry, 75 Haxey, 78 Stow, 83 Corringham, 84 Saundby, 87 Epworth, 88 Sturton-le-Steeple, 89 Misterton. *other numbers* Gainsborough

01428 60 Hindhead Surrey, 64 Haslemere, 65 Haslemere, 66 Haslemere, 68 Chiddingfold, Witley & Wormley, 70 Northchapel, 71 Headley Down, 72 Liphook, 74 Milland, 75 Passfield, *other numbers* Haslemere

01429 22 Hartlepool Cleveland, 23 Hartlepool, 26 Hartlepool, 27 Hartlepool, 82 Thornley, 83 Wellfield, 85 Hartlepool, 86 Hartlepool, 87 Greatham, 88 Trimdon

01430 41 Eastrington, 42 North Cave, 43 Howden Goole, 44 Gilberdyke, 81 Dalton Holme, 82 North Newbold, 86 Holme on Spalding Moor, *other numbers* Market Weighton

01431 2 Helmsdale Sutherland, 3 Kinbrace

01432 76 Burghill, 82 Burley Gate, 83 Canon Pyon, 84 Carey, 85 Bartestree Cross, 86 Fownhope, 87 Holme Lacy, 88 Sutton St Nicholas, 89 Tarrington, *other numbers* Hereford

01433 Hope Valley Derbys. 60 MCL Hope Valley, 62 Hope, 63 Grindleford, 65 Hathersage, 67 Edale

01434 22 Bellingham Hexham Northumberland, 23 Wark, 24 Greenhaugh, 25 Kielder, 27 West Woodburn, 32 Haltwhistle, 344 Bardon Mill, 345 Whitfield, 38 Alston, 60 Hexham, 63 Corbridge, 672 Great Whittington, 673 Slaley, 674 Newbrough, 675 Blanchand Consett, 676 Slaley, 681 Humshaugh, 682 Riding Mill, 683 Allendale, 684 Haydon Bridge, 685 Allenheads, 688 Haydon Bridge

01435 81 Horam Road Heathfield East Sussex, 83 Rushlake Green, 86 Heathfield, 87 Mayfield, 88 Burwash, *other numbers* Heathfield

99

01436 81 Garelochhead Helensburgh Dunbartonshire, 82 Rhu, **831** Clynder, **84** Kilcreggan, **85** Coulport, **86** Luss, *other numbers Helensburgh*

01437 53 Maenclochog Clunderwen Dyfed, 54 Llawhaden, **56** Clunderwen, **71** Camrose, **72** St Davids, **73** Clarbeston, , **74** Treffgarne, **75** Rhos, **76** Haverfordwest, **77** Haverfordwest, **78** Broadhaven, **87** Treffgarne, **89** Johnston

01438 31 Stevenage Herts, 35 Stevenage, **36** Stevenage, **71** Welwyn & Tewin, **72** Stevenage, **73** Stevenage, **74** Stevenage, **75** Stevenage, **76** Stevenage, **77** MCL Stevenage, **78** MCL Stevenage, **79** Bulls Green, **81** Knebworth, **82** Codicote, **83** Kimpton, **84** Welwyn, **861** Walkern, **862** Walkern, **869** Benington, **87** Whitwell, **88** Shephall, *other numbers Stevenage*

01439 748 Nunnington York, 77 Helmsley, **788** Ampleforth, **798** Bilsdale

01440 6 Haverhill Suffolk, 70 Haverhill, **71** Haverhill, **73** Steeple Bumpstead, **783** Thurlow, **785** Ridgewell, **786** Hundon, **788** Ridewell, **82** Wickhambrook

01442 2 Hemel Hempstead Herts, 30 Hemel Hempstead, **34** MCL Hemel Hempstead, **39** TC Hemel Hempstead, **58** JCGL Hemel Hempstead, **6** Hemel Hempstead, **70** Berkhamsted, **82** Tring, **83** Bovingdon, **841** Little Gaddesden, **842** Little Gaddesden, **843** Little Gaddesden, **844** Hemel Hempstead, **845** Hemel Hempstead, **846** Hemel Hempstead, **85** Aldbury Common, **86** Berkhamsted, **87** Berkhamsted, **88** MCL Hemel Hempstead, **89** Tring, *other numbers Hemel Hempstead*

01443 20 Newtown Llantwit Mid Glam., 22 Llantrisant Pontyclun, **23** Llantrisant Pontyclun, **40** Pontypridd, **41** Treharris, **42** Tonypandy, **43** Tonypandy, **44** Tonypandy, **45** Nelson Treharris, **47** Mountain Ash, **48** Pontypridd, **49** Pontypridd, **61** Rhondda Valley/Pontypridd, **67** Tonyrefail, **68** Porth, **69** Ynysowen, **71** Bedlinog, **73** Ferndale, **74** Abercynon, **75** Ferndale, **77** Treorchy, **79** Ynysybwl, **81** Hengoed, **82** Bargoed, **83** Bargoed, **84** Treforest, **86** Hengoed, **87** Bargoed

01444 23 Burgess Hill West Sussex, 24 Burgess Hill, **25** Burgess Hill, **31** MCL Haywards Heath, **40** Handcross, **46** Warninglid, **47** Wivelsfield Green, **48** Lindfield, **81** Balcombe, **831** Scaynes Hill, **87** Burgess Hill, **881** Bolney, **89** Ardingly, *other numbers Haywards Heath*

01445 2 Gairloch Ross-shire, 71 Gairloch, **720** Achnasheen, **731** Aultbea, **741** Badachro, **760** Kinlochewe, **771** North Erradale,

100

781 Poolewe, 790 Diabaig, 791 Torridon, 81 Diabaig, 83 Badachro, 84 Kinlochewe, 85 North Erradale, 86 Poolewe, 88 Achnasheen, 42 Barry

01446 43 MCL Barry South Glam, 70 Barry, 71 Rhoose, 72 Barry, 73 Barry, 74 Barry, 75 St Athan, 76 Peterston-super-Ely, 77 Cowbridge, 78 Bonvilston, 79 Llantwit Major

01449 60 MCL Stowmarket Suffolk, 61 Stowmarket, 67 Stowmarket, 71 Stonham, 72 Needham Market, 73 Rattlesden, 74 Bildeston, 760 Coddenham, 765 Mendlesham, 766 Mendlesham, 767 Mendlesham, 77 Stowmarket, 78 Bacton, 79 Coddenham

01450 3 Hawick Roxburghshire, 85 Teviotdale, 86 Bonchester Bridge, 87 Denholm, 88 Borthwickbrae

01451 81 Bourton-on-the-Water Cheltenham Glos, 82 Bourton-on-the-Water, 83 Stow-on-the-Wold, 84 Windrush, 85 Guiting Power, 86 Northleach, 87 Stow-on-the-Wold

01452 37 Barnwood Gloucester, 51 MCL Gloucester, 61 Barnwood, 62 Barnwood, 63 Barnwood, 65 Barnwood, 70 Hartpury, 71 Churchdown, 72 Hardwicke, 73 Twigworth, 74 Saul, 75 Minsterworth, 76 Westbury-on-Severn, 77 Bisley, 78 Tirley, 79 Tibberton, 81 Painswick, 83 Longhope, 84 Staunton Court, 85 Churchdown, 86 Witcombe, 88 Hardwicke, other numbers Gloucester

01453 51 Berkeley Glos, 52 Wotton-under-Edge, 54 Dursley, 73 Brimscombe, 75 Stroud, 6 Stroud, 79 Stonehouse, 81 Berkeley, 82 Stonehouse, 83 Nailsworth, 84 Wotton-under-Edge, 86 Uley, 87 Amberley, 88 Brinscombe, 89 Cambridge

01454 20 Almondsbury Bristol, 21 Badminton, 22 Rangeworthy, 23 Didmarton, 25 Winterbourne, 26 Falfield, 27 Chipping, 28 Thornbury, 281 Thornbury, 282 Chipping Sodbury, 29 Wickwar, 31 Chipping Sodbury, 32 Chipping Sodbury, 33 Chipping Sodbury, 41 Thornbury, 42 Thornbury, 61 Almondsbury, 62 Almondsbury, 63 Pilning, 77 Winterbourne, 88 MCL Rangeworthy, 88 UACL Rangeworthy, 89 MCL Rangeworthy

01455 20 Leire Leics, 21 Stoke Golding, 22 Wolvey, 26 MCL, 27 Sapcote, 28 Sutton Elms, 29 Market Bosworth, 55 Lutterworth, 82 Desford, 84 Earl Shilton, 85 Earl Shilton, 88 Thurlaston, other numbers Hinckley

01456 41 Cannich Beauly Inverness-shire, 45 Drumnadrochit, 47 Glenurquhart, 48 Gorthleck

01457 76 Mottram Hyde Cheshire, 82 Saddleworth, 83 Mossley, 85 Glossop, 86 Glossop, 87 Saddleworth, 88 MCL Glossop.

89 *Glossop*

01458 21 Ashcott Bridgwater Somerset, 22 Charlton Mackrell, 24 Long Sutton, 25 Langport, 27 Somerton, 29 MCL Glastonbury, 4 Street, 5 Baltonsborough, 83 Glastonbury, 84 Street, 85 Baltonsborough, 86 Meare

0459 Mobile Communications – other licensed operators

01460 22 South Chard Chard Somerset, 23 Buckland St Mary, 24 South Petherton, 28 Isle Brewers, 3 Winsham, 5 Ilminster, 6 Chard, 7 Crewkerne

01461 20 Annan Dumfriesshire, 3 Gretna, 4 Eastriggs, 5 Kirtlebridge, 6 Waterbeck, 7 Cummertrees, 8 Kirkpatrick Fleming

01462 42 Hitchin Herts, 43 Hitchin, 44 Hitchin, 45 Hitchin, 47 Letchworth, 48 Letchworth, 49 Baldock, 67 Letchworth, 68 Letchworth, 70 Langford, 71 Shillington, 73 Stotfold, 74 Ashwell, 75 MCL Hitchin, 76 Offley, 79 Weston, 81 Shefford, 83 Stotfold, 85 Shefford, 89 Baldock, *other numbers* Hitchin

01463 2 Macdhui Inverness, 71 Macdhui, 73 Kessock, 74 Kiltarlity, 75 Dores, 76 Struy, 77 Daviot, 78 Beauly Beauly, 79 Culloden, 81 Munlochy, 83 Drumchardine, 86 Dochgarroch, 7 Muir of Ord, 88 Macdhui

01464 20 Insch Aberdeenshire, 3 Kennethmont, 4 Colpy, 5 Old Rayne, 6 Rhynie, 7 Ythanwells, 8 Insch, 831 Kennethmont, 841 Colpy, 851 Old Rayne, 861 Rhyme, 881 Yi-hanwells

01465 Girvan Ayrshire, 81 Dailly, 82 Barrhill, 83 Ballantrae, 84 Pinwherry, 86 Barr, 87 Old Dailly, 88 Colmonell, 89 Lendalfoot

01466 Huntly Aberdeenshire, 6 Cornhill, 700 Glass, 702 Cabrach, 711 Rothiemay, 720 Gartly, 730 Forgue, 740 Drumblade, 751 Cornhill, 760 Cairnie, 771 Knock, 78 Aberchirder, 81 Rothiemay, 82 Forgue, 84 Drumblade, 85 Glass, 86 Knock, 87 Cairnie, 88 Gartly, 89 Cabrach

01467 Inverurie Aberdeenshire, 632 Kintore, 642 Kemnay, 651 Monymusk, 671 Wartle, 681 Pitcaple, 80 MCL Inverurie

01469 51 DCL 53 Barrow-on-Humber, 54 Killingholme, 55 Immingham, 56 Roxton, 57 Immingham, 80 Wootton Ulceby

01470 511 Glendale Portree, Isle of Skye, 522 Dunvegan, 532 Skeabost Bridge, 542 Uig, 552 Duntulm Isle, 562 Staffin, 572 Struan, 582 Edinbane, 592 Waternish

102

01471 822 Broadford Isle of Skye, **833** Isle Ornsay, **844** Ardvasar, **855** Tarskavaig, **866** Loch Scavaig Isle of Skye

01472 31 DCL, **6** Cleethorpes, **20** Cleethorpes, **21** Humberston, **22** Waltham, **276** Scartho, **277** Scartho, **278** Scartho, **28** Healing, **29** Cleethorpes, **37** Swallow, **38** Marshchapel, **39** Binbrook, **75** Scartho, **81** Humberston, **82** Waltham, **84** North Thoresby, **85** Caistor, **87** Scartho, **88** Healing, **other numbers** Grimsby

01473 20 MCL Ipswich, **31** Great Wenham, **327** Holbrook, **328** Holbrook, **37** Charsfield, **61** Kesgrave, **62** Kesgrave, **637** Kesgrave, **652** Hintlesham, **654** Nacton, **657** Offton, **658** Offton, **659** Nacton, **730** Copdock, **735** Grundisburgh, **736** Waldringfield, **737** Charsfield, **738** Grundisburgh, **780** Woolverstone, **781** Woolverstone, **785** Witnesham, **787** Shotley, **788** Shotley, **81** Hadleigh, **82** Hadleigh, **83** Claydon, **89** Helmingham, **other numbers** Ipswich

01474 3 Gravesend Kent, **5** Gravesend, **70** Longfield, **81** Meopham, **82** Shorne, **83** Southfleet, **85** West Kingsdown, **87** Ash Green, **other numbers** Gravesend

01475 52 Wemyss Bay, **53** Millport, **54** Langbank, **568** Fairlie, **63** Gourock, **67** Largs, **68** Largs, **70** Port Glasgow, **72** Greenock, **74** Port Glasgow, **78** Greenock, **88** Greenock, **89** Greenock

01476 44 Grantham Lincs, **53** Great Ponton, **55** Corby Glen, **58** Ingoldsby, **83** Great Ponton, **86** Buckminster, **87** Knipton, **other numbers** Grantham

01477 50 Smallwood Sandbach Cheshire, **53** Holmes Chapel, **54** Holmes Chapel, **57** Lower Withington

01478 61 Portree Isle of Skye, **64** Carbost, **65** Sligachan, **66** Raasay

01479 81 Aviemore Inverness-shire, **821** Nethybridge, **83** Boat-of-Garten, **84** Carrbridge, **5** Dulnain Bridge, **861** Cairngorm, **87** Grantown-on-Spey

01480 21 St Neots Cambs, **22** St Neots, **30** St Ives, **32** Huntingdon, **37** CCL, **38** CCL, **39** CCL, **40** St Neots, **46** St Ives, **47** St Neots, **48** St Ives, **49** St Ives, **81** Buckden, **83** Papworth, **86** Kimbolton, **88** Croxton, **89** Woolley, **other numbers** Huntingdon

01481 Guernsey CI, **82** Alderney, **83** Sark

01482 Hull North Humberside

103

01483 200 Dunsfold Surrey, 202 Shere, 203 Shere, 204 Cranleigh, 205 Shere, 208 Hascombe, 21 Clandon & Ripley, 22 Clandon & Ripley, 23 Worplesdon, 24 MCL Guildford, 25 MCL Guildford, 26 Cranleigh, 27 Cranleigh, 28 East Horsley, 29 MCL Guildford, 3 Guildford, 41 Godalming, 42 Godalming, 44 Guildford, 45 Guildford, 46 Guildford, 47 Brookwood, 48 Brookwood, 5 Guildford, 6 Guildford, 71 Woking, 72 Woking, 730 Woking, 732 Woking, 733 Woking, 734 Guildford, 735 Woking, 736 Woking, 737 Woking 74 Woking, 75 Woking, 76 Woking, 77 Woking, 78 MCL Guildford, 79 Brookwood, 81 Compton, Normandy & Puttenham, 82 CBTL Guildford, 84 LBCL Guildford, 86 Godalming, 89 Bramley, *other numbers Guildford*

01484 400 Brighouse West Yorkshire, 401 Brighouse, 405 Brighouse, 406 Brighouse, 460 Milnsbridge, 60 Kirkburton, 64 Milnsbridge, 65 Milnsbridge, 66 Holmfirth, 7 Brighouse, 84 Slaithwaite, 85 Meltham, 86 Skelmanthorpe, 88 MCL Huddersfield, *other numbers Huddersfield*

01485 21 Brancaster King's Lynn Norfolk, 23 Syderstone, 512 Thornham, 518 Docking, 520 Great Massingham, 525 Holme, 528 East Rudham, 53 Hunstanton, 54 Dersingham, 570 Heacham, 571 Heacham, 572 Heacham, 578 Syderstone, 6 Hillington

01487 3 Abbots Ripton Cambs, 74 Somersham, 77 Abbots Ripton, 82 Warboys, 83 Sawtry, 84 Somersham, 89 CCL, *other numbers Ramsey*

01488 60 Boxford & Kintbury Berks, 61 MCL, 63 Chaddleworth, 64 Great Shefford, 65 Kintbury, 66 Inkpen, 68 Hungerford, *other numbers Lambourn*

01489 55 Locksheath Southampton, 56 Locksheath, 57 Locksheath, 58 Locksheath, 60 NCL Locksheath, 77 Botley, 78 Botley, 79 Botley, 81 MCL Locksheath, 86 Durley, 87 Droxford, 88 Locksheath, 89 Bishops Waltham

01490 41 Corwen Clwyd, 42 Cerrigydrudion, 43 Glyndwr, 44 Llandrillo, 45 Bryneglwys, 46 Maerdy, 81 Maerdy, 83 Glyndwr, 84 Llandrillo, 85 Bryneglwys

01491 41 Henley-on-Thames Oxon, 57 Henley-on-Thames, 60 MCL, 61 Watlington, 62 Rotherfield Greys, 63 Turville Heath, 64 Nettlebed, 65 Cholsey, 66 MCL, 67 Upper Basildon, 68 Checkendon, 69 MCL, 82 Wallingford, 83 Wallingford, 86 TC Thames Valley, 87 Goring-on-Thames, *other numbers Henley-on-Thames*

01492 51 Old Colwyn Clwyd, **54** Rhos-on-Sea Gwynedd, **56** Aberconwy, **57** Aberconwy, **58** Aberconwy, **59** Aberconwy, **62** Penmaenmawr, **64** Llanrwst, **65** Tynygroes, **66** Dolgarrog, **68** Dolwen, **86** Llandudno, **87** Llandudno, other numbers Colwyn Bay

01493 33 Great Yarmouth Norfolk, **36** Fleggburgh, **37** Caister-on-Sea, **38** Ormesby, **39** Winterton-on-Sea, **41** Gorleston, **44** Gorleston, **45** Gorleston, **48** Fritton, **60** Gorleston, **65** Gorleston, **66** Gorleston, **68** MCL Great Yarmouth, **70** Freethorpe, **72** Caister-on-Sea, **73** Ormesby, **74** Martham, **75** Acle, **78** Burgh Castle, **8** Great Yarmouth

01494 42 High Wycombe Bucks, **430** High Wycombe, **431** Amersham, **432** Amersham, **433** Amersham, **434** Amersham, **435** Amersham, **436** High Wycombe, **437** High Wycombe, **438** High Wycombe, **439** High Wycombe, **44** High Wycombe, **45** High Wycombe, **46** High Wycombe, **47** High Wycombe, **480** Radnage, **481** Bledlow Ridge, **482** Radnage, **483** Radnage, **484** Radnage, **485** Radnage, **486** Radnage, **487** Radnage, **488** Hampden Row, **489** Hampden Row, **49** High Wycombe, **51** High Wycombe, **52** High Wycombe, **53** High Wycombe, **54** Little Chalfont, **55** High Wycombe, **56** Naphill, **57** High Wycombe, **58** JCGL High Wycombe, **60** MCL High Wycombe, **61** MCL High Wycombe, **67** Beaconsfield, **68** Beaconsfield, **71** Holmer Green, **72** Amersham, **73** Amersham, **75** Cholesbury, **76** Little Chalfont, **77** Chesham, **78** Chesham, **79** Chesham, **81** Penn, **83** The Lee, **86** Great Missenden, **87** Chalfont St Giles, **88** Lane End, **89** Great Missenden, other numbers High Wycombe

01495 20 Ynysddu Newport Gwent, **21** Abertillery, **22** Blackwood, **24** Newbridge, **27** Cross Keys, **29** Blaina, **30** Ebbw Vale, **31** Brynmawr, **32** Abertillery, **33** MCL Pontypool, **35** Ebbw Vale, **37** CWM Ebbw Vale, **71** Tredegar, **72** Tredegar, **75** Pontypool, **76** Pontypool, **77** Talywain, **78** Little Mill, **79** Blaenavon

01496 30 Port Ellen Isle of Islay, **81** Bowmore, **82** Jura, **84** Port Askaig, **85** Port Charlotte, **86** Portnahaven

01497 82 Hay on Wye Hereford, **83** Clifford, **84** Glasbury, **85** Painscastle

01499 Inveraray Argyll, **5** Furnace, **6** Cairndow

0500 MCL

01501 73 Armadale Bathgate West Lothian, **74** Whitburn, **75** Harthill, **76** Stoneyburn, **77** Fauldhouse, **785** Auchengray, **82** Shotts

105

01502 475 Barnby Beccles Suffolk, **476** Barnby, **478** Blythburgh, **50** Lowestoft, **51** Lowestoft, **52** Lowestoft, **53** Lowestoft, **56** Lowestoft, **572** Lowestoft, **573** Lowestoft, **574** Lowestoft, **575** Brampton, **578** Wangford, **58** Lowestoft, **675** Wrentham, **677** Aldeby, **678** Aldeby, **70** Blythburgh, **71** Beccles, **72** Southwold, **73** Blundeston, **74** Kessingland

01503 22 Lanreath Looe Cornwall, **23** St Germans, **24** Widegates, **25** Downderry, **26** Looe, **27** Polperro, **3** St Germans, **5** Downderry, **7** Polperro

01504 301 Cross Londonderry, **33** Claudy, **38** Strabane, **39** Dunamanagh, **61** MCL Londonderry, **722** Limavady, **74** Dungiven, **750** Bellarena, **76** Limavady, **781** Feeny, **81** Eglinton, **84** Bready, **86** Campsie, **88** Strabane, **other numbers** Londonderry

01505 3 Johnstone Renfrewshire, **34** CBTL, **50** Beith, **61** Bridge-of-Weir, **68** Kilbirnie, **7** Kilbarchan, **81** Bredland, **82** MCL, **84** Lochwinnoch, **85** Uplawmoor, **86** Bishopton, **87** Kilmalcolm, **88** Bishopton

01506 3 Livingston West Lothian, **4** Livingston, **47** MCL, **49** MCL, **5** Bathgate, **63** Bathgate, **65** Bathgate, **67** Linlithgow, **81** Dechmont, **82** Bo'ness, **83** Philpstoun, **84** Linlithgow, **85** Broxburn, **87** West Calder, **88** Mid Calder, **89** Winchburgh

01507 31 Burgh-on-Bain Lincoln, **32** South Cockerington, **33** Saltfleetby, **34** Stenigot, **35** North Somercotes, **36** Fulstow, **44** Sutton-on-Sea, **45** Withern, **46** Alford, **47** Mablethorpe, **48** Swaby, **49** Huttoft, **52** Horncastle, **53** Tetford, **56** Mareham-le-Fen, **57** Baumber, **58** Winceby, **other numbers** Louth

01508 3 Long Stratton, **39** MCL, **47** Swainsthorpe, **480** Thurton, **482** Wootton, **488** Fundenhall, **489** Framingham, **492** Framingham, **493** Framingham, **494** Framingham, **495** Framingham, **498** Hempnall, **499** Hempnall, **51** Kirby Cane, **52** Loddon, **532** Long Stratton, **533** Long Stratton, **538** Surlingham, **54** Raveningham, **55** Brooke, **57** Mulbarton

01509 25 Loughborough, **41** Quorn, **50** Shepshed, **60** Shepshed, **62** Quorn, **646** Hathern, **65** Shepshed, **67** Kegworth, **68** Kegworth, **81** Sileby, **82** LCL, **83** MCL, **84** Hathern, **85** East Leake, **88** Wymeswold, **89** Woodhouse, **other numbers** Loughborough

0151 Liverpool, 200 Central, **207** North, **210** Energis, **220** Stoneycroft, **221** Stoneycroft, **222** Central, **224** Central, **225** Central, **226** Stanley, **228** Stoneycroft, **229** Central, **230** Stoneycroft, **231** Central, **235** Central, **236** Central, **237** Central, **239** Central, **242** Central, **250** Stoneycroft, **251** Central, **252** Stoneycroft, **254** Stoneycroft, **255** Central, **256** Stanley, **258**

Central, 259 Stoneycroft, 260 Anfield, 261 Anfield, 263 Anfield, 264 Anfield, 270 Stanley, 280 CNW, 281 CNW, 282 CNW, 283 CNW, 284 CNW, 285 CNW, 286 CNW, 287 CNW, 288 CNW, 289 CNW, 298 North, 326 Eastham, 327 Eastham, 328 Eastham, 334 Bromborough, 336 Neston, 339 Hooton, 342 Heswall, 343 Bromborough, 346 Bromborough, 347 Hooton, 348 Hooton, 350 Ellesmere Port, 353 Neston, 355 Ellesmere Port, 356 Ellesmere Port, 357 Ellesmere Port, 373 Ellesmere Port, 419 Hale, 420 Widnes, 421 Gateacre, 422 Widnes, 423 Widnes, 424 Widnes, 425 Hale, 426 Prescot, 427 Cressington Park, 428 Gateacre, 430 Prescot, 431 Prescot, 432 Prescot, 443 Huyton, 448 Hunts Cross, 449 Huyton, 471 MCL, 472 MCL, 473 MCL, 474 MCL, 475 MCL, 476 MCL, 480 Huyton, 481 483 Hunts Cross, 485 Hunts Cross, 486 Hunts Cross, 487 Netherley, 488 Netherley, 489 Huyton, 493 Prescot, 494 Cressington Park, 495 Widnes, 498 Netherley, 520 Maghull, 521 Aintree, 523 Aintree, 524 Aintree, 525 Aintree, 526 Maghull, 527 Maghull, 529 Aintree, 530 Aintree, 531 Maghull, 545 Simonswood, 546 Simonswood, 547 Simonswood, 548 Simonswood, 549 Simonswood, 555 Royal, 571 O. 600 Mountwood, 604 Arrowebrook, 605 Arrowebrook, 606 Arrowebrook, 608 Mountwood, 609 Mountwood, 618 Prestel, 625 Caldy, 630 Wallasey, 631 Wallasey, 632 Hoylake, 637 Wallasey, 638 Wallasey, 639 Wallasey, 641 Rockferry, 643 Rockferry, 644 Rockferry, 645 Rockferry, 647 Birkenhead, 648 Irby, 649 Arrowebrook, 650 Birkenhead, 651 Claughton, 652 Claughton, 653 Claughton, 666 Birkenhead, 670 Claughton, 677 Arrowebrook, 678 Arrowebrook, 691 Wallasey, 700 Central, 702 Royal, 703 Royal, 705 Royal, 706 Royal, 707 Royal, 708 Royal, 709 Royal, 722 Childwall, 724 Allerton, 726 Lark Lane, 727 Lark Lane, 728 Lark Lane, 729 Allerton, 733 Sefton Park, 734 Sefton Park, 735 Sefton Park, 737 Childwall, 738 Childwall, 777 Royal, 794 Royal, 801 Liverpool, 802 Liverpool, 920 Waterloo, 922 Bootle, 924 Great Crosby, 928 Waterloo, 929 Hightown, 931 Great Crosby, 932 Great Crosby, 933 Bootle, 934 Bootle, 944 Bootle, 949 Waterloo, 951 Bootle, 955 Bootle, 966 Waterloo

01520 2 Lochcarron Strathcarron Ross-shire, 3 Kishorn, 4 Applecross, 5 Shieldaig, 6 Achnashellach
01522 Lincoln, 50 Birchwood, 595 Sudbrooke Park, 68 Birchwood, 69 Birchwood, 70 Saxilby, 72 Waddington, 73 Scampton, 75 Sudbrooke Park, 77 Spalford, 78 Bassingham, 79 Washingborough, 81 Navenby, 86 Swinderby, 88 DCL, other numbers Lincoln
0523 MCL

01524 22 Hornby Lancaster, **24** Ingleton , **25** Clapham, **26** Bentham, **271** Kirkby, **272** Kirkby, **274** Tunstall, **276** Barbon, **40** Morecambe, **41** Morecambe, **42** Morecambe, **70** Silverdale, **72** Carnforth, **73** Carnforth, **75** Galgate, **76** Arnside, **77** Caton, **78** Burton, **79** Forton, **81** Halton-on-Lune, **82** Hest Bank, **83** Morecambe, **850** Heysham, **851** Heysham, **852** Heysham, **853** Heysham, **854** Heysham, **855** Heysham, **858** Overton, **859** Heysham, **86** Heysham, **89** MCL Lancaster, other numbers Lancaster
01525 21 Hockliffe Leighton Buzzard Beds, **22** Eaton Bray, **23** Heath & Reach, **24** Stewkley, **26** Great Brickhill, **27** Soulbury, **28** Ridgmont, **29** Woburn, **37** Leighton Buzzard, **40** Ampthill, **71** Flitwick, **72** Flitwick, **75** CBTL, **77** MCL Leighton Buzzard, **83** Leighton Buzzard, **84** Ampthill, **85** Leighton Buzzard, **86** Silsoe, **87** Toddington, other numbers Leighton Buzzard
01526 32 Metheringham Lincs, **34** Coningsby, **35** Woodhall Spa, **37** Martin, **38** Horsington, **39** Bardney, **83** Ruskington, **86** Billinghay
01527 40 South & West Redditch Worcs, **45** SBC, **49** MCL, **50** Ipsley & South East Redditch, **51** Ipsley & South East Redditch, **52** Ipsley & South East Redditch, **54** South & West Redditch, **55** South & West Redditch, **57** Bromsgrove, **58** North & Central Redditch, **59** North & Central Redditch, **6** North & Central Redditch, **82** Hanbury, **83** Bromsgrove, **85** Studley, **86** Wychbold, **87** Bromsgrove, **89** Astwood Bank, other numbers Redditch
01528 522 Dalwhinnie Inverness-shire, **544** Laggan
01529 24 Billingborough Lincs, **42** Swaton, **45** Culverthorpe, **46** Heckington, **48** South Rauceby, **49** Folkingham, **5** Culverthorpe, **6** Heckington, other numbers Sleaford
01530 22 Osgathorpe Leics, **23** Bagworth, **24** Markfield, **25** MCL, **26** Ibstock, **27** Measham, **41** Ashby-de-la-Zouch, **56** Ashby-de-la-Zouch, other numbers Coalville
01531 63 Ledbury Herefordshire, **64** Bosbury, **65** Bromesberrow, **66** Much Marcle, **67** Trumpet Ledbury, **82** Newent, **89** Dymock
01534 Jersey
01535 21 BCCL, **27** Cullingworth Bradford, **West Yorkshire**, **63** Cross Hills, **64** Haworth, **65** Steeton Keighley, **West Yorkshire**, **62** MCL Keighley, **67** MCL Keighley, other numbers Keighley

108

01536 20 Corby Northants, 26 Corby, 27 Corby, 33 Cranford, 37 Brigstock, 38 MCL, 39 TC, 40 Corby, 418 Rothwell, 42 Burton Latimer, 44 Corby, 45 Great Oakley, 46 Great Oakley, 71 Rothwell, 72 Burton Latimer, 74 Great Oakley, 76 Desborough, 77 Rockingham, 79 Broughton, other numbers Kettering

01538 26 Ipstones Stoke-on-Trent, 300 Blackshaw, 304 Onecote, 306 Rudyard, 308 Waterhouses, 33 Rudyard, 36 Churnetside, 37 Leek, 38 Leek, 39 Leek, 70 Oakamoor, 72 Tean, 75 Cheadle, 77 MCL

01539 430 Ambleside Cumbria, 431 Ambleside, 432 Ambleside, 433 Ambleside, 434 Ambleside, 435 Grasmere, 436 Hawkshead, 437 Langdale, 440 Windermere, 441 Coniston, 442 Windermere, 443 Windermere, 444 Windermere, 445 Windermere, 446 Windermere, 447 Windermere, 448 Windermere, 48 Windermere, 530 Newby Bridge, 531 Newby Bridge, 532 Grange-over-Sands, 533 Grange-over-Sands, 534 Grange-over-Sands, 535 Grange-over-Sands Cumbria, 536 Cartmel, 537 Grange-over-Sands, 552 Witherslack, 558 Flookburgh, 560 Sedgwick, 561 Sedgwick, 562 Milnthorpe, 563 Milnthorpe, 564 Milnthorpe, 567 Crooklands, 568 Crosthwaite, 569 Sedgwick, 620 Sedbergh, 621 Sedbergh, 623 Newbiggin-on-Lune, 624 Orton, 625 Dent, 821 Staveley, 822 Staveley, 823 Selside, 824 Grayrigg. other numbers Kendal

01540 651 Kincraig, 66 Kingussie, 673 Newtonmore

01542 81 Drummuir Keith Banffshire, 83 Buckie, 84 Cullen, 85 Clochan, 86 Mulben, 87 Grange, 88 Keith

01543 27 Heath Hayes Cannock Staffs, 36 Brownhills, 37 Brownhills, 40 MCL, 422 Hednesford, 423 Hednesford, 424 Hednesford, 425 Hednesford, 426 Hednesford, 43 Whittington, 444 Fradley, 450 Heath Hayes, 452 Brownhills, 453 Brownhills, 454 Brownhills, 46 Cannock, 47 Yoxall, 48 Shenstone, 49 Armitage, 50 Cannock, 57 Cannock, 66 Burntwood, 68 Burntwood, 82 SBC, 87 Hednesford, other numbers Lichfield

01544 21 New Radnor Presteigne Powys, 22 Gladestry, 23 Kington, 26 Presteigne, 31 Weobley, 32 Eardisley, 34 Lyonshall, 35 New Radnor, 37 Gladestry, 38 Pembridge Leominster, Herefordshire

01545 55 Pontshaen Llandysul Dyfed, 56 New Quay, 57 Aberaeron, 58 Llanarth, 59 Pontshaen

01546 5 Kilmartin Lochgilphead Argyll, 60 Lochgilphead, 7 Tayvallich, 81 Ford, 83 Crinan, 85 Achnamara, 86 Minard, 88 Minard

01547 3 Leintwardine Craven Arms Shropshire, **4** Bucknell, **51** Beguildy, **510** Beguildy, **52** Knighton, **53** Bucknell, **54** Leintwardine, **55** Llangunllo, **56** Whitton, **6** Whitton, **81** Llangunllo

01548 51 Chivelstone Kingsbridge Devon, **52** East Allington, **53** Frogmore, **55** Loddiswell, **58** Torcross, **81** Bigbury-on-Sea, **82** Gara Bridge, **83** Modbury, **84** Salcombe, **other numbers** Kingsbridge

01549 Lairg Sutherland, **40** Lairg, **411** Altnaharra, **421** Invershin, **431** Merkland, **441** Rosehall, **81** Altnaharra, **82** Invershin, **83** Merkland, **84** Rosehall

01550 2 Llandovery, **4** Gwynfe, **5** Cynghordy, **6** Rhandirmwyn, **72** Llandovery, **74** Gwynfe, **75** Cynghordy, **76** Rhandirmwyn, **77** Llangadog

01551 5 Llangurig Llanidloes Powys

01553 617 Saint Germans King's Lynn Norfolk, **62** MCL King's Lynn, **630** Ashwicken, **631** Castle Rising, **636** Gayton, **67** South Wootton, **68** South Wootton, **81** Watlington, **82** Terrington St Clement, **84** Middleton, **other numbers** King's Lynn

01554 71 MCL Llanelli Dyfed, **74** Llanelli, **75** Llanelli, **77** Llanelli, **81** Trimsaran, **82** Llangennech, **83** Burry Port, **89** Kidwelly

01555 66 Lanark, **7** Carluke, **81** Forth, **82** Coalburn, **840** Carnwath, **85** Douglas, **86** Crossford, **87** Carstairs, **88** Douglas, **89** Lesmahagow

01556 50 Castle Douglas Kirkcudbrightshire, **60** Palnackie, **61** Dalbeattie, **62** Kippford, **63** Rockcliffe, **64** Auchencairn, **65** Kirkpatrick, **66** Haugh of Urr, **67** Crossmichael, **68** Bridge of Dee, **69** Crocketford

01557 22 Ringford Castle Douglas Kirkcudbrightshire, **3** Kirkcudbright, **5** Dundrennan, **6** Twynholm, **7** Borgue, **81** Gatehouse, **83** Townhead, **84** Mossyard

01558 65 Pumpsaint Llanwrda Dyfed, **66** Dryslwyn, **68** Talley, **82** Llandeilo

01559 35 Maesycrugiau Pencader Dyfed, **36** Llandysul, **37** Velindre, **38** Pencader, **39** Maesycrugiau

01560 32 Darvel Ayrshire, **4** Stewarton, **6** Fenwick, **7** Moscow

01561 32 Auchenblae Laurencekirk Kincardineshire, **34** Fettercairn, **36** Inverbervie, **37** Laurencekirk

01562 53 MCL, 70 Blakedown Kidderminster Worcs, 71 Romsley, 72 Midland Cable, 73 Belbroughton, 77 Chaddesley Corbett, 85 Wolverley, 88 Hagley, other numbers Kidderminster

01563 2 Kilmarnock Ayrshire, 3 Kilmarnock, 4 Kilmarnock, 5 Kilmarnock, 7 Kilmarnock, 82 Galston, 83 Symington, 84 Fiveways, 85 Drybridge, 852 Kilmarnock, 86 Craigie, 88 Fiveways

01564 70 Earlswood Warks, 11 MCL, 73 Knowle, 74 Tanworth-in-Arden, 77 Arley, 78 Lapworth, 79 Henley-in-Arden, 82 Wythall

01565 61 Knutsford Cheshire, 72 Lower Peover, 73 Pickmere, 77 Arley, 83 Bucklow Hill, 87 Mobberley, 88 Mobberley, other numbers Knutsford

01566 77 Launceston Cornwall, 781 Canworthy Water, 782 Coads Green, 783 Lewdown, 784 Lifton, 785 North Petherwin, 86 Pipers Pool

01567 82 Killin Perthshire, 83 Lochearnhead

01568 61 Leominster Herefordshire, 70 Kingsland, 72 Ivington, 75 Leysters, 76 Steens Bridge, 77 Wigmore, 78 Yarpole, 79 Bodenham, 84 Bodenham, 86 Wigmore, 87 Leysters, 88 Ivington

01569 730 Newtonhill Stonehaven Kincardineshire, 74 Drumlithie, 75 Catterline, 76 Stonehaven, 80 MCL Stonehaven

01570 42 Lampeter Dyfed, 43 Cwrtnewydd, 45 Llangybi, 47 Aeron, 48 Llanvbydder, 49 Llangybi

01571 822 Assynt Sutherland, 833 Drumbeg, 844 Lochinver, 855 Stoer

01572 71 Belton Leics, 73 Manton, 74 Morcott, 76 Thistleton, 78 Wymondham, 81 Cottesmore, 82 Uppingham, 84 Wymondham, 85 Manton, 86 Belton, 87 Morcott, other numbers Oakham

01573 2 Kelso Roxburghshire, 41 Gordon, 42 Yetholm, 43 Lempitlaw, 44 Morebattle, 45 Roxburgh, 46 Smailholm, 47 Stichill

01574 2 Larne Co Antrim, 31 MCL Larne, 583 Ballygally, 841 Glenarm, 885 Carnlough

01575 53 Craigton Kirriemuir Angus, 54 Cortachy, 55 Clova, 56 Lintrathen, 57 Kirriemuir, 582 Glenisla

01576 2 Lockerbie Dumfriesshire, 3 Ecclefechan, 4 Johnstone Bridge, 5 Kettleholm, 6 Boreland, 7 Bankshill

01577 83 Glenfarg Perth, *84 Fossoway, 85 Cleish Hills, 86 Kinross*

01578 71 Lauder Berwickshire, *72 Lauder, 73 Stow, 74 Westruther, 75 Oxton, 76 Fountainhall*

01579 2 Dobwalls Liskeard Cornwall, *32 Dobwalls, 34 Liskeard, 35 St Dominick, 36 Rilla Mill, 37 Stoke Climsland, 38 Callington, 5 St Dominick, 6 Rilla Mill, 8 Callington*

01580 20 Ticehurst East Sussex, *21 Goudhurst, 24 Benenden, 29 Biddenden, 71 Cranbrook, 75 Hawkhurst, 76 Tenterden, 80 Frittenden, 81 Etchingham, 83 Staplecross, 850 Sandhurst, 852 Frittenden, 86 Hurst Green, 87 Flimwell, 88 Robertsbridge, 89 Staplehurst, other numbers Cranbrook*

01581 2 Cairnryan Stranraer Wigtownshire, *3 Glenluce, 4 Dunragit, 5 Auchenmalg, 6 New Luce*

01582 2 Luton Beds. *3 Luton, 40 Luton, 41 Luton, 42 Luton, 431 Luton Airport, 432 Luton, 435 Luton, 44 MCL Luton, 45 Luton, 46 Harpenden, 47 Dunstable, 48 Luton, 49 Leagrave, 50 Leagrave, 53 Luton, 56 Leagrave, 57 Leagrave, 58 Leagrave, 59 Leagrave, 60 Dunstable, 61 CBTL, 62 TC Luton, 63 MCL Luton, 64 ECL Luton, 66 Dunstable, 67 Dunstable, 69 Dunstable, 71 Harpenden, 72 Luton, 73 Luton, 74 Luton, 76 Harpenden, 79 Redbourn, 83 Wheathampstead, 84 Markyate, 85 Houghton Regis, 86 Houghton Regis, 87 Whipsnade, 88 Hexton, other numbers Luton*

01583 2 Glenbar Tarbert Argyll, *3 Carradale, 4 Tayinloan, 421 Glenbarr, 431 Carradale, 441 Tayinban, 5 Gigha*

01584 70 Eardiston Tenbury Wells Worcs. *71 Brimfield, 73 Seifton, 74 Richards Castle, 75 Stoke St Milborough, 76 Munslow, 77 Bromfield, 78 Newnham Bridge, 79 Newnham Bridge, 81 Tenbury Wells, 82 Stoke St Milborough, 83 Richards Castle, 85 Bromfield, 86 Seifton, 87 Ludlow, 88 Eardiston, 89 Cleehillstone*

0585 Cellnet Cellular Radio

01586 5 Campbeltown Argyll, *1 Machrihanish, 82 Kilkenzie, 83 Southend*

01588 61 Linley Bishops Castle Shropshire, *62 Church Stoke, 63 Bishops Castle, 64 Clun, 65 Linley, 66 Little Brampton, 67 Craven Arms, 68 Lydbury, 7 Little Brampton, 8 Lydbury*

01590 2 Brockenhurst Lymington Hants, *612 Beaulieu, 616 Bucklers Hard, 64 Milford-on-Sea, 65 East End, 67 Lymington, 68*

Sway, 69 MCL Lymington

01591 1 Llangammarch Wells Powys, 3 Llanwrtyd, 61 Llanwrtyd, 62 Llangammarch

01592 20 Kirkcaldy Fife, 26 Kirkcaldy, 61 Glenrothes, 62 Glenrothes, 63 Glenrothes, 64 Kirkcaldy, 65 Kirkcaldy, 71 Buckhaven, 72 Cardenden, 74 Glenrothes, 75 Glenrothes, 76 Glenrothes, 77 Glenrothes, 78 Lochgelly, 84 Scotlandwell, 86 Ballingry, 87 Burntisland, 88 Kinglassie, 89 Kinghorn

01593 2 Lybster Caithness, 3 Dunbeath, 4 Latheron, 5 Berriedale, 721 Lybster, 731 Dunbeath, 741 Latheron, 751 Berriedale

01594 51 Blakeney Glos, 52 Netherend, 53 St Briavels, 54 Drybrook, 56 Whitecroft, 59 MCL Dean, 81 Coleford, 82 Cinderford, 83 Coleford, 84 Lydney, 86 Lydbrook

01595 69 Lerwick, 71 Walls, 72 Weisdale, 75 Foula, 76 Fair Isle, 809 Walls, 81 Bixter, 82 Bressay, 830 Weisdale, 84 Gott, 85 Hamnavoe, 86 Reawick, 87 Sandness, 873 Papa Stour, 88 Scalloway, 89 Skellister

01597 81 Rhayader Powys, 82 Llandrindod-Wells, 83 Llananno, 84 Llananno, 85 Penybont, 86 Newbridge on Wye, 87 Pantydwr, 88 Pantydwr, 89 Newbridge-on-Wye

01598 3 Parracombe Barnstaple Devon, 4 North Molton, 5 Lynton, 71 Brayford, 72 Brendon, 73 Brendon, 74 North Molton, 75 Lynton, 76 Filleigh, 77 Parracombe

01599 Kyle Ross-shire, 511 Glenshiel, 522 Glenelg, 53 Kyle, 544 Plockton, 555 Dornie, 566 Balmacara, 577 Stromeferry, 588 Killian, 81 Glenshiel, 82 Glenelg, 84 Plockton, 85 Dornie, 86 Balmacara, 87 Stromeferry, 88 Killian

01600 71 Monmouth Gwent, 74 Dingestow, 75 Skenfrith, 77 Monmouth, 78 Llantilio, 83 Dingestow, 84 Skenfrith, 85 Llantilio, 86 Trelleck, 89 Symonds Yat

01603 20 MCL Norwich, 26 Drayton, 270 Sth Walsham, 278 Buxton, 279 Buxton, 71 Brundall, 720 Salhouse, 721 Salhouse, 722 Salhouse, 726 Costessey, 73 Coltishall, 74 Costessey, 754 Hevingham, 755 Hevingham, 758 Barnham Broom, 759 Barnham Broom, 781 Wroxham, 782 Wroxham, 783 Wroxham, 784 Wroxham, 81 Hethersett, 86 Drayton, 87 Reepham, 88 Honingham, 89 St Faiths, other numbers Norwich

113

01604 40 Weston Favell Northampton, 41 Weston Favell, 44 Northampton, 45 TC, 49 Moulton, 50 Creaton, 58 Duston, 59 Duston, 64 Moulton, 66 Hardingstone, 670 Moulton, 671 Moulton, 672 Moulton, 673 Moulton, 674 Hardingstone, 675 Hardingstone, 676 Hardingstone, 677 Hardingstone, 68 Maidwell, 69 Yardley, 70 Hardingstone, 71 Kingsthorpe, 72 Kingsthorpe, 73 MCL, 74 Guilsborough, 75 Duston, 76 Hardingstone, 77 East Haddon, 781 Walgrave St Peters, 784 Weston Favell, 785 Weston Favell, 786 Weston Favell, 787 Weston Favell, 790 Moulton, 791 Kingsthorpe, 792 Kingsthorpe, 793 Kingsthorpe, 794 Moulton, 797 Moulton, 81 Earls Barton, 82 Chapel Brampton, 83 Kislingbury, 84 Chapel Brampton, 85 Blisworth, 86 Roade, 87 Hackleton, 88 Brixworth, 89 Cogenhoe, other numbers Northampton

01606 5 Winsford Cheshire, 30 Sandiway, 31 Northwich, 70 Hartford, 72 Hartford, 73 Middlewich, 74 Hartford, 75 Hartford, 76 Hartford, 77 Hartford, 78 Hartford, 79 Hartford, 83 Middlewich, 85 Weaverham, 86 Winsford, 87 Hartford, 88 Sandiway, 89 Comberbach, other numbers Northwich

01608 64 Chipping Norton, 650 Moreton-in-Marsh, 651 Moreton-in-Marsh, 652 Moreton-in-Marsh, 653 Moreton-in-Marsh, 654 Moreton-in-Marsh, 657 Kingham, 658 Kingham, 659 Kingham, 66 Shipston-on-Stour, 674 Barton-on-the-Heath, 676 Chadlington, 677 Enstone, 678 Enstone, 679 Enstone, 682 Ilmington, 683 Great Tew, 684 Long Compton, 685 Brailes, 686 Little Cherington, 73 Hook Norton, 80 MCL Chipping Norton, 81 Charlbury, other numbers Chipping Norton

01609 74 Kirkby Fleetham Northallerton North Yorkshire, 76 Northallerton, 77 Northallerton, 78 Northallerton, 881 Great Smeaton, 882 East Harlsey, 883 Osmotherley

0161 Manchester, 200 City Centre, 202 Newton Heath & Collyhurst, 203 Newton Heath & Collyhurst, 204 Newton Heath & Collyhurst, 205 Newton Heath & Collyhurst, 214 City Centre, 220 Openshaw, Gorton, Reddish & Denton, 223 Openshaw, Gorton, Reddish & Denton, 224 Fallowfield & Rusholme, 225 Fallowfield & Rusholme, 226 Moss Side, 227 Moss Side, 228 City Centre, 230 Openshaw, Gorton, Reddish & Denton, 231 Openshaw, Gorton, Reddish & Denton, 232 Moss Side, 234 City Centre, 236 City Centre, 237 City Centre, 238 City Centre, 239 City Centre, 242 City Centre, 245 City Centre, 247 City Centre, 248 Fallowfield & Rusholme, 256 Fallowfield & Rusholme, 257 Fallowfield & Rusholme, 272 Ardwick & Longsight, 273 Ardwick & Longsight, 274 Ardwick &

115

& Cadishead, 785 Eccles & Patricroft, 786 Eccles & Patricroft, 787 Eccles & Patricroft, 788 Eccles & Patricroft, 789 Eccles & Patricroft, 790 Worsley & Little Hulton, 792 Broughton, 793 Swinton & Pendlebury, 794 Swinton & Pendlebury, 795 Blackley & Cheetham Hill, 796 Whitefield & Unsworth, 797 Bury, 798 Prestwich & Heaton Park, 799 Worsley & Little Hulton, 81 City Centre, 827 City Centre, 828 City Centre, 829 City Centre, 830 City Centre, 831 City Centre, 832 City Centre, 833 City Centre, 834 City Centre, 835 City Centre, 836 City Centre, 837 City Centre, 838 City Centre, 839 City Centre, 848 Old Trafford & Trafford Park, 856 Old Trafford & Trafford Park, 860 Chorlton, 861 Chorlton, 862 Chorlton, 864 Stretford, Longford & Urmston, 865 Stretford, Longford & Urmston, 866 Stretford, Longford & Urmston, 869 Old Trafford & Trafford Park, 872 Old Trafford & Trafford Park, 873 Old Trafford & Trafford Park, 875 Old Trafford & Trafford Park, 876 Old Trafford & Trafford Park, 877 Old Trafford & Trafford Park, 881 Chorlton, 882 Chorlton, 886 Old Trafford & Trafford Park, 888 Old Trafford & Trafford Park, 902 Northenden & Wythenshawe, 903 Hale & Ringway, 904 Hale & Ringway, 905 Sale & Ashton-on-Mersey, 910 Manchester, 911 Manchester, 926 Altrincham & Bowdon, 927 Altrincham & Bowdon, 928 Altrincham & Bowdon, 929 Altrincham & Bowdon, 930 MCL, 931 MCL, 941 Altrincham & Bowdon, 942 Altrincham & Bowdon, 945 Northenden & Wythenshawe, 946 Northenden & Wythenshawe, 947 Northenden & Wythenshawe, 950 MCL, 951 MCL, 952 MCL, 953 MCL, 954 MCL, 955 MCL, 956 MCL, 957 MCL, 958 MCL, 959 MCL, 962 Sale & Ashton-on-Mersey, 968 Sale & Ashton-on-Mersey, 969 Sale & Ashton-on-Mersey, 972 Sale & Ashton-on-Mersey, 973 Sale & Ashton-on-Mersey, 975 Sale & Ashton-on-Mersey, 976 Sale & Ashton-on-Mersey, 980 Hale & Ringway, 998 Northenden & Wythenshawe

01620 81 Gifford Haddington East Lothian, 82 Haddington, 83 Garvald, 84 Gullane, 85 Dirleton, 86 East Linton, 87 Whitekirk, 88 Athelstaneford, 89 North Berwick

01621 74 Latchingdon Chelmsford, 772 Southminster, 773 Southminster, 774 Southminster, 776, Bradwell-on-Sea, 778 Tillingham, 779 Tillingham, 782 Burnham-on-Crouch, 783 Burnham-on-Crouch, 784 Burnham-on-Crouch, 785 Burnham-on-Crouch, 786 Burnham-on-Crouch, 788 Goldhanger, 81 Tiptree, 82 Purleigh, 84 Maldon, 85 Maldon, 86 Tollesbury, 873 Bradwell-on-Sea, 875 Maldon, 89 Wickham

01622 61 MCL, *63 Bearsted Maidstone Kent*, *71 Aylesford*, *72 Barming*, *73 Bearsted*, *74 Loose*, *78 Aylesford*, *79 Aylesford*, *81 Wateringbury*, *82 Hunton*, *83 Marden*, *84 Sutton Valence*, *85 Lenham*, *86 Otham*, *87 East Peckham*, **880** *Hollingbourne*, **882** *Aylesford*, **883** *Aylesford*, **884** *Wormshill*, **89** *Headcorn*, **other numbers** *Maidstone*

01623 411 Bilsthorpe Notts, *44 Sutton-in-Ashfield*, *45 DCL*, *49 Blidworth*, *51 Sutton-in-Ashfield*, *52 Sutton-in-Ashfield*, *55 Sutton-in-Ashfield*, *72 Kirkby-in-Ashfield*, *74 Shirebrook*, *75 Kirkby-in-Ashfield*, *78 MCL*, *79 Blidworth*, *81 Pleasley*, *82 Edwinstowe*, *83 New Ollerton*, *84 Warsop*, *86 New Ollerton*, *87 Blisthorpe*, *88 Farnsfield*, **other numbers** *Mansfield*

01624 61 Douglas Isle of Man, *62 Douglas*, *63 Douglas*, *66 Douglas*, *67 Douglas*, *68 Douglas*, *80 St Johns*, *81 Ramsey*, *82 Castletown*, *83 Port Erin*, *83 Port St Mary*, *84 Peel*, *85 Marown*, *86 Laxey*, *87 Kirk Michael*, *88 Kirk Andreas*, *89 Sulby*, **other numbers** *Douglas*

01625 52 Wilmslow Cheshire, *53 Wilmslow*, *54 Wilmslow*, *56 Bollington*, *57 Bollington*, *58 Alderley Edge*, *59 Alderley Edge*, *60 Macclesfield*, *71 Wilmslow*, *82 Prestbury*, *85 Poynton*, *86 Chelford*, *87 Poynton*, **88** *MCL Macclesfield*, **89** *Chelford*, **other numbers** *Macclesfield*

01626 7 Teignmouth Devon, *82 Bickington*, *83 Bovey Tracey*, *85 Chudleigh*, *86 Dawlish*, *87 Shaldon*, *88 Dawlish*, *89 Starcross*, **other numbers** *Newton Abbot*

01627 84 Wormshill Sittingbourne Kent

01628 2 Maidenhead Berks, *3 Maidenhead*, *40 Marlow*, *41 MCL*, *42 MCL*, *43 MCL*, *47 Marlow*, *48 Marlow*, *49 Marlow*, *50 Maidenhead*, *52 Bourne End*, *53 Bourne End*, *54 TCC*, *55 AT*, *58 Maidenhead*, *59 Maidenhead*, *60 Burnham*, **644** *Maidenhead Berks*, **646** *Marlow*, **648** *Bourne End*, *66 Burnham*, *70 Maidenhead*, *71 Maidenhead*, *72 Maidenhead*, *73 Maidenhead*, *74 Maidenhead*, *75 Maidenhead*, *76 Maidenhead*, *77 Maidenhead*, *78 Maidenhead*, *79 MCL*, **810** *Bourne End*, **811** *Bourne End*, **812** *Maidenhead*, **813** *Maidenhead*, **815** *Maidenhead*, **817** *Maidenhead*, **819** *Bourne End*, *82 Littlewick Green*, *84 Maidenhead*, *85 Bourne End*, *89 Marlow*, **other numbers** *Maidenhead*

01629 53 Dethick Derbys, *54 Carsington*, *63 Youlgrave*, *64 Great Longstone*, *65 Winster*, *73 Darley Dale*, *77 Matlock*, *81 Bakewell*,

117

82 Wirksworth, 83 Darley Dale, 85 Carsington, **other numbers Matlock**

01630 62 Wetwood Staffordshire, 63 Tern Hill, 64 Pipe Gate, 65 Market Drayton, 66 Cheswardine, 67 Ashley, 68 Hodnet, 69 Market Drayton, 82 Wetwood, 86 Cheswardine

01631 5 Oban Argyll, 71 Connel, 72 Ledaig, 73 Appin, 74 Duror, 75 Bonawe, 76 Lismore, 77 Kilmore

01633 40 Penhow Newport Gwent, 41 Llanwern, 42 Caerleon, 43 Caerleon 44 Machen, 45 Tredunnock, 47 MCL Newport, 48 Cwmbran, 60 Risca, 61 Risca, 64 Cwmbran 66 CBTL, 68 Castleton, 83 Cwmbran, 86 Cwmbran, 87 Cwmbran, 88 Magor, 89 Rhiwderin, **other numbers Newport**

01634 20 Bluebell Hill Medway Kent, 22 Cliffe, 23 Rainham, 24 Snodland, 25 Hoo, 26 Rainham, 27 Allhallows, 28 Gillingham, 29 Strood, 3 Rainham, 5 Gillingham, 6 Bluebell Hill, 7 Strood, 85 Gillingham, 86 Bluebell Hill, 87 MCL, **other numbers Chatham**

01635 20 Hermitage Berks, 24 Chieveley, 25 Highclere, 26 Headley, 27 Burghclere, 28 East Illsey, 294 Thatcham, 297 Kingsclere, 298 Kingsclere, 299 Kingsclere, 3 Newbury, 4 Newbury, 50 Newbury, 51 Newbury, 52 Newbury, 55 Newbury, 56 Newbury, 572 Newbury, 577 Compton, 578 Compton, 579 Compton, 58 Newbury, 81 MCL Newbury, 82 TC Thames Valley, 86 Thatcham, 87 Thatcham, **other numbers Newbury**

01636 49 MCL, 52 East Stoke, 62 Fenton Claypole, 63 Caunton, 68 DCL, 81 Southwell, 82 Sutton-on-Trent, 83 Bleasby, 89 Collingham, **other numbers Newark**

01637 83 Crantock Newquay Cornwall, 85 Newquay, 86 St Mawgan, 87 Newquay, 88 St Columb

01638 500 Ousden Newmarket Suffolk, 507 Stetchworth, 508 Stetchworth, 51 Mildenhall, 52 Eriswell, 53 Eriswell, 54 Mildenhall, 55 Kentford, 570 Six Mile Bottom, 577 Exning, 578 Exning, 58 Mildenhall, 60 CCL Newmarket, 71 Mildenhall, 72 Fordham, 73 Cheveley, 74 Burwell, 75 Kentford, 78 Isleham, **other numbers Newmarket**

01639 6 Neath West Glam, 70 Seven Sisters, 71 Resolven, 72 Glyn Neath, 73 Abercrave, 75 Crynant, 76 CBTL, 81 Briton Ferry, 82 Briton Ferry, 83 Upper Cwmtwrch, 84 Glantawe, 85 Cymmer, 87 Port Talbot, 88 Port Talbot, 89 Port Talbot

01641 2 Bettyhill Thurso Caithness, 3 Melvich, 4 Strathy, 52 Bettyhill, 53 Melvich, 54 Strathy, 56 Strathnaver, 57 Halladale, 6

Strathnaver, 7 Halladale

01642 30 Marton, **31** Marton, **32** Marton, **33** MCL Middlesbrough, **34** MCL Middlesbrough, **35** MCL Middlesbrough, **36** Norton, **37** Haverton Hill, **38** MCL Middlesbrough, **43** Eston Grange, **44** Eston Grange, **45** Eston Grange, **46** Eston Grange, **47** Redcar, **48** Redcar, **49** Redcar, **52** Norton, **53** Norton, **54** Seal Sands, **55** Norton, **56** Haverton Hill, **57** Hartburn, **58** Hartburn, **59** Stainton, **60** Stockton, **61** Stockton, **62** Stockton, **63** Stockton, **66** Stockton, **67** Stockton, **70** Hutton, **71** Stokesley, **72** Great Ayton, **75** Ingleby, **76** Ingleby, **77** Wainstones, **78** Eaglescliffe, **79** Eaglescliffe, **81** Linthorpe, **82** Linthorpe, **85** Linthorpe, other numbers Middlesbrough

01643 7 Minehead Somerset, **82** Dunster, **83** Exford, **84** Timberscombe, **85** Winsford, **86** Porlock

01644 2 New Galloway Castle Douglas Kirkcudbrightshire, 3 Dalry Castle, 4 Corsock Castle, 5 Laurieston Castle, 6 Carsphairn Castle, 7 Parton Castle

0645 Mercury LocalCall

01646 60 Neyland Milford Haven Dyfed, **62** Pembroke, **63** Dale, **64** Angle, **65** Carew, **66** Castlemartin, **67** Lamphey, **68** Pembroke, **69** Milford Haven

01647 21 Drewsteignton Exeter Devon, **22** Manaton, **23** Whiddon Down, **24** Cheriton Bishop, **27** Lustleigh, **35** Christow, **40** Moretonhampstead, **43** Chagford, **44** Moretonhampstead, **5** Christow, **61** Tedburn St Mary, **7** Lustleigh

01648 2 Draperstown, **386** Bellaghy, **40** Swatragh, **418** Ballyronan, **42** Maghera, **43** Maghera, **44** Maghera, **45** Maghera, **46** Castledawson, **5** Toomebridge, **6** Castledawson, **73** Coagh, **74** Moneymore, **751** Tulnacross, **76** Cookstown, other numbers Magherafelt

01650 51 Cemmaes Road, **52** Llanbrynmair, **53** Dinas Mawddwy

01651 80 Methlick Ellon Aberdeenshire, **82** Rothienorman, **83** MCL Oldmeldrum, **842** Udny Ellon, **851** Tarves Ellon, **862** Newmachar, **872** Oldmeldrum, **88** Whiterashes, **891** Fyvie

01652 61 Saxby-all-Saints Brigg, South Humberside, **62** Searby, **63** Barton-on-Humber, **64** Kirton Lindsey, **65** Brigg, **66** Barton-on-Humber, **67** North Kelsey, **68** Barnetby

119

01653 61 Whitwell-on-the-Hill Malton North Yorkshire, 62 Hovingham, 64 Coneysthorpe, 65 Kirby Misperton, other numbers Malton

01654 70 Machynlleth Powys, 71 Tywyn, 761 Corris, 767 Aberdovey, 781 Glandyfi, 782 Abergynolwyn, 79 Pennal

01655 Maybole Ayrshire, 3 Turnberry, 4 Crosshill, 5 Kirkmichael, 6 Kirkoswald, 7 Straiton, 740 Crosshill, 750 Kirkmichael, 760 Kirkoswald, 770 Straiton

01656 72 Aberkenfig Bridgend Mid Glam, 73 Maesteg, 74 Kenfig Hill, 77 Porthcawl, 78 Porthcawl, 79 Wick, 81 Maesteg, 84 Ogmore Valley, 86 Pencoed, 87 Pontycymmer, 88 Southerndown, 89 Wick, other numbers Bridgend

01659 5 Sanquhar Dumfriesshire, 6 Kirkconnel, 74 Leadhills
0660 MCL

01661 80 MCL Wylam Northumberland, 82 Ponteland, 83 Prudhoe, 84 Stocksfield, 85 Wylam, 86 Ponteland, 87 Ponteland, 881 Belsay, 886 Stamfordham

01662 2 Omagh Co Tyrone, 52 Aughnacloy Co Tyrone, 54 Clogher, 56 Ballygawley, 57 Aughnacloy, 48 Gortin, 65 Sion Mills, 6 Newtownstewart, 67 Castlederg, 75 Beragh, 761 Carrickmore, 77 Mountfield, 83 Drumquin, 84 Fintona, 898 Dromore

01663 50 Newmills Stockport Cheshire, 71 Whaley Bridge, 73 Whaley Bridge, 74 New Mills, 75 Chinley, 76 Disley, 88 MCL New Mills

01664 42 Rearsby Leics, 43 Rotherby, 44 Scalford, 45 Somerby, 46 Waltham-on-the-Wolds, 47 Whissendine, 76 Scalford, 77 Somerby, 78 Waltham-on-the-Wolds, 79 Whissedine, 81 Asfordby, 82 Nether Broughton, 84 Gaddesby, 85 DCL, 86 MCL, other numbers Melton Mowbray

01665 51 Alnwick Northumberland, 570 Longframlington, 574 Whittingham, 575 Shilbottle, 576 Embleton, 577 Longhoughton, 578 Powburn, 579 Chariton Mires, 589 Chathill, 60 Alnwick, 711 Amble, 72 Seahouses, 83 Alnmouth

01666 50 Tetbury Glos, 51 Brinkworth, 57 Crudwell, 837 Hullavington, 838 Hullavington, 84 Sherston, 86 Minety, 88 Westonbirt, 89 Leighterton, other numbers Malmesbury

120

01667 404 Cawdor, 45 Nairn, 462 Ardersier, 493 Croy

01668 213 Belford Northumberland, 214 Bamburgh, 215 Chatton, 216 Milfield, 217 Wooperton, 28 Wooler, 5 Chatton, 6 Milfield, 7 Wooperton

01669 2 Rothbury Morpeth Northumberland, 30 Netherton, 40 Hepple, 50 Harbottle, 620 Rothbury, 621 Rothbury, 630 Netherton, 640 Hepple, 650 Harbottle

01670 35 Blyth Northumberland, 36 Blyth, 50 Morpeth, 51 Morpeth, 52 Ashington, 530 Bedlington, 531 Bedlington, 533 Morpeth, 534 Morpeth, 54 Blyth, 59 Cramlington, 71 Cramlington, 72 Hartburn, 73 Cramlington, 74 Scots Gap, 76 Red Row, 772 Hartburn, 774 Scots Gap, 775 Whalton, 787 Felton, 788 Longhorsley, 789 Stannington, 79 Ulgham, 81 Ashington, 82 Bedlington, 85 Ashington, 86 Lynemouth

01671 40 Newton Stewart, 82 Creetown, 83 Kirkcowan, 84 Bargrennan

01672 20 Ramsbury Marlborough Wilts, 4 Aldbourne, 51 Marlborough, 52 Ramsbury, 53 Avebury, 54 Aldebourne, 56 Pewsey, 6 Pewsey, 81 Burbage, 84 Ogbourne-St-George, 85 Woodborough, 86 Lockeridge, 87 Great Bedwyn, 89 MCL Marlborough

01673 81 Bishop Norton, 82 Owersby Moor, 83 Tealby, 84 Market Rasen, 85 Wragby, 86 Welton, 87 Normanby-by-Spital, 88 Wickenby

01674 67 Montrose Angus, 81 Bridge-of-Dun, 82 Farnell, 83 Hillside, 84 Northwaterbridge, 85 St Cyrus

01675 41 MCL, 44 Hampton-in-Arden, 46 Coleshill, 47 Curdworth, 48 Furnace End

01676 51 Meriden West Midlands, 52 Meriden, 53 Berkswell, 54 Fillongley, 57 MCL

01677 42 Bedale North Yorkshire, 45 Constable Burton, 46 Jervaulx, 47 Well Bedale

01678 3 Llanderfel Bala Gwynedd, 4 Llanuwchllyn, 52 Bala, 53 Llanderfel, 54 Llanuwchllyn

01680 2 Craignure Isle of Mull, 300 Aros, 4 Kinlochspelve, 812 Craignure, 814 Kinlochspelve

01681 4 Pennyghael Isle of Mull, 5 Tiroran, 700 Fionnphort, 700 Iona, 704 Pennyghael, 705 Tiroran

01683 Moffat Dumfriesshire, 3 Beattock

121

01684 27 Tewkesbury Glos, 29 Tewkesbury, 31 Hanley Swan, 4 Colwall, 54 Colwall, 59 Upton-on-Severn, 7 Bredon, 77 Bredon, 83 Birtsmorton, 85 Tewkesbury, 86 MCL, other numbers Malvern

01685 81 Hirwaun Aberdare Mid Glam, 84 Rhymney, 87 Aberdare, 88 Aberdare, other numbers Merthyr Tydfil

01686 41 Llanidloes Powys, 42 Carno, 43 Trefeglwys, 44 Llangurig, 45 Newtown, 61 Newtown, 62 Newtown, 63 Abermule, 64 Berriew, 65 Tregynon, 66 Montgomery, 67 Kerry, 68 Caersws

01687 Mallaig Inverness-shire, 45 Arisaig, 46 Mallaig, 47 Lochailort, 5 Arisaig, 7 Lochailort

01688 Tobermory Isle of Mull, 4 Dervaig, 5 Ulva Ferry

01689 80 Lodge Hill Kent, 81 MCL, 82 Orpington, 83 Orpington, 84 Lodge Hill, 85 Farnborough, 86 Farnborough, 87 Orpington, 88 Farnborough, 89 Orpington

01690 4 Capel Curig Betws-Y-Coed Gwynedd, 6 Dolwyddelan, 71 Betws-Y-Coed, 72 Capel Curig, 73 Betws-Y-Coed, 75 Dolwyddelan, 76 Penmachno, 77 Pentrefoelas

01691 61 Queens Head Oswestry Shropshire, 62 Ellesmere, 64 Llanfyllin, 65 Oswestry, 66 Oswestry, 67 Oswestry, 68 Knockin, 70 Llansilin, 71 Glyn Ceiriog, 73 Llanwddyn, 74 Pennant, 75 Dudleston Heath, 76 Llanarmon, 77 Chirk, 78 Llanhaeadr, 82 Llansantffraid, 83 Llanymynech

01692 4 North Walsham Norfolk, 50 North Walsham, 535 Smallburgh, 536 Smallburgh, 538 Stalham, 59 Swanton Abbott, 58 Stalham, 59 Hickling, 63 Horning, 64 MCL North Walsham, 65 Walcott, 670 Potter Heigham, 678 St Benets, 69 Swanton Abbot, 73 Rostrevor, 75 Warrenpoint, 76 Kilkeel, 77 Warrenpoint

01693 82 Jerrettspass, 83 Bessbrook, 84 Killeavy, 85 Mayobridge, 86 Crossmaglen, 878 Newtownhamilton, 88 Forkhill, other numbers Newry

01694 72 Church Stretton Shropshire, 73 Acton Burnell, 75 Leebotwood, 77 Longville, 78 Marshbrook

01695 2 Skelmersdale Lancs, 3 Skelmersdale, 42 Aughton Green, 50 Skelmersdale, 51 Skelmersdale, 52 Skelmersdale, 53 Skelmersdale, 54 Skelmersdale, 55 Skelmersdale, 56 Skelmersdale, 57 Ormskirk, 58 Ormskirk, 62 Upholland, 63 Upholland, 72

Skelmersdale, 73 Skelmersdale

06966 Jersey Premium Rate Services

01697 32 Aspatria Cumbria, 33 Silloth, 34 Wigton, 35 Kirkbride, 36 Abbeytown, 37 Low Ireby, 472 Armathwaite, 473 Southwaite, 476 Raughton Head, 478 Caldbeck, 72 Brampton, 73 Brampton, 740 Hallbankgate, 741 Brampton, 746 Hallbankgate, 747 Gilsland, 748 Roadhead

01698 26 Motherwell Lanarkshire, 27 Motherwell, 28 Hamilton, 35 Wishaw, 37 Wishaw, 38 Cambusnethan, 42 Hamilton, 45 Hamilton, 50 MCL, 71 Blantyre, 73 Holytown, 74 Bellshill, 79 Stonehouse, 81 Uddingston, 82 Blantyre, 83 Holytown, 84 Bellshill, 85 Bothwell, 86 Cleland, 87 Salsburgh, 88 Larkhall, 89 Hamilton, 50 Rothesay

01700 81 Tighnabruaich Argyll, 82 Kilfinnan, 83 Kilchattan Bay, 84 Colintraive

01702 20 Hawkwell Hockley Essex, 21 Great Wakering, 23 Hullbridge, 25 Canewdon, 27 MCL, 29 Shoeburyness, 420 Eastwood, 421 Eastwood, 47 Leigh-on-Sea, 48 Leigh-on-Sea, 51 Eastwood, 52 Eastwood, 53 Rochford, 54 Rochford, 55 Hadleigh, 58 Thorpe Bay, 7 Leigh-on-Sea, other numbers Southend-on-Sea

01703 20 Hythe Hants, 21 Southampton, 22 Southampton, 23 Southampton, 24 Fawley, 25 Chandlers Ford, 26 Chandlers Ford, 27 Chandlers Ford, 28 Lyndhurst, 29 Ashurst, 30 MCL, 31 MCL, 32 MCL, 33 Southampton, 38 Southampton, 39 MCL, 40 Bursledon, 42 Woolston, 43 Woolston, 44 Woolston, 45 Hamble, 46 Moorhill, 47 Moorhill, 49 MCL, 51 Shirley, 52 Shirley, 53 Southampton, 55 Hampton, 58 Hampton, 59 Hampton, 60 Fair Oak, 61 Eastleigh, 62 Eastleigh, 63 Southampton, 64 Eastleigh, 65 Eastleigh, 66 Totton, 67 Hampton, 68 Woolston, 69 Fair Oak, 70 Shirley, 71 Southampton, 72 Southampton, 73 Rownhams, 74 Rownhams, 76 Bassett, 77 Shirley, 78 Shirley, 79 Shirley, 81 Cadnam, 82 Southampton, 83 Southampton, 84 Hythe, 86 Totton, 87 Totton, 88 Totton, 89 Fawley

01704 2 Churchtown Merseyside, 500 Southport, 501 Southport, 502 Southport, 505 Churchtown, 506 Churchtown, 507 Churchtown, 51 Southport, 53 Southport, 54 Southport, 55 Birkdale, 56 Birkdale, 57 Ainsdale, 82 Rufford, 83 Formby, 84 Halsall, 86 MCL, 87 Formby, 88 Scarisbrick, 89 Burscough

123

Waterloo, 262 Paddington, 263 Holloway, 265 City of London & Wapping, 266 Lords, 267 Kentish Town, 268 Howland Street, 269 Holborn, 270 Westminster, 271 Westminster, 272 Whitehall, 273 Westminster, 274 Brixton, 275 Dalston, 276 Whitehall, 277 Walworth & New Cross, 278 King's Cross, 279 Whitehall, 280 City of London, 281 Holloway, 282 MCL, 283 City of London, 284 Kentish Town, 285 MCL, 286 Lords & Maida Vale, 287 Gerrard Street, 288 Canonbury, 289 Lords & Maida Vale, 290 Mayfair, 297 Gerrard Street, 304 MCL, 305 MCL, 306 MCL, 308 ECTL, 315 MCL, 320 St Paul's, 321 Westminster, 322 St Paul's, 323 Bloomsbury, 324 Clerkenwell, 325 St Paul's, 326 Brixton, 327 St Paul's, 328 Kilburn & Maida Vale, 329 MCL, 330 Moorgate, 331 MCL, 333 MCL, 334 MCL, 335 MCL, 336 Clerkenwell, 337 City of London, 338 MCL, 339 MCL, 344 MCL, 345 ECTL, 350 Battersea, 351 Chelsea, 352 Chelsea, 353 City of London, 354 Canonbury, 355 Mayfair, 356 City of London, 357 Southwark, 358 Peckham & New Cross, 359 Highbury, 362 O, 363 ECTL, 369 MCL, 370 Earl's Court, 371 West Kensington & Parsons Green, 372 Maida Vale, 373 Earl's Court, 374 Moorgate, 375 Bishopsgate, 376 Chelsea & Kensington Gardens, 377 City of London, 378 Southwark, 379 Holborn, 380 Euston, 381 Fulham, 382 City of London, 383 Euston, 384 Parsons Green, 385 Fulham, 386 Fulham, 387 Euston, 388 Euston, 389 Whitehall, 391 Euston, 394 Bermondsey, 396 MCL, 397 Southwark, 401 Waterloo, 402 Paddington, 403 Southwark, 404 Holborn, 405 Holborn, 406 St Paul's, 407 Southwark, 408 Mayfair, 409 Mayfair, 410 MCL, 411 MCL, 412 MCL, 413 MCL, 414 MCL, 415 MCL, 416 MCL, 417 MCL, 418 MCL, 425 MCL, 426 Bishopsgate, 430 Clerkenwell, 431 Hampstead, 433 Hampstead, 434 Soho, 435 Hampstead, 436 Howland, 437 Soho, 438 Covent Garden, 439 Soho, 454 MCL, 457 MCL, 465 MCL, 467 Marylebone, 473 Albert Dock, Plaistow & Canning Town, 474 Plaistow, Canning Town & Albert Dock, 476 Plaistow, Canning Town & Albert Dock, 477 MCL, 480 City of London & Wapping, 481 City of London & Wapping, 482 Kentish Town, 483 St John's Wood, 484 Euston, 485 Kentish Town, 486 St Marylebone, 487 St Marylebone, 488 City of London & Wapping, 489 City of London, 490 Clerkenwell, 491 Mayfair, 492 Holborn, 493 Mayfair, 494 Gerrard Street (Soho), 495 Mayfair, 496 Moorgate, 497 Covent Garden, 498 Nine Elms, 499 Mayfair, 510 Poplar, 511 Plaistow, Canning Town & Albert Dock, 512 Poplar, 513 Canary Wharf, 515 Poplar, 516 Canary Wharf, 522 MCL, 525 MCL, 528 MCL, 537 Poplar, 538 Poplar, 548 MCL, 555 BT ACD, 580 Bloomsbury, 581 Kensington, 582 Vauxhall, 583 City of London, 584 Kensington, 585 Battersea, 586 St John's Wood, 587 Vauxhall, 588 City of

London, 589 South Kensington, 600 City of London, 601 City of London, 602 West Kensington, 603 West Kensington, 604 Maida Vale, 605 West Kensington, 606 City of London, 607 Barnsbury, 608 Clerkenwell, 609 Barnsbury, 610 Fulham & West Kensington, 611 Holborn, 612 Howland Street, 613 City of London, 615 St Paul's, 617 MCL, 618 Prestel, 620 Southbank, 621 City of London. 622 Nine Elms, 623 City of London, 624 Maida Vale, 625 Kilburn & Maida Vale, 626 City of London, 627 Nine Elms, 628 City of London, 629 Mayfair, 630 Victoria, 631 Bloomsbury, 632 Bloomsbury, 633 Bloomsbury, 634 City of London, 635 Peckham & New Cross, 636 Bloomsbury, 637 Bloomsbury, 638 City of London, 639 Peckham & New Cross, 649 MCL, 652 MCL, 662 City of London. 696 MCL, 700 Lower Holloway, 701 Camberwell & Walworth, 702 City of London & Wapping, 703 Camberwell & Walworth, 704 Lower Holloway, 705 Featurenet, 706 Paddington, 707 Featurenet, 708 Camberwell & Walworth, 709 City of London & Wapping. 710 City of London, 711 MCL, 712 MCL, 713 Harrison Street, 714 MCL, 715 Canary Wharf, 716 MCL, 717 MCL, 718 Canary Wharf, 719 Canary Wharf, 720 Nine Elms, 721 Westminster, 722 St John's Wood, 723 Paddington, 724 Paddington, 725 North Paddington, 726 City of London, 727 Bayswater & Notting Hill, 728 Euston, 729 Shoreditch, 730 Sloane Square, 731 Fulham, 732 Peckham & New Cross, 733 Brixton, 734 Soho, 735 Kennington & Walworth, 736 Fulham, 738 Brixton & Nine Elms, 739 Shoreditch, 747 Whitehall, 753 MCL, 757 MCL, 762 St Paul's, 765 MCL, 772 MCL, 774 MCL, 775 MCL, 779 MCL, 782 MCL, 790 Shoreditch, 791 Stephney Green, 792 Bayswater, 793 Vauxhall, 794 Hampstead, 795 Chelsea & Kensington Gardens, 796 City, 797 MCL, 798 Pimlico, 799 Westminster, 813 MCL, 814 MCL, 815 MCL, 816 MCL, 817 MCL, 820 Vauxhall, 821 Victoria, 822 City of London, 823 Belgravia & South Kensington, 824 Sloane, 825 MCL, 826 Moorgate, 827 MCL, 828 Victoria, 829 St Paul's, 830 MCL, 831 Holborn, 832 City of London, 833 King's Cross, 834 Victoria, 835 Earls Court, 836 Covent Garden, 837 King's Cross, 838 South Kensington, Sloane Square & Belgravia, 839 Whitehall, 860 MCL, 865 MCL, 872 MCL, 873 MCL, 880 MCL, 887 MCL, 895 MCL, 896 MCL, 901 MCL, 910 MCL, 911 MCL, 912 MCL, 915 MCL, 916 MCL, 917 MCL, 918 MCL, 919 MCL, 920 Moorgate, 921 Waterloo, 922 Waterloo, 923 Kingsland Green, 924 Brixton, 925 Whitehall, 926 Brixton, 927 Soho, 928 Waterloo, 929 Monument, 930 Westminster, 931 Fulham, 932 Pimlico, 933 Pimlico, 934 Waterloo, 935 St Marylebone, 936 City of London, 937 Kensington, 938 Kensington, 939 Southwark, 945 MCL, 955 MCL, 956 MCL, 957 MCL, 962 MCL, 971 MCL, 972

MCL, 973 MCL, 975 MCL, 976 Pimlico, Westminster, Whitehall, 978 Nine Elms, Battersea, Brixton, 982 MCL, 987 Poplar

01720 4 Isles of Scilly Penzance Cornwall

01721 70 MCL Peebles, 72 Peebles, 73 Eddleston, 74 Kirkton Manor, 75 Drochil Castle, 76 Stobo Peebles

01722 32 Salisbury Wilts, 33 Salisbury, 39 MCL, 41 Salisbury, 42 Salisbury, 43 Salisbury, 710 Alderbury, 711 Alderbury, 714 Fovant, 716 Teffont, 72 Farley, 73 Middle Woodford, 74 Wilton, 77 Coombe Bissett, 78 Broadchalke, 79 Stapleford, 82 Salisbury

01723 50 Cayton Bay North Yorkshire, 51 Filey, 58 Cayton Bay, 85 Snainton, 86 West Ayton, 87 Cloughton, 88 Hackness, 89 Hunmanby, other numbers Scarborough

01724 71 Crowle South Humberside, 72 Burton-on-Stather, 73 Winterton, 76 Scotter, 78 Keadby, 79 Eastoft, other numbers Scunthorpe

01725 2 Downton Salisbury Wilts, 53 Rockbourne, 516 Tollard Royal, 517 Cranborne, 55 Handley, 59 MCL, 89 Martin Cross

01726 81 Par Cornwall, 82 Nanpean, 83 Fowey, 84 Mevagissey, 85 Stenalees, 86 Fraddon, 87 Polruan, 88 Grampound Road, 89 Roche, other numbers St Austell

01727 37 Welwyn Garden City, 71 JCGL, 81 St Albans, 82 Bowmansgreen, 83 St Albans, 84 St Albans, 85 St Albans, 86 St Albans, 87 Park Street, 88 MCL, 89 St Albans

01728 45 Aldeburgh Suffolk, 60 Saxmundham, 621 Framlingham, 628 Worlingworth, 635 Leiston, 638 Badingham, 642 Leiston, 643 Leiston, 648 Westleton, 65 Saxmundham, 660 Peasenhall, 662 Rendham, 663 Rendham, 668 Yoxford, 685 Earl Soham, 688 Snape, 689 Snape, 72 Framlingham, 73 Westleton, 74 Wickham Market, 79 Peasenhall, 83 Leiston, 86 Debenham

01729 830 Airton Skipton North Yorkshire, 840 Long Preston, 850 Hellifield, 860 Horton-in-Ribblesdale, other numbers Settle

01730 81 Midhurst West Sussex, 821 Rogate, 823 East Meon, 824 Privett, 825 Harting, 827 Hawkley, 828 Privett, 829 West Meon, 89 Liss, other numbers Petersfield

01731 28 Thorney Toll Cambs, 29 Mereside

01732 22 West Malling Maidstone Kent, 3 Tonbridge, 4 Sevenoaks, 52 West Malling, 59 MCL, 70 Four Elms, 71 Sevenoaks, 74

Sevenoaks, 75 Ide Hill, 76 Seal, 77 Tonbridge, 78 Borough Green, 81 Plaxtol, 82 Fairseat, 83 Hildenborough, 84 West Malling, 85 Hadlow, 86 Edenbridge, 87 West Malling, 88 Borough Green, other numbers Sevenoaks

01733 20 Whittlesey Cambs, 21 Crowland, 22 Eye, 23 Orton, 24 Yaxley, 25 Glinton, 26 Westwood, 27 Thorney, *28 MCL, 32 Werrington, 33 Westwood, 35 Whittlesey, 36 Orton, 37 Orton, 380 Castor, 382 Werrington, 39 Orton, 41 Peterborough, 46 MCL, 47 MCL, 57 Werrington, 81 Newborough, 840 Turves, 842 Westwood, 844 Mereside, 849 Thorney Toll, other numbers Peterborough*

01734 20 Reading (South) & Whitley Berks, 21 *Reading (South) & Whitley,* 220 *Reading (South) & Whitley,* 222 *Reading (South) & Whitley,* 223 *Reading (South) & Whitley,* 224 *Reading (South) & Whitley,* 225 *Heckfield,* 23 *Reading (South) & Whitley,* 41 *Hurst, Shurlock Row & Twyford,* 25 MCL, 26 Earley Reading, 27 Sonning & Woodley, 28 ECL, 29 Earley, 30 Theale, 31 *Reading (South) & Whitley,* 320 Hurst, Shurlock Row & Twyford, 321 Hurst, Shurlock Row & Twyford, 322 Tilehurst, 323 Theale, 324 Eversley, 326 Heckfield, 327 Theale, 328 Eversley, 33 Mortimer, 34 Hurst, Shurlock Row & Twyford, 35 Earley, 36 Wokingham, 39 Reading, 40 Wargrave, 41 Tilehurst, 42 Tilehurst, 43 Tilehurst, 44 Woodley, 45 Tilehurst, 46 Caversham, 47 Caversham, 48 Caversham, 49 MCL, 5 Reading Berks, 60 Reading, 61 TC, 62 TC, 63 MCL, 64 MCL, 66 Reading, 671 BCL, 69 Woodley, 70 Silchester, 71 Woolhampton, 72 Kidmore End, 73 Eversley, 742 Wokingham, 744 Bradfield, 745 Bradfield, 75 *Reading (South) & Whitley,* 760 Aborfield, 763 Aborfield, 764 Pangbourne, 765 Pangbourne, 77 Wokingham, 81 Tadley, 820 Tadley, 821 Tadley, 822 Tadley, 824 Tadley, 825 Tadley, 826 Tadley, 827 Tadley, 828 Hurst, Shurlock Row & Twyford, 83 Burghfield Common, 84 Pangbourne, 85 *Reading (South) & Whitley,* 86 *Reading (South) & Whitley,* 87 *Reading (South) & Whitley,* 88 Spencers Wood, 89 Wokingham, **other numbers Reading**

01736 71 Marazion Cornwall, 73 Mousehole, 74 Cockwells, 75 Hayle, 76 Germoe, 78 St Just, 79 St Ives, 81 St Buryan, 85 Leedstown, 87 Sennen, **other numbers Penzance**

01737 2 Reigate Surrey, 3 Burgh Heath, 55 Downland, 64 Merstham, 73 Reserved for Mercury, 76 Redhill, 77 Redhill, 78 Redhill, 81 Tadworth, 82 Nutfield Ridge, 83 Mogador, 84 Betchworth

01738 5 Scone Perth, 583 Almondbank, 71 Caputh, 73 Gask, 787 Bankfoot, 81 Bridge-of-Earn, 82 Stanley, 84 Methven, 85 Abernethy, 88 Glencarse, 89 Glenalmond, 89 MCL, other numbers Perth

01740 62 Sedgefield Stockton-on-Tees Cleveland, 63 Stillington, 65 Ferryhill, 79 MCL

01743 70 Upton Magna Shrewsbury Shropshire, 71 Dorrington, 74 Nesscliffe, 76 Cross Houses, 79 Pontesbury, 81 Nesscliffe, 82 Yockleton, 85 Montford Bridge, 86 Hanwood, 87 Bayston Hill, 88 Halfway Hous, 89 Worthen, other numbers Shrewsbury

01744 2 St Helens Lancs, 3 St Helens, 45 St Helens, 46 St Helens, 5 St Helens, 61 St Helens, 69 St Helens, 73 St Helens, 74 St Helens, 75 St Helens, 77 St Helens, 81 Marshall's Cross, 82 Marshall's Cross, 83 Marshall's Cross, 85 Marshall's Cross, 88 Rainford, 89 Billinge

01745 54 Llannefydd Denbigh Clwyd, 55 Nantglyn, 56 Mostyn, 57 Dyserth, 58 St Asaph, 59 Rhuddlan, 70 Nantglyn, 71 Bodfari, 72 Llanfairtalhaiarn, 73 Trefnant, 76 Llangernyw, 77 Llansannan, 78 Llanynys, 79 Llannefydd, 81 Denbigh, 82 Abergele, 83 Abergele, 84 Llanfairtalhaiarn, 85 Prestatyn, 86 Llangernyw, 87 Llansannan, 88 Prestatyn, 89 Llanynys, other numbers Rhyl

01746 31 Morville Bridgnorth Shropshire, 32 Stottesdon, 33 Burwarton, 34 Ditton Priors, 35 Middleton Scriven, 36 Brockton, 37 MCL, 4 Worfield, 5 Ackleton, 710 Claverley, 712 Ditton Priors, 714 Morville, 716 Worfield, 718 Stottesdon, 780 Quatt, 781 Quatt, 783 Ackleton, 785 Brockton, 787 Burwarton, 789 Middleton Scriven, 86 Highley, other numbers Bridgnorth

01747 5 Shaftesbury Dorset, 81 Fontmell Magna, 822 Gillingham, 823 Gillingham, 824 Gillingham, 825 Gillingham, 826 Gillingham, 828 Donhead, 829 Donhead, 830 East Knoyle, 838 East Stour, 84 Bourton, 86 Mere, 87 Tisbury, 89 Hindon

01748 81 Old Catterick Richmond North Yorkshire, 82 Richmond, 83 Catterick Camp, 85 Richmond, 87 Catterick Camp, 884 Reeth, 886 Gunnerside

01749 33 Shepton Mallet, 34 Shepton Mallet, 67 Wells, 68 Wells, 81 Bruton, 82 Royal Bath & West, 83 Evercreech, 84 Oakhill, 85 Upton Noble, 66 Ditcheat, 87 Priddy, 88 Cranmore, 89 Pilton

01750 2 Selkirk, 32 Ashkirk, 42 Cappercleuch, 52 Ettrick Bridge, 62 Ettrick Valley, 76 Yarrowford, 82 Yarrow

01751 41 Lastingham York, 43 Kirbymoorside, 46 Lockton, 47 Pickering

129

01752 61 Cornwood Ivybridge Devon, 64 Shaugh Prior, 65 Holbeton, 81 Torpoint, 82 Millbrook, 84 Saltash, 85 Landrake, other numbers Plymouth

01753 212 Langley Berks, 218 Slough, 22 Slough, 51 Slough, 52 Slough, 53 Slough, 54 Langley, 55 Slough, 56 Slough, 57 Slough, 58 Langley, 59 Langley, 60 MCL, 612 Langley, 615 Slough, 618 Slough, 619 Slough, 62 Windsor, 63 Slough, 641 Slough, 642 Farnham Common, 643 Farnham Common, 644 Farnham Common, 645 Farnham Common, 646 Farnham Common, 647 Farnham Common, 648 Farnham Common, 65 Iver, 66 Fulmer, 67 MCL, 68 Colnbrook, 69 Slough, 71 TCC, 73 TCC, 74 TCC, 75 Windsor, 78 JCGL, 79 MCL, 81 MCL, 82 Slough, 83 Windsor, 84 Windsor, 85 Windsor, 86 Windsor, 87 Slough, 88 Gerrards Cross, 89 Gerrards Cross, other numbers Slough

01754 81 Burgh Lines, 82 Friskney, 83 Little Steeping, 85 Scremby, 87 Chapel St Leonards, 88 Wainfleet, 89 Scremby, other numbers Skegness

01756 71 Bolton Abbey Skipton North Yorkshire, 72 Burnsall, 73 Cracoe, 75 Grassington, 76 Kettlewell, 77 Arncliffe, 74 Gargrave, other numbers Skipton

01757 Selby North Yorkshire, 228 Gateforth, 248 Riccall, 249 Riccall, 268 Cawood, 269 Cawood, 270 Burn, 28 Bubwith, 61 Camblesforth, 63 Hemingbrough

01758 61 Pwllheli Gwynedd, 70 Pwllheli, 71 Abersoch, 72 Nefyn, 74 Llanbedrog, 75 Llithfaen, 76 Aberdaron, 77 Tudweiliog, 83 Botwnnog, 86 Aberdaron, 88 Rhiw

01759 30 Pocklington York, 31 Melbourne, 35 MCL, 36 Bishop Wilton, 37 Stamford Bridge, 38 Wilberfoss

01760 3 Narborough Kings Lynn Norfolk, 4 Holme, 72 Swaffham, 755 Castle Acre, 756 Gt Cressingham, 22 West Harptree, 23 Stratton-on-the-Fosse, 24 Chewton Mendip, 29 MCL Mendip

01761 41 Midsomer Norton Bath Avon, 42 Midsomer Norton, 43 Radstock, 45 Temple Cloud, 46 Blagdon, 47 Timsbury, 49 Compton Dando

01762 318 Poyntzpass Newry Co Down, 320 Craigavon, 321 Lurgan, 322 Lurgan, 323 Lurgan, 324 Lurgan, 325 Lurgan, 326

Lurgan, 327 Lurgan, 328 Lurgan, 329 Lurgan, 340 Derryadd, 341 Craigavon, 342 Craigavon, 343 Craigavon, 344 Craigavon, 345 Craigavon, 346 Craigavon, 347 Lurgan, 348 Lurgan, 349 Lurgan, 82 Waringstown, 83 Gilford, 84 Tandragee, 85 Annaghmore, 87 Richhill, 88 Waringstown, 89 Loughgall, other numbers Portadown

01763 20 Fowlmere Royston Herts, 22 CCL, 24 Royston 25 Royston, 26 Melbourn, 27 Buntingford, 281 Cottered, 287 Kelshall, 288 Broadfield, 289 Great Hormead, 83 Chrishall, 84 Barkway, 85 Steeple Morden

01764 Crieff Perthshire, 65 Crieff, 66 Auchterarder, 67 Comrie, 681 Muthill, 682 Blackford, 683 Madderty, 684 Dunning, 685 St Fillans

01765 620 Sawley North Humberside, 635 North Stainley, 640 Melmerby, 658 Kirkby Malzeard, 677 Bishop Monkton, 689 Masham, other numbers Ripon

01766 51 Porthmadog Gwynedd, 52 Criccieth, 53 Garndolbenmaen, 54 Trawsfynydd, 59 Maentwrog, 75 Garndolbenmaen, 76 Ffestiniog, 77 Penrhyndeudraeth, 78 Harlech, 81 Chwilog, 83 Blaenau, 85 Maentwrog, 86 Beddgelert, 87 Trawsfynydd, 89 Beddgelert

01767 20 MCL, 26 Potton, 31 Biggleswade, 32 CCL, 60 Biggleswade, 62 Northill, 63 Wrestlingworth, 64 Blunham, 65 Gamlingay, 67 Great Gransden, 68 Sandy, 69 Sandy, other numbers Sandy

01768 34 Brough Kirkby Stephen Cumbria, 35 Appleby, 36 Kirkby Thore, 37 Kirkby Stephen, 482 Glenridding, 483 Greystoke, 484 Skelton, 486 Pooley Bridge, 770 Buttermere, 771 Langwathby, 772 Keswick, 773 Keswick, 774 Keswick, 775 Keswick, 776 Bassenthwaite Lake, 777 Borrowdale, 778 Braithwaite, 779 Threlkeld, 881 Langwathby, 882 Culgaith, 884 Culgaith, 885 Calthwaite, 886 Culgaith, 887 Culgaith, 894 Plumpton, 896 Croglin, 897 Lazonby, 898 Lazonby, other numbers Penrith

01769 52 Ashreigney Chulmleigh Devon, 54 Chittlehamholt, 55 Bishops Nympton, 56 High Bickington, 57 South Molton, 58 Chulmleigh, 6 High Bickington

01770 30 Brodick Isle of Arran, 60 Lamlash, 70 Whiting Bay, 81 Corrie, 82 Kildonan, 83 Lochranza, 84 Machrie, 85 Pirnmill, 86 Shiskine, 87 Sliddery

01771 2 Mintlaw Peterhead Aberdeenshire, 3 New Deer, 4 Maud, 5 Strichen, 613 Maud, 62 Mintlaw, 637 Strichen, 644 New

131

Deer, 653 New Pitsligo, 7 New Pitsligo

01772 40 Preston Lancs, 42 Leyland, 43 Leyland, 45 Leyland, 48 Energis, 49 MCL, 60 Croston, 61 Longton, 621 Leyland, 622 Leyland, 623 Leyland, 624 Leyland, 625 Leyland, 63 Freckleton, 64 Leyland, 670 Freckleton, 671 Kirkham, 672 Kirkham, 673 Kirkham, 679 Freckleton, 68 Kirkham, 690 Catforth, 691 Catforth, 781 Longridge, 782 Longridge, 783 Longridge, 784 Longridge, 785 Longridge, 786 Longridge, 81 Hesketh Bank, 83 MCL, 845 Freckleton, 846 Freckleton, 85 Freckleton, 86 Broughton, 87 Samlesbury, other numbers Preston

01773 510 Pinxton Derbys, 511 Pinxton, 520 Alfreton, 521 Alfreton, 522 Alfreton, 523 Alfreton, 525 Belper, 53 Langley Mill, 54 Leabrooks, 55 Cowers Lane, 58 Pinxton, 59 Tibshelf, 60 Leabrooks, 71 Langley Mill, 72 Ripley, 76 Langley Mill, 78 DCL, 81 Pinxton, 82 Belper, 83 Alfreton, 84 MCL, 85 Ambergate, 86 Pinxton, 87 Tibshelf, other numbers Ripley

01775 63 Deeping St Nicholas Lincs, 64 Pinchbeck Bars, 67 Tongue End, 68 Surfleet, 75 Risegate, 77 Spalding, 82 Donington, 84 Gosberton, 88 Deeping St Nicholas, other numbers Spalding

01776 7 Stranraer Wigtownshire, 81 Portpatrick, 82 Lochans, 83 Sandhead, 84 Drummore, 853 Kirkcolm, 86 Ardwell, 87 Leswalt

01777 22 Dunham-on-Trent Newark Notts, 24 Rampton, 81 Ranskill, 83 Gamston, 87 Tuxford, other numbers Retford

01778 31 Bourne Lincs, 32 Edenham, 33 Witham-on-the-Hill, 39 Bourne Lincs, 42 Bourne, 44 Dowsby, 56 Greatford, 57 Morton, 590 Witham-on-the-Hill, 591 Edenham, other numbers Market Deeping

01779 81 Cruden Bay Peterhead Aberdeenshire, 82 Longside, 838 St Fergus, 84 Hatton, 872 Peterhead

01780 41 Castle Bytham Lincs, 44 Duddington, 45 Bulwick, 46 Empingham, 47 King's Cliffe, 72 North Luffenham, 74 Bainton, 78 Wansford, 83 Duddington, other numbers Stamford

01782 20 Hanley Stoke-on-Trent Staffs, 21 Hanley, 22 Hanley, 26 Hanley, 27 Hanley, 28 Hanley, 29 Stoke-on-Trent, 30 Ash Bank, 31 Longton/Fenton, 32 Longton/Fenton, 33 Longton/Fenton, 34 Longton/Fenton, 37 Barlaston, 38 Blythe Bridge, 39 Blythe Bridge, 4 Stoke-on-Trent/Fenton, 50 Endon, 51 Biddulph, 522 Biddulph, 523 Biddulph, 524 Burslam/Tunstall, 53 Milton, 54 Milton,

132

other numbers Swansea

01793 41 MCL Swindon Wilts, 44 MCL, 45 MCL, 70 Blunsdon, 71 Ashbury, 72 Blunsdon, 731 Broad Hinton, 74 Chiseldon, 75 Cricklade, 76 Highworth, 77 Purton, 78 Shrivenham, 79 Wanborough, 81 Wroughton, 82 Stratton St Margaret, 83 Stratton St Margaret, 842 Wootton Bassett, 843 Wootton Bassett, 845 Wroughton, 848 Wootton Bassett, 849 Wootton Bassett, 85 Wootton Bassett, 861 Highworth, 87 Toothill, 88 Toothill, 89 Toothill, other numbers Swindon

01794 2 West Wellow Romsey Hants, 30 Broughton, 34 Lockerley, 38 Kings Somborne, 39 Earldoms, 40 Lockerley, 41 Lockerley, 51 Romsey, 52 Romsey, 6 Braishfield, 83 Romsey, 88 Whiteparish, 89 MCL

01795 4 Sittingbourne Kent, 51 Leysdown-on-Sea, 52 Teynham, 53 Faversham, 58 Sheerness, 59 Faversham, 6 Sheerness, 83 Milstead, 84 Newington, 87 Minster, 880 Eastchurch, 886 Doddington, 89 Eastling, other numbers Sittingbourne

01796 47 Pitlochry, 461 Blair Atholl, 482 Ballinluig, 483 Calvine

01797 22 Rye East Sussex, 23 Peasmarsh Rye, 25 Northiam, 26 Beckley, 27 Wittersham, 28 Iden, 34 Brookland, 36 New Romney, other numbers Rye

01798 34 Petworth West Sussex, 81 West Chiltington, 831 Bury, 861 Lodsworth, 865 Fittleworth, 867 Graffham, 869 Sutton, 87 Pulborough, other numbers Pulborough

01799 50 CCL Saffron Walden Essex, 53 Great Chesterford, 54 Newport, 55 Clavering, 57 MCL, 584 Ashdon, 586 Gt Sampford, 59 Radwinter, other numbers Saffron Walden

0800 BT Freefone

0801 Cellnet Cellular Radio

01803 3 St Marychurch Torquay Devon, 5 Paignton, 60 Chelston, 61 Shiphay Collaton, 62 Churston, 663 Paignton, 664 Paignton, 665 Paignton, 666 Paignton, 668 Paignton, 69 Chelston, 71 Blackawton, 72 Dittisham, 73 Harbertonford, 75 Kingswear, 76 Staverton, 77 Stoke Fleming, 78 Stoke Gabriel, 81 Ipplepen, 83 Dartmouth, 84 Churston, 85 Brixham, 86 Totnes, 87 Kingskerswell, 88 Brixham, other numbers Torquay

134

01805 3 Beaford Winkleigh Devon, 4 Dolton, 60 Langtree, 62 Torrington, 68 Beaford, 69 Bolton
01806 22 Brae Shetland, 23Hillswick, 24 Sullom Voe, 3 North Roe, 4 Ollaberry, 5 Out Skerries, 503 Hillswick, 515 Out Skerries, 522 Brae, 533 North Rae, 544 Ollaberry, 566 Symbister, 577 Vidlin, 588 Voe, 6 Symbister, 7 Vidlin, 8 Vo
01807 50 Ballindalloch Banffshire, 51 Advie, 58 Tomintoul, 59 Glenlivet
01808 2 Tomatin Inverness-shire, 3 Farr, 4 Glenmazeran, 51 Tomatin, 52 Farr, 53 Glenmazeran
01809 511 Tomdoun Inverness-shire, 501 Invergarry Inverness-shire

0181 200 Colindale, 201 Mill Hill, Elstree, Colindale, Hendon & Golders Green, 202 Hendon, 203 Hendon, 204 Kingsbury, 205 Colindale, 206 Kingsbury, 207 Elstree, 208 Cricklewood, 209 Golders Green, 211 Stamford Hill & Bowes Park, 215 ECTL 220 MCL, 224 MCL, 227 ECTL, 231 Ealing, Greenford & Isleworth, 232 Isleworth, 233 MCL, 235 MCL, 237 Hammersmith, 238 MCL, 239 MCL, 240 MCL, 241 MCL, 242 MCL, 243 MCL, 244 MCL, 245 CLP, 247 Kingston, 248 MCL, 252 MC, 264 O, 275 Barnet, 289 NCL, 290 Bromley, 291 Forest Hill, 292 MCL, 293 Greenwich, 294 Eltham, 295 Chislehurst, 297 Lee Green, 298 Bexleyheath, 299 Dulwich & Camberwell, 300 Sidcup, 301 Bexleyheath, 302 Sidcup, 303 Bexleyheath, 304 Bexleyheath, 305 Greenwich, 306 ECTL 307 MCL, 308 Sidcup, 309 Sidcup, 310 Thamesmead, 311 Thamesmead, 312 Greenwich, 313 Bromley, 314 Catford & Rushey Green, 316 Woolwich & Plumstead, 317 Woolwich & Plumstead, 318 Lewisham, 319 Woolwich, Eltham & Greenwich, 330 Worcester Park, 332 Richmond, 335 Worcester Park, 336 New Malden, 337 Worcester Park, 339 Thames Ditton/Surbiton, 340 Crouch End, 341 Crouch End, 342 Crouch End & Enfield, 343 Finchley & North Finchley, 344 Ponders End, 345 Edmonton, 346 Finchley, 347 Crouch End, 348 Crouch End, 349 Finchley, 360 Winchmore Hill, 361 New Southgate, 362 New Southgate & Enfield, 363 Enfield, 364 Enfield, Ponders End & Barnet, 365 Bowes Park, Tottenham & Muswell Hill, 366 Enfield, 367 Enfield, 368 New Southgate, 369 North Finchley, 370 Enfield, 381 Mill Hill, Edgware, Golders Green & Elstree, 384 MCL, 385 Wembley & Stanmore, 386 JCGL, 390 Surbiton, 391 Chessington, 392 Mortlake, 393 Ewell, 394 Ewell, 395 MCL, 397 Chessington, 398 Thames Ditton, 399 Surbiton, 401 MCL, 402 MCL, 419 MCL, 420 Bushey Heath, Hatch End, Stanmore, 421 Hatch End, 422 South Harrow, 423 South Harrow, 424 Harrow, 426 South Harrow & Pinner, 427 Harrow, 428 Hatch End, 429 Pinner & Eastcote, 440 Barnet, 441 Hadley Green &

Barnet, **442** Clapton, Stamford Hill & Muswell Hill, **443** Ponders End, **444** Muswell Hill, **445** North Finchley, **446** North Finchley, **447** Palmers Green & Barnet, **449** Barnet, **450** Cricklewood & Dollis Hill, **451** Willesden, **452** Cricklewood & Dollis Hill, **453** Harlesden, **455** Golders Green, **456** Colindale, **458** Golders Green, **459** Willesden, **460** Bromley, **461** Catford & Bellingham, **462** Hayes, **463** Lee Green, **464** Bromley, **466** Chislehurst & Bickley, **468** Chislehurst & Bickley, **469** Deptford, **470** Upton Park, **471** Upton Park, **472** Upton Park, **475** Upton Park, **476** MCL, **478** Ilford, **479** MCL, **482** MCL, **490** MCL, **491** ECTL, **500** Hainault, **501** Hainault, **502** Loughton, **503** Gants Hill, Goodmayes, Highams Park, Upton Park, Stratford & Walthamstow, **504** Woodford & Buckhurst Hill, **505** Woodford & Buckhurst Hill, **506** Woodford, **507** Barking, **508** Loughton, **509** Walthamstow, **514** Ilford, **517** Dagenham, **518** Ilford, Leytonstone & Wanstead, **519** Stratford & Forest Gate, **520** Walthamstow, **521** Walthamstow, **23** Highams Park, **524** Chingford, **526** Dagenham, **527** Highams Park, **528** MCL, **529** Chingford, **530** Wanstead, **531** Highams Park, **532** Leytonstone, Loughton & Wanstead, **533** Hackney, **534** Stratford & Forest Gate, **535** MCL, **536** Stratford & Forest Gate, **539** Leytonstone, **540** Merton & South, **541** Kingston, **542** Merton & South Wimbledon, **543** Merton & South Wimbledon, **544** Merton & South Wimbledon, **545** Merton & South Wimbledon, **546** Kingston, **547** Kingston, **549** Kingston, **550** Gants Hill, **551** Gants Hill, **552** Upton Park, **553** Ilford, **554** Ilford, **555** Stratford & Forest Gate, **556** Leytonstone, **557** MCL, **558** Leytonstone, **559** Chingford, Hainault & Woodford, **560** Isleworth & Brentford, **561** Hayes & Cranford, **562** London Airport, Heathrow & Harlington, **563** Hammersmith, **564** London Airport, Heathrow, **565** MCL, **566** Greenford & Perivale, **567** Ealing, **568** Isleworth, **569** Hayes, **570** Hounslow & Heston, **571** Southall, **572** Hounslow & Heston, **573** Hayes & Cranford, **574** Southall, **575** Greenford, **576** Shepherd's Bush, **577** Hounslow, **578** Greenford, **579** Ealing, **581** MCL, **590** Seven Kings & Goodmayes, **591** Barking, **592** Dagenham, **593** Dagenham, **594** Barking, **595** Dagenham, **597** Seven Kings & Goodmayes, **598** Seven Kings & Goodmayes, **599** Seven Kings & Goodmayes, **606** Hayes, **640** Kenley, **641** Sutton & Cheam, **642** Sutton & Cheam, **643** Sutton & Belmont, **644** Sutton & Cheam, **645** Purley & Kenley, **646** Mitcham & Morden, **647** Wallington & Carshalton, **648** Mitcham & Morden, **649** Croydon, **650** Beckenham, **651** Sanderstead & Selsdon, **652** Sutton & Cheam, **653** Beulah Hill, **654** Addiscombe & South Norwood, **655** Addiscombe & South Norwood, **656** Addiscombe & South Norwood, **657** Sanderstead & Selsdon, **658** Beckenham, **659** Sydenham & Penge, **660** Purley

Wandsworth, **876** Mortlake, **877** Wandsworth, **878** Mortlake, **879** Wimbledon, **880** Clapton, Stamford Hill & Tottenham, **881** Wood Green & Bowes Park, **882** Palmers Green, **883** Muswell Hill, **884** Edmonton, **885** Tottenham, **886** Palmers Green, **887** Edmonton, **888** Wood Green & Bowes Park, **889** Wood Green & Bowes Park, **890** Felthan & East Bedfont, **891** Twickenham, **892** Twickenham, **893** Feltham, Southall & Twickenham, **894** Twickenham, **895** MCL, **896** Acton, **897** London Airport Heathrow & Harlington, **898** Twickenham, **899** MCL, **900** Wembley, **902** Wembley, **903** Wembley, **904** North Wembley, **905** Edgware, Elstree, Golders Green, **906** Mill Hill, **907** Kenton, **908** North Wembley, **909** Kenton, **910** Featurenet, **913** MCL, **914** MCL, **919** Featurenet, **924** ECTL **940** Richmond & Kew, **941** East Molesey & Hampton, **942** New Malden, **943** Teddington, **944** Wimbledon, **945** MCL, **946** Wimbledon, **947** Wimbledon, **948** Richmond & Kew, **949** New Malden, **950** Bushey Heath, **951** Edgware, **952** Edgware, **953** Elstree, **954** Stanmore, **958** Edgware, **959** Mill Hill, **960** Kensal Green, **961** Harlesden & Stonebridge Park, **963** Harlesden, **964** Kensal Green, **965** Harlesden, **966** South Harrow, **967** MCL, **968** Kensal Green, **969** Kensal Green, **970** MCL, **971** Wimbledon, **974** Chessington & Kingston, **975** MCL, **977** Teddington, **979** East Molesey & Hampton, **980** Bow & Mile End, **981** Bow & Mile End, **982** MCL, **983** Goodmayes & Mile End, **984** Dagenham, **985** Hackney, **986** Hackney, **988** Leytonstone, **989** Wanstead, **990** London Airport, **991** Perivale, Alperton & North Ealing, **992** Acton, **993** Acton, **994** Chiswick, **995** Chiswick, **996** Chiswick, **997** Perivale, Alperton & North Ealing, **998** Perivale, Alperton & North Ealing

01820 **62** Banbridge Co Down, **63** Rathfriland, **650** Ballyward, **662** Banbridge, **651** Ballinaskeagh, **671** Katesbridge

01821 **640** Balbeggie, **642** Errol, **650** Kinrossie, **670** Rait

01822 **81** Mary Tavy Tavistock Devon, **82** Lydford, **83** Gunnislake, **84** Bere Alston, **85** Yelverton, **86** Chillaton, **87** Milton Abbot, **88** Postbridge, **89** Princetown, other numbers Tavistock

01823 **40** Milverton Taunton Somerset, **41** West Monkton, **42** Blagdon Hill, **43** Bishops Lydeard, **44** Henlade, **45** Kingston St Mary, **46** Bradford-on-Tone, **48** Hatch Beauchamp, **49** North Curry, **60** Churchstanton, **62** Henlade, **66** Wellington, **67** Greenham, **68** Hemyock, **69** Burrowbridge, **72** MCL, other numbers Taunton

01824 **3** Llanarmon-yn-Ial Mold Clwyd, **6** Cyffylliog, **70** Ruthin, **71** Cyffylliog, **75** Clawdd Newydd, **78** Llanarmon-Yn-Ial Mold, **79**

Llandynog
01825 71 Nutley Uckfield East Sussex, 72 Newick, 73 Busted, 740 Chelwood Gate, 75 Isfield, 76 Uckfield, 79 Danehill, 83 Hadlow Down, 84 Halland, 87 Chiddingly, 88 Halland, 89 Framfield, other numbers Uckfield
01826 21 Tealing Dundee, 22 Longforgan, 23 Newbigging, 24 Gauldry, 25 Kellas, 26 Auchterhouse
01827 25 Fazeley, 26 Fazeley, 28 Fazeley, 33 Polesworth, 37 Clifton Campville, 38 Harlaston, 71 Atherstone, 72 Atherstone, 83 Newton Regis, 7 Hurley, 88 Twycross, 89 Polesworth, other numbers Tamworth
01828 27 Coupar Angus Blairgowrie Perthshire, 28 Coupar, 3 Alyth, 4 Meigle, 5 Newtyle, 62 Coupar, 63 Alyth, 640 Meigle, 650 Newtyre, 670 Burrelton, 68 Inchture, 7 Burrelton, 83 MCL, 86 Inchture
01829 25 Tilston Malpas Cheshire, 26 Bunbury, 27 Farndon, 70 Tattenhall, 71 Tattenhall, 72 Cholmondeley, 73 Tarporley, 74 Tarvin, 75 Kelsall, 76 Little Budworth, 781 Huxley, 782 Broxton
01830 30 Capheaton Newcastle upon Tyne, 40 Kirkwhelpington, 50 MCL, 52 Otterburn, 530 Capheaton, 540 Kirkwhelpington
0831 VGP
01832 2 Benefield Northants, 22 Cotterstock, 28 Elton, 29 Winwick, 5 Benfield, 71 Bythorn, 72 Clopton, 73 Thrapston, 74 Thrapston, 85 MCL, other numbers Oundle
01833 21 Barningham Richmond North Yorkshire, 22 Forest-in-Teesdale, 28 Bowes, 31 Barnard Castle, 37 Barnard Castle, 40 Middleton-in-Teesdale, 50 Cotherstone, 621 Barningham, 622 Forest-in-Teesdale, 627 Whorlton, 628 Bowes, 631 Barnard Castle, 637 Barnard Castle, 640 Middleton-in-Teesdale, 65 Cotherstone, 66 Staindrop, 69 Barnard Castle
01834 81 Saundersfoot Dyfed, 83 Llanteg, 84 Tenby, 86 Narberth, 87 Manorbier, 88 Llanteg, 89 Martletwy
01835 82 St Boswells Melrose Roxburghshire, 83 Ancrum, 4 Camptown, 85 Crailing, 86 Crailing, 86 Jedburgh, 87 Lilliesleaf
0836 VGP, 4 VGP
01837 81 Hatherleigh Okehampton Devon, 82 North Tawton, 83 Winkleigh, 84 Sticklepath, 85 Exbourne, 86 Bridestowe, 87 Bratton Clovelly, 89 North Tawton, other numbers Okehampton

139

01838 2 Dalmally, 3 Crianlarich, 4 Tyndrum

0839 MCL

01840 21 Camelford Cornwall, 23 St Gennys, 25 Boscastle, 26 Otterham Station, 7 Tintagel

01841 52 St Merryn Padstow Cornwall, 53 Padstow, 4 Rumford

01842 7 Thetford Norfolk, 81 Brandon, 82 Feltwell, 85 Thetford, 86 Lakenheath, 87 Mundford, 89 Elvedon

01843 2 Margate Kent, 4 Birchington, 5 Ramsgate, 6 Broadstairs, 82 Minster, 83 Westgate, 84 Birchington, 85 Ramsgate, 86 Broadstairs, other numbers Thanet

01844 20 Long Crendon Aylesbury Bucks, 21 Thame, 23 Brill, 25 MCL, 26 Thame, 271 Princes Risborough, 272 Princes Risborough, 273 Princes Risborough, 274 Princes Risborough, 275 Princes Risborough, 276 Princes Risborough, 277 Great Milton, 278 Great Milton, 279 Great Milton, 28 Tetsworth, 29 Haddenham, 33 Ickford, 34 Princes Risborough, 35 Kingston Blount, other numbers Thame

01845 50 Hutton Sessay Thirsk North Yorkshire, 52 Thirsk, 53 Upsall, 56 Sinderby, 57 Topcliffe, 58 Kirby Wiske, 9 Sutton

01846 50 MCL, 61 Moira Craigavon Co Armagh, 621 Maze, 622 Maze, 63 Baillies Mills, 64 Stoneyford, 65 Aghalee, 68 Hillsborough, 69 Dromore, other numbers Lisburn

01847 6 Thurso Caithness, 89 Thurso, 55 Tongue, 56 Talmine, 601 Talmine, 611 Tongue, 81 Reay, 82 Castletown, 83 Halkirk, 84 Westerdale, 85 Barrock, 86 Forss, 87 Bridge of Westfield, 89 Thurso

01848 2 Moniaive Thornhill Dumfriesshire, 3 Thornhill, 5 Durisdeer, 6 Marrburn

01849 41 MCL, 43 Templepatrick Ballyclare Co Antrim, 420 Crumlin, 421 Crumlin, 422 Crumlin, 423 Crumlin, 45 Crumlin, 47 Randalstown, other numbers Antrim

0850 Cellnet Cellular Radio

01851 612 Great Bernera, 621 Callanish, 643 Carloway, 672 Timsgarry, 70 Stornoway, 71 Shawbost, 81 Port of Ness, 82 Back, 83 Balallan, 84 Barvas, 85 Borve, 86 Crossbost, 870 Garrabost, 88 Gravir, 89 North Tolsta

140

01852 2 Kilmelford Oban Argyll, 3 Balvicar, 314 Luing, 316 Kilninver, 4 Luing, 5 Barbreck, 6 Kilninver

01854 61 Ullapool Ross-shire, 622 Achiltibuie, 633 Dundonnell, 655 Lochbroom, 666 Strathkanaird

01855 2 Ballachulish Argyll, 3 Onich, 4 Kinlochleven, 5 Ardgour, 6 Kingshouse, 811 Ballachulish, 821 Onich, 831 Kinlochleven, 841 Ardgour, 851 Kingshouse

01856 70 Longhope Stromness Orkney, 71 Balfour, 72 Birsay, 73 Burray, 74 Deerness, 5 Evie, 76 Finstown, 77 Harray, 78 Holm, 79 Hoy, 81 Orphir, 82 Rousay, 83 St Margarets Hope, 84 Sandwick, 85 Stromness, 86 Tankerness, 87 Kirkwall

01857 2 Eday Orkney, 3 North Ronaldsay, 4 Papa Westray, 5 Sanday, 6 Stronsay, 600 Sanday, 616 Stronsay, 622 Eday, 633 North Ronaldsay, 644 Papa Westray, 677 Westray, 7 Westray

01858 52 Clipston Northants, 53 Dingley, 54 East Langton, 55 Hallaton, 56 Medbourne Green, 57 Welford, 82 MCL, 83 Medbourne Green, 88 Hushands Bosworth, 89 Hallaton, other numbers Market Harborough

01859 50 Harris, 520 Leverburgh, 530 Manish, 540 Scalpay, 550 Scarista, 560 Scarp

0860 Cellnet

01861 50 Glenanne Armagh, 51 Armagh, 52 Armagh, 53 Keady, 54 Benburb, 55 Markethill, 56 Caledon

01862 810 Dornoch Sutherland, 82 Edderton, 832 Fearn, 84 Kildary, 85 Nigg, 86 Nigg Station, 87 Portmahomack, 88 Whiteface, 89 Tain

01863 766 Ardgay Ross-shire, 755 The Craigs

01864 2 Crawford Biggar Lanarkshire, 4 Crawfordjohn, 5 Elvanfoot

01865 20 Oxford Oxon, 22 Cowley, 22 Headington, 22 Summertown, 24 Oxford, 25 Oxford, 26 Oxford, 27 Oxford, 28 Oxford, 29 Oxford, 30 Standlake, 31 Summertown, 32 Boars Hill, 33 Charlton on Otmoor, 340 Berinsfield, 341 Berinsfield, 343 Nuneham Courtenay, 350 Oxford, 351 Stanton St John, 358 Stanton St John, 361 Garsington, 368 Garsington, 37 Kidington, 38 MCL, 390 Frilford Heath, 391 Marcham, 400 Stadhampton, 407 Clifton Hampden, 41 Cowley, 48 MCL, 5 Summertown, 6 Headington, 71 Cowley, 72 Oxford, 73 Boars Hill, 740 Headington, 741 Headington, 742 Headington, 743 Headington, 744 Headington, 745

141

Cowley, **746** Cowley, **747** Cowley, **748** Cowley, **749** Cowley, **75** Headington, **77** Cowley, **78** Cowley, **79** Oxford, **81** Oxford, **82** Longworth, **84** Kidlington, **858** Warborough, **86** Cumnor, **872** Wheatley, **873** Wheatley, **874** Wheatley, **875** Wheatley, **876** Wheatley.
88 Eynsham, **89** Stadhampton, other numbers Oxford
01866 2 Taynuilt Argyll, **3** Kilchrenan, **4** Lochavich, **822** Taynuilt, **833** Kilchrenan, **844** Lochavich
01867 30 Clifton Hampden Abingdon Oxon, **32** Warborough, **33** Charlton-on-Otmoor, **36** Garsington, **38** Nuneham, **5** Kidlington, **7** Wheatley
01868 72 Dungannon, **73** Stewartstown, **74** Coalisland, **752** Dungannon, **753** Dungannon, **754** Dungannon, **758** Pomeroy, **759** Pomeroy, **76** Donaghmore, **78** Moy
01869 23 Upper Heyford Oxford Oxon, **24** Bicester, **25** Bicester, **27** Stratton, **32** Bicester, **331** Tackley, **337** Deddington, **338** Deddington, **339** Deddington, **340** Steeple Aston, **343** Middleton, **345** Fritwell, **346** Fritwell, **347** Steeple Aston, **348** Steeple Aston. **35** Bletchington, **36** Bicester, **37** Deddington, **38** Deddington, **39** Deddington, **40** Steeple Aston, **47** Steeple Aston, **81** Croughton Brackley, **87** MCL, other numbers Bicester
01870 60 Benbecula Isle of, **610** Carnan, **620** Grogarry
01871 81 Castlebay, **89** North Bay
01872 50 Veryan Truro Cornwall, **51** Mitchell, **52** Tresillian, **53** Tregony, **54** Zelah, **55** St Agnes, **57** Perranporth, **58** Portscatho, **8** Devoran, other numbers Truro
01873 81 Crickhowell Powys, **82** Cross Ash, **83** Gilwern, **84** Gobion, **85** Abergavenny, **86** Longtown Castle, **87** Longtown Castle, **88** Nantyderry, **89** Crucorney
01874 61 Brecon Powys, **62** Brecon, **63** Sennybridge, **65** Llangorse, **66** Llanfrynach, **67** Talybont-on-Usk, **69** Merthyr Cynog, **71** Talgarth, **73** Bwlch, **75** Llyswen, **84** Llangorse, **86** Llanfrynach, **87** Talybont-on-Usk, **89** Merthyr Cynog
01875 30 Temple Gorebridge Midlothian, **32** Ford Pathhead, **34** Pencaitland, **40** MCL, **6** Tranent, **81** Port Seton, **81** Prestonpans, **82** Gorebridge, **830** Temple Gorebridge, **833** Humbie, **835** Heriot, **85** Longniddry, **87** Aberlady

142

01876 500 Lochmaddy, 510 Bayhead, 540 Berneray, 560 Sollas, 500 Locheport

01877 33 Callander Perthshire, 375 Port of Menteith, 376 Trossachs, 382 Aberfoyle, 384 Strathyre, 387 Kinlochard, 386 Inversnaid

01878 700 Lochboisdale, 710 Bornish, 720 Eriskay

01879 2 Scarinish Isle of Tiree, 3 Coll Isle of, 22 Scarinish, 23 Coll

01880 3 Ormsary Lochgilphead Argyll, 4 Clachan, 6 Skipness, 73 Whitehouse, 74 Clachan, 76 Skipness, 77 Ormsary, 82 Tarbert

0881 MCL

01882 632 Kinloch Rannoch, 633 Bridge of Gaur, 634 Tummel Bridge

01883 33 Caterham Surrey, 34 Caterham, 62 Upper Warlingham, 65 Woldingham, 71 Oxted, 72 Oxted, 73 Oxted, 74 Godstone, 81 Reserved for Mercury

01884 26 Kentisbeare Cullompton Devon, 27 Plymtree, 3 Cullompton, 82 Sampford Peverell, 84 Craddock, 85 Bickleigh, 88 Rackenford, other numbers Tiverton

01885 40 Pencombe Bromyard Herefordshire, 41 Kyre, 48 Bromyard, 49 Munderfield

01886 81 Shelsley Beauchamp Worcs, 82 Knightwick, 83 Leigh Sinton, 880 Ridgeway Cross, 884 Suckley, 888 Wichenford

01887 82 Aberfeldy Perthshire, 83 Kenmore, 84 Strattay, 86 Bridge of Balgie, 87 Glenlyon

01888 511 Auchterless, 544 Cuminestown, 55 King Edward, 56 Turriff

01889 22 Hamstall Ridware Rugeley Staffs, 26 Hollington, 27 Weston, 500 Dapple Heath, 502 Field, 503 Rugeley, 504 Hamstall Ridware, 505 Hilderstone, 507 Hollington, 508 Sandon, 56 Uttoxeter, 57 Rugeley, 58 Rugeley, 59 Rocester, 88 Little Haywood, 75 Eyemouth

01890 76 Reston Eyemouth Berwickshire, 77 Coldingham, 78 Ayton, 81 Chirnside, 82 Crookham, 83 Birgham, 84 Leitholm, 85 Mindrum, 86 Swinton, 87 Whitsome, 88 Coldstream

0891 BT Premium Rate Services

143

01892 5 Tunbridge Wells Kent, *6 Crowborough*, 70 Tunbridge Wells, 72 Brenchley, 73 Collier Street, 74 Fordcombe, *75 Frant*, 77 Hartfield, 78 Wadhurst, *82 Pembury*, 83 Paddock Wood, 85 Rotherfield, 86 Langton, 87 Penshurst, 89 Lamberhurst, *other numbers Tunbridge Wells*

0893 BT Mobile Communications (Radio Paging)

0894 BT Premium Rate Service

01895 2 Uxbridge, *4 West Drayton*, 6 Ruislip, 81 Uxbridge, *82 Harefield*, 83 Denham, 84 MCL, 85 MCL, 86 MCL, 89 JCGL

01896 7 Galashiels Selkirkshire, *82 Melrose*, 83 Innerleithen, 84 Earlston, 85 Clovenfords, 86 Blainslie, 87 Walkerburn

0897 BT Premium Rate Service

0898 BT Premium Rate Services

01899 Biggar, 3 Tinto, *4 Broughton*, 5 Lamington, 6 Skirling, 7 Tweedsmuir, 81 Dunsyre

01900 81 Maryport Cumbria, 82 Cockermouth, *85 Lorton*, 88 Allonby, *other numbers Workington*

01902 303 Fallings Park Wolverhampton West Midlands, 304 Fallings Park, 305 Fallings Park, 307 Fallings Park, 324 Wombourne, 326 Wombourne, 33 Penn, 34 Penn, 350 Horseley Fields, 351 Horseley Fields, 352 Horseley Fields, 353 Bilston, 354 Bilston, 36 Willenhall, 37 Albrighton, 38 Finchfield, 39 Fordhouses, 40 Bilston, 43 Wolverhampton, 44 MCCL, 45 Horseley Fields, 46 ECL, 48 MCL, 49 Bilston, 60 Willenhall, 61 Willenhall, 62 Penn Wolverhampton, 63 Willenhall, 64 MCL, 65 MCCL, 66 Sedgeley, 67 Sedgeley, 68 MCCL, 69 MCL, 70 Pattingham, 72 Fallings Park, 73 Fallings Park, 74 Tettenhall, 75 Tettenhall, 76 Finchfield, 774 Tettenhall, 78 Fordhouses, 790 Standeford, 791 Standeford, 793 Tettenhall, 794 Standeford, 84 Codsall, 85 Brewood, 86 Fallings Park, 87 Horseley Fields, 88 Sedgeley, 89 Wombourne, *other numbers Wolverhampton*

01903 20 Worthing/Central Worthing West Sussex, 21 Worthing, 22 Worthing, 23 Worthing, 24 Worthing, 25 Worthing, 26 Swandean, 27 Swandean, 28 Worthing, 50 Worthing, 51 Worthing, 52 NCL, 69 Swandean, 70 Worthing, 71 Littlehampton, 72 Littlehampton, 73 Littlehampton, 74 Storrington, 75 Lancing, 76 Lancing, 77 Rustington, 78 Rustington, 81 Steyning, 82 Worthing, 83 Swandean, 84 MCL, 850 Rustington, 851 Lancing, 859 Rustington, 871 Patching, 872 Findon, 873 Findon, 874 Findon, 877

144

Findon. 879 Steyning, 88 Arundel, 89 Ashington, other numbers Worthing
01904 40 Stockton on Forest North Yorkshire. 41 Melrosegate, 43 Melrosegate, 448 Wheldrake, 45 MCL, 468
Flaxton Moor, 47 Beningbrough. 48 Dunnington, 49 Strensall, 69 Clifton, 608 Elvington, 70 Dringhouses, 728 Escrick, 738 Rufforth.
744 Appleton Roebuck, 75 Haxby, 76 Haxby, 78 Acomb, 79 Acomb, other numbers York
01905 33 Cotheridge Worcester, 34 Spetchley, 35 St Peters, 36 St Peters, 37 Severn, 38 Upton Snodsbury, 39 Himbleton, 42 St
Johns, 45 Fernhill Heath, 62 Ombersley, 64 Hallow, 69 Himbleton, 74 St Johns, 75 Fernhill Heath, 76 St Peters, 77 Droitwich, 79
Droitwich, 82 Kempsey, 83 Powick, 84 Peopleton, 85 MCL, 87 Worcester, other numbers Worcester
01908 20 Bradwell Abbey Milton Keynes Bucks. 21 Newport Pagnell, 22 Wolverton, 23 Bradwell Abbey, 24 Bradwell Abbey, 25
Stony Stratford, 26 Stony Stratford, 27 Milton Keynes, 28 Woburn Sands, 29 Bradwell Abbey, 30 Bradwell Abbey, 31 Wolverton.
32 Wolverton, 33 Wolverton, 342 Milton Keynes, 343 Bradwell Abbey, 344 Bradwell Abbey, 345 Shenley, 346 Shenley, 347
Bradwell Abbey, 348 Bradwell Abbey, 349 Bradwell Abbey, 35 Bradwell Abbey, 36 Milton Keynes, 37 Milton Keynes, 50 Shenley,
51 Hanslope, 52 Shenley, 53 Shenley, 54 Yardley Gobion, 55 Stoke Goldington, 56 Stony Stratford, 570 Stony Stratford, 571
Wicken, 572 Wicken, 573 Wicken, 574 Wicken, 58 Woburn Sands, 60 Bradwell Abbey, 61 Newport Pagnell, 62 Newport Pagnell, 63
Milton Keynes, 64 Milton Keynes, 65 Milton Keynes, 66 Milton Keynes, 67 Bradwell Abbey, 68 Bradwell Abbey, 69 Bradwell
Abbey, 83 MCL, 84 MCL, 85 MCL, other numbers Milton Keynes
01909 Worksop Notts, 51 Kiveton, 54 North Carlton, 55 Dinnington, 56 Dinnington, 59 Blyth, 72 Whitwell, 73 North Carlton, 77
Kiveton, other numbers Worksop
0191 021 BT Phone Base, 2 North Tyneside Code Area, 200 Newcastle City, 201 MCL, 202 MCL, 203 MCL, 212 Jesmond, 213
Gosforth, 214 Kenton, 215 Benton, 216 Killingworth, 217 Wideopen, 221 Newcastle City, 222 Newcastle City, 223 Gosforth, 224
Newcastle, 225 Gosforth, 226 Newcastle West, 227 Newcastle City, 229 Lemington, 230 Newcastle City, 231 Newcastle City,
232 Newcastle City, 233 Newcastle City, 234 Wallsend, 235 Newcastle City, 236 Wideopen, 237 Seaton Delaval, 238 Newcastle
Eas, 244 Newcastle City, 250 Dudley, 251 Whitley Bay, 252 Whitley Bay, 253 Whitley Bay, 257 North Shields, 258 North Shields,

259 North Shields, 260 Newcastle City, 261 Newcastle City, 262 Wallsend, 263 Wallsend, 264 Lemington, 265 Newcastle East, 266 Benton, 267 Lemington, 268 Killingworth, 270 Benton, 271 Kenton, 272 Newcastle West, 273 Newcastle West, 274 Denton Burn, 275 Denton Burn, 276 Newcastle East, 279 Gosforth, 281 Jesmond, 284 Gosforth, 285 Gosforth, 286 Kenton, 288 Denton Burn, 293 North Shields, 295 Wallsend, 296 North Shields, 297 Whitley Bay, 298 Seaton Delaval, 3 Durham Code Area, 301 MCL, 370 Beamish, 371 Sacriston, 372 Sherburn Hill, 373 New Brancepeth, 374 Durham, 377 Coxhoe, 378 Meadowfield, 383 Durham, 384 Durham, 385 Fencehouses, 386 Durham, 387 Chester-le-Street, 388 Chester-le-Street, 4 South Tyneside Code Area, 401 MCL, 402 MCL, 410 Birtley, 413 Ryton, 414 Blaydon, 415 Washington, 416 Washington, 417 Washington, 418 Washington, 419 Washington, 427 South Shields, 428 Jarrow, 430 Jarrow, 438 Felling, 454 South Shields, 455 South Shields, 456 South Shields, 460 Dunston, 461 Dunston, 469 Felling, 477 Gateshead, 478 Gateshead, 482 Low Fell, 483 Jarrow, 487 Low Fell, 488 Whickham, 489 Jarrow, 490 Gateshead, 491 Low Fell, 492 Birtley, 493 Dunston, 495 Felling, 496 Whickham, 497 Low Fell, 499 Blaydon, 5 Wearside Code Area, 501 MCL, 510 Sunderland City, 511 East Herrington, 512 Houghton-le-Spring, 513 Seaham, 514 Sunderland City, 515 Sunderland City, 516 Sunderland North, 517 Hetton-le-Hole, 518 Peterlee, 519 Boldon, 520 East Herrington, 521 Ryhope, 522 East Herrington, 523 Ryhope, 526 Hetton-le-Hole, 527 Easington, 528 East Herrington, 529 Whitburn, 534 Hylton, 536 Boldon, 537 Boldon, 548 Sunderland, 549 Sunderland, 563 Houghton-le-Spring, 564 Sunderland City, 565 Sunderland City, 567 Sunderland City, 569 Sunderland City, 581 Seaham, 584 Houghton-le-Spring, 586 Peterlee, 587 Peterlee 01920 42 CBTL, 43 Dane End Ware Herts, 44 Ware, 46 Ware, 48 Ware, 82 Puckeridge, 83 Wetton-at-Stone, 86 Ware, 87 Stanstead Abbotts, 88 Ware

01922 40 Bloxwich Walsall West Midlands, 41 Cheslyn Hay, 43 MCL, 47 Bloxwich, 49 Bloxwich, 5 Aldridge, 68 Pelsall, 69 Pelsall, 701 Cheslyn Hay, 71 Bloxwich, 742 Aldridge, 743 Aldridge, 744 Aldridge, 745 Aldridge, 747 Aldridge, 85 Walsall, other numbers Walsall

01923 20 Watford Herts, 21 Watford, 22 Watford, 23 Watford, 24 Watford, 25 Watford, 26 Kings Langley, 27 Kings Langley, 28 Chorleywood, 41 MCL, 46 JCGL, 6 Garston, 7 Rickmansworth, 81 Watford, 82 Northwood, 83 Northwood, 85 Radlett, 891 Garston,

146

892 *Garston,* 893 *Garston,* 894 *Garston,* 895 *Garston,* 896 *Rickmansworth,* **897** *Rickmansworth,* **898** *Rickmansworth,* **899** *Rickmansworth,* **900** *Rickmansworth*

01924 22 **Normanton West Yorkshire,** 23 *Horbury/Ossett,* 24 *Sandal,* 25 *Sandal,* 26 *Horbury/Ossett,* 27 *Horbury/Ossett,* 280 *Horbury/Ossett,* 40 *Heckmondwike,* 41 *Heckmondwike,* 42 *Batley,* 43 *Dewsbury,* 44 *Batley,* 45 *Dewsbury,* 46 *Dewsbury,* 47 *Batley,* 48 *Mirfield,* 49 *Mirfield,* 81 *MCL,* 82 *Lofthouse Gate,* **830** *Bretton,* **839** *Lofthouse Gate,* 84 *Flockton,* 86 *Crofton,* 87 *Lofthouse Gate,* 89 *Normanton, other numbers Wakefield*

01925 22 *Newton-le-Willows,* 28 *Padgate,* 29 *Newton-le-Willows,* **461** *Penketh,* **66** *MCL,* **70** *MCL,* 72 *Penketh,* 73 *Norcott Brook,* 74 *Moore,* 75 *Lymm,* 76 *Culcheth,* 78 *Warrington,* 79 *Penketh,* 81 *Padgate,* 82 *Padgate,* **830** *Padgate,* **831** *Padgate,* **837** *Padgate,* **838** *Padgate,* **839** *Padgate,* 85 *Padgate,* 87 *Padgate,* 88 *Padgate, other numbers Warrington*

01926 40 *Warwick,* 41 *Warwick,* **484** *Haseley Knob,* **488** *Moreton Morrell,* 49 *Warwick,* 5 *Kenilworth,* 61 *Harbury,* 62 *Barford,* 63 *Marton,* 64 *Kineton,* 65 *Moreton Morrell,* 81 *Southam,* 82 *MCL,* 84 *Claverdon,* 85 *Kenilworth,* 86 *Kenilworth, other numbers Leamington Spa*

01928 51 *Runcorn Cheshire,* **52** *MCL,* 56 *Runcorn,* 57 *Runcorn,* 58 *Runcorn,* 59 *Runcorn,* 70 *Runcorn,* 71 *Runcorn,* 72 *Helsby,* 73 *Frodsham,* 74 *Manley,* 75 *Runcorn,* 76 *Helsby,* 78 *Kingsley,* 79 *Runcorn*

01929 40 **Bindon Abbey Dorset,** 41 *West Lulworth,* 42 *Swanage,* 43 *Worth Matravers,* 44 *Studland,* 45 *Morden,* 46 *Bindon Abbey,* 47 *Bere Regis,* 48 *Corfe Castle,* **49** *MCL,* 55 *Wareham*

01931 **712** *Hackthorpe Penrith Cumbria,* **713** *Bampton,* **714** *Morland,* **715** *Ravensworth,* **716** *Shap*

01932 2 *Walton-on-Thames Surrey,* 5 *Byfleet,* 7 *Chertsey,* 7 *Sunbury-on-Thames,* **81** *MCL,* 82 *Weybridge,* 83 *Weybridge,* 84 *Weybridge,* 85 *Weybridge,* 86 *Cobham,* 87 *Ottershaw,* **88** *MCL,* **89** *MCL*

01933 31 **Rushden Northants,** 33 *Wellingborough,* 38 *Telecential,* 40 *Harrowden,* 41 *Rushden,* 46 *Raunds,* 5 *Rushden,* 62 *Raunds,* 65 *Irthlingborough,* 66 *Bozeat,* 67 *Harrowden,* 68 *Finedon, other numbers Wellingborough*

01934 51 **Worle Weston-super-Mare Avon,** 52 *Worle,* 71 *Wedmore,* 73 *Axbridge,* 74 *Cheddar,* 75 *Edingworth,* 81 *Bleadon,* 82

Banwell, 83 Yatton, 84 Winscombe, 85 Churchill, 86 Wrington, 87 Yatton, *other numbers Weston-super-Mare*

01935 60 MCL Yeovil Somerset, 81 Sherborne, 82 Martock, 83 Evershot, 84 Ilchester, 85 Marston Magna, 86 West Coker, 87 Yetminster, 88 Chiselborough, 89 Corscombe, *other numbers Yeovil*

01936 5 Bridgemere Nantwich Cheshire, 51 MCL, 53 Tadcaster

01937 54 Boston Spa Wetherby West Yorkshire, 55 Barkston Ash, 57 Collingham Bridge, 59 Spofforth, 83 Tadcaster, 84 Boston Spa, *other numbers Wetherby*

01938 50 Meifod Powys, 55 Welshpool, 56 Chirbury, 57 Trewern, 58 Forden, 59 Guilsfield, 72 Chirbury, 75 Guilsfield, 81 Llanfair, 82 Llangadfan, 83 Castle Caereinion, 85 Castle Caereinion

01939 20 Lee Brockhurst Shrewsbury Shropshire, 21 Hadnall, 22 Clive, 23 Wem, 25 Shawbury, 26 Baschurch, 27 Cockshutt, 29 Bomere Heath

01941 1 H, 2 H, 20 SBC Wigan Lancs, 21 Orrell, 22 Orrell, 26 Leigh, 27 Ashton-in-Makerfield, 29 Ashton-in-Makerfield

01942 50 MCL Wigan Lancs, 51 SBC, 52 Hindley, 53 Hindley, 54 Hindley, 55 Hindley, 56 Hindley, 57 Hindley, 58 Hindley, 59 Hindley, 60 Leigh, 62 Orrell, 67 Leigh, 68 Leigh, 70 SBC, 71 Ashton-in-Makerfield, 72 Ashton-in-Makerfield, 75 Wigan, 81 Westhoughton, 83 Aspull, 84 Westhoughton, 85 Westhoughton, 86 Platt Bridge, 87 Atherton, 88 Atherton, 89 Atherton, *other numbers Wigan*

01943 46 Otley West Yorkshire, 60 Ilkley, 81 Ilkley, 83 Addingham, 84 MCL, 85 Otley, 86 Burley-in-Wharfdale, 87 Guiseley, 88 Blubberhouses

01944 71 Sherburn Malton North Yorkshire, 72 West Heslerton, 73 West Lutton, 75 Rillington, 76 North Grimston

01945 41 Wisbech St Mary Cambs, 42 Tydd, 43 Marshland, 44 Sutton, 45 Guyhirn, 70 Parson, 76 Tydd, 77 Upwell, 78 Walpole, 85 Sutton St James, 86 Friday Bridge, 87 Newton, 88 Terrington, *other numbers Wisbech*

01946 721 Seascale Cumbria, 723 Eskdale, 724 Holmrook, 725 Gosforth, 726 Wasdale, 727 Seascale, 728 Seascale, 729 Seascale, 77 Seascale, 78 Seascale, 81 Cleator Moor, 82 Egremont, 83 Harrington, 84 Beckermet, 86 Lamplugh, *other numbers Whitehaven Cumbria*

148

01947 60 Whitby North Yorkshire, 81 Sleights, 82 Whitby, 83 Sandsend, 84 Hinderwell, 88 Robin Hoods Bay, 893 Sandsend, 895 Grosmont, 896 Goathland, 897 Glaisdale

01948 66 Whitchurch Shropshire, 71 Bettisfield, 73 Redbrook Maelor, 74 Hanmer, 75 Bettisfield, 76 Calverhall, 77 Threapwood Malpas, 78 Redbrook Maelor, 83 Hanmer, 84 Prees, 85 Hampton Heath, 86 Malpas, 87 Burleydam, 88 Whixall, 89 Calverhall, other numbers Whitchurch

01949 20 East Bridgford Notts, 21 East Bridgford, 27 MCL, 4 Bottesford, 5 Whatton, 6 Harby, 81 Kinoulton, 83 Bingham, 84 Bottesford, 85 Whatton, 86 Harby, 87 DCL

01950 2 Bigton Shetland, 3 Cunningsburgh, 422 Bigton, 431 Sandwick, 46 Sumburgh, 477 Cunningsburgh, 5 Sandwick, 6 Sumburgh

01951 2 Colonsay Isle of Islay, 41 MCL, 43 Ironbridge, 46 Shifnal

01952 50 Dawley Telford Shropshire, 51 Cressage, 54 Great Bolas, 55 Sambrook, 58 Cuckoo Oak, 59 Stirchley, 60 Donington, 61 Oakengates, 62 Oakengates, 63 Dawley, 66 Stirchley, 67 Donington, 68 Cuckoo Oak, 69 Great Chatwell, 71 Norton, 72 Much Wenlock, 73 Norton, 74 Uppington, 75 Ryton Shifnal, 76 Weston-U-Lizard, 77 High Ercall, 78 Childs Ercall, 81 Newport, 82 Newport, 84 Childs Ercall, 85 Weston-u-Lizard, 86 Uppington, 87 Ryton Shifnal, 88 Broseley, other numbers Telford

01953 45 Attleborough Norfolk, 48 Caston Attleborough, 49 Great Hockham, 60 Wymondham, 68 Garboldisham, 71 East Harling, 78 Banwell, 81 Garboldisham, 85 Hingham, 86 New Buckenham, 881 Watton, 882 Watton, 883 Watton, 884 Watton, 885 Watton, 886 Watton, 887 Quidenham, 888 Quidenham

01954 20 CCL Cambridge, 21 Madingley, 23 Swavesey, 24 MCL, 25 Cottenham, 260 Willingham, 261 Willingham, 267 Elsworth, 71 Caxton, 78 Crafts Hill

01955 Wick Caithness, 60 Wick, 611 John O'Groats, 621 Watten, 631 Keiss, 641 Lyth, 651 Thrumster, 661 Gillock, 81 John O'Groats, 82 Watten, 83 Keiss, 84 Lyth, 85 Thrumster, 86 Gillock

0956 MCL

149

01957 Mid Yell Shetland, *70* Midyell, *711* Baltasand, *722* Burraroe, *733* Ketlar, *744* Gutcher, *755* Vyeasound, *766* West Sandwick, *81* Baltasund, *82* Burravoe, *83* Fetlar, *84* Gutcher, *85* Uyeasound, *86* West Sandwick

0958 MCL

01959 51 Knockholt Sevenoaks Kent, *52* Otford, *53* Knockholt, *54* Biggin Hill, *56* Westerham, *57* Biggin Hill & Tatsfield

01960 31 MCL Ballyclare, *32* Ballyclare, *34* Ballyclare, *350* Carrickfergus, *351* Carrickfergus, *352* Ballyclare, *353* Whitehead, *354* Ballyclare, *36* Carrickfergus, *37* Whitehead, *382* Islandmagee

01962 70 MCL Winchester, Hants *71* Twyford, *72* Sparshott, *73* Alresford, *75* Hursley, *76* Sutton Scotney, *771* Bramdean, *772* Ropley, *773* Ropley, *774* Micheldever, *775* Hursley, *776* Sparshott, *777* Owslebury, *779* Itchen Abbas, *792* Itchen Abbas, *797* Sparshott, *82* Winchester, *84* Winchester, *85* Winchester, *86* Winchester, *87* Winchester, *88* Harestock

01963 21 Holnest Sherborne Dorset, *22* Corton Denham, *23* Bishop's Caundle, *24* Wheathill, *25* Milborne, *35* Castle Cary, *36* Stalbridge, *37* Templecombe, *4* North Cadbury, **other numbers** Wincanton

01964 52 Aldbrough, *53* Hornsea, *54* Leven, *55* Leconfield, *56* Skirlaugh, *62* Keyingham, *63* Patrington, *65* Spurn Point, *67* Burton Pidsea, **other numbers** Withernsea

01967 40 Strontian, *411* Kingairloch, *421* Morvern, *431* Argyll, *83* Kingairloch, *85* Salen

01968 40 MCL Penicuik, *66* West Linton, *67* Penicuik, *682* Dolphinton

01969 2 Leyburn North Yorkshire, *40* Coverdale, *50* Bainbridge, *622* Leyburn, *640* Coverdale, *650* Bainbridge, *663* Aysgarth, *667* Hawes

01970 61 Aberystwyth, *62* Aberystwyth, *82* Bow Street, *83* Talybont, *84* Capel Bangor, *85* Ponterwyd, *87* Borth, *88* Capel, *89* Ponterwyd

01971 500 Lochmore Lairg Sutherland, *502* Scourie, *51* Durness, *52* Kinlochbervie

01972 500 Glenborrodale, *510* Kilchoan

0973 0

150

01974 20 Llanon Dyfed, **21** Bronant, **24** Llanilar, **25** Bronant, **26** Crosswood, **27** Nebo, **28** Pontrhydygroes, **29** Tregaron, **7** Llanilar, **82** Llangeitho, **83** Pontrhydfendigaid

01975 56 Alford Aberdeenshire, **571** Kildrummy, **581** Muir-of-Fowlis, **641** Glenkindie, **651** Strathdon

0976 0

01977 51 Castleford West Yorkshire, **52** Castleford, **55** Castleford, **603** Castleford, **604** Castleford, **607** Knottingley, **608** South Elmsall, **61** Hemsworth, **62** Wentbridge, **64** South Elmsall, **66** Whitley Bridge, **67** Knottingley, **68** South Milford, **other numbers** Pontefract

01978 71 Overton-on-Dee, **76** Caergwrle, **78** Bangor-on-Dee, **79** Llandegla, **81** Ruabon, **82** Ruabon, **83** Rhosllanerchrugog, **84** Rhosllanerchrugog, **85** Gresford, **86** Llangollen, **other numbers** Wrexham

0979 7 Jersey Cellular Radio (GSM), **3** Bulford Camp

01980 4 Tidworth Stonehenge Salisbury Witts, **5** Durrington Walls, **610** Idminston, **611** Idminston, **612** Amesbury, **613** Amesbury, **615** Amesbury, **620** Shrewton, **621** Shrewton, **622** Amesbury, **623** Amesbury, **624** Amesbury, **625** Amesbury, **627** Amesbury, **630** Upavon, **631** Bulford Camp, **635** Amesbury, **64** Cholderton, **66** Amesbury, **69** MCL, **7** Netheravon, **84** Tidworth, **86** Winterslow

01981 21 Wormbridge Hereford, **22** Bridge Sollars, **23** Michaelchurch, **24** Pontrilas, **25** Madley, **50** Moccas, **51** Michaelchurch, **54** Wormelow, **55** Peterchurch, **58** St Weonards, **59** Bridge Sollars

01982 55 Builth Wells Powys, **56** Erwood, **57** Hundred House

01983 20 Cowes Isle of Wight, **28** Cowes, **29** Cowes, **40** Sandown, **52** Newport, **53** Calbourne, **55** Chale Green, **56** Ryde, **6** Ryde, **72** Chillerton, **73** Niton, **74** Brighstone, **5** Freshwater, **76** Yarmouth, **78** Calbourne, **81** Ryde, **82** Newport, **84** Godshill, **85** Ventnor, **86** Shanklin, **87** Bembridge, **88** Wootton Bridge, **other numbers** Isle of Wight

01984 4 Washford Watchet Somerset, **5** Stogumber, **61** Crowcombe, **62** Wiveliscombe, **631** Watchet, **632** Williton, **633** Williton, **634** Watchet, **65** Stogumber, **66** Lydeard St Lawrence, **7** Lydeard St Lawrence, **8** Crowcombe

01985 24 Wylye Warminster Witts, **6** Wylye, **840** Sutton Veny, **841** Sutton Veny, **844** Maiden Bradley, **85** Codford St Marys,

151

other numbers Warminster

01986 781 Ilketshall Suffolk, **782** St Cross, **784** Bramfield, **785** Linstead, **788** Homersfield, **79** Ubbeston, **83** Halesworth, **84** Bramfield, **86** Homersfield, **87** Halesworth, **89** Bungay

01988 4 Wigtown Newton Stewart Wigtownshire, **5** Whithorn, **6** Garlieston, **7** Port William, **84** Kirkinner, **85** Sorbie, **86** Mochrum

01989 72 Gorsley Ross-On-Wye Herefordshire, **73** Harewood End, **74** How Caple, **75** Lea, **77** Llangarron, **78** Upton Bishop, **86** How Caple, *other numbers Ross-on-Wye*

0990 BT National Call

0992 40 ACC Hoddesdon Herts, **50** Hertford, **511** Bayford, **513** Hertford, **52** North Weald, **55** Hertford, **56** Epping, **57** Epping, **58** Hertford, **61** MCL, **62** Waltham Cross, **63** Waltham Cross, **64** Waltham Cross, **65** Lea Valley, **7** Lea Valley, **81** Theydon Bois, **82** MCL, **85** MCL, **89** Nazeing, *other numbers Hoddesdon*

01993 70 Witney Oxon, **71** Witney, **760** Asthall Leigh, **77** Witney, **81** Woodstock, **82** Burford, **83** Shipton-under-Wychwood, **84** Carterton, **85** Bampton Castle, **86** Ramsden, **87** Asthall Leigh, **88** Freeland, **89** Stonesfield, *other numbers Witney*

01994 23 St Clears Carmarthen Dyfed, **24** Whitland, **41** Hebron, **42** Laugharne, **44** Llanboidy, **45** Pendine, **48** Madox, **5** Pendine, **01995 60** Garstang Preston Lancs, **61** Chipping Preston, **64** Brock, **670** Great Eccleston, **671** Great Eccleston, **672** Great Eccleston, **679** St Michaels, **69** MCL

01997 3 Urray Ross-shire, **414** Garve, **421** Strathpeffer, **433** Urray, **455** Aultguish, **466** Scatwell, **477** Strathconon, **5** Aultguish, **6** Scatwell, **7** Strathconon

Section 3
International codes

Most international calls can now be made direct. As from April 16, 1995 the code to dial abroad from the UK has changed from 010 to 00. Although the international dialling code for calls to the UK remains 44, callers from abroad must include the extra 1 in the customer's number.

To call an international number simply look up the country in the aphabetical list and follow the simple instructions.

Many countries include an initial 0 in the area code when telephone numbers are quoted, this 0 should not be dialled except when dialling former USSR countries when the 0 must be dialled or when the initial 0 is included in this book.

Area codes in Finland, Iceland, Spain and Turkey often have an initial 9 instead of an 0, this 9 should not be dialled.

If there is a *'Direct'* number included at the end of a country's list, visitors to the UK can made a reverse charge or credit card call home via an operator in their own country, they are charged in the caller's home country.

To help you make your calls at an appropriate time of day, basic time differences have been included for Greenwich Mean Time *(GMT)*. Allow for any local seasonal time differences in the country you are dialling and for British Summer Time.

Codes from the UK look like this –

International access code	Country code	Area code	Customer's personal number
00	1	415	480 11234

If you have problems contact the international operator on 155 or international directory enquiries on 153.

Afghanistan 00 93
GMT + 4½ hrs, charge band 13

Albania 00 355
Durres 52, Elbasan 545, Korce 824, Tirana 42,
GMT + 1 hr, charge band 3

Algeria 00 213
Algiers 2, Annaba 8, Batna 4, Bechar 7, Bejaia 5, Biskra 4, Blida
3, Bord Bou Arreridj 5, Boumerdes 2, Chlef 3, Constantine 4, El-
oued 4, Ghardaia 9, Guelma 8, Jijel 5, Khenchela 4, Laghouat 9,
Mascara 6, Medea 3, Mila 4, Mostaganem 6, Oran 6, Oum-El-
Bouaghi 4, Ouargla 9, Relizane 6, Saida 7, Setif 5, Sidi Bel Abbes
7, Skikda 8, Tamanrasset 9, Tiaret 7, Tindouf 7, Tipaza 2, Tizi-
Ouzou 3, Tlemcen 7
GMT + 1 hr, charge band 3

Andorra 00 33 628
GMT + 1 hr, charge band 1

Angola 00 244
Lobito 711, Luanda 2, Namibe 64, all other areas via operator
GMT + 1 hr, charge band 13

Anguilla 00 1 809
GMT -4 hrs, charge band 5

Antarctica (Australian territory) 00 672
Davis Base 106, Macquarie Island 139, Mawson Base 117
Current UK time + between 4½-10 hrs, charge band 13

Antigua and Barbuda 00 1 809
GMT -4 hrs, charge band 5

Antilles Netherlands 00 599 Bonaire 7, Curacao 9, Saba 4, St
Eustacius 3, St Maarten 5
GMT -4 hrs, charge band 8

Argentina 00 54
Avellaneda 776, Bahia Blanca 91, Balcarce 266, Buenos Aires
1, Catamarca 833, Cordoba 51, Formosa 717, Las Calera 51,
La Plata 21, Mar del Plata 23, Mendoza 61, Neuquen 99, Parana
43, Punta Alta 932, Resistencia 722, Rio Cuarto 586, Rio Grande
964, Rosario 586, Salta 87, San Juan 64, San Lorenzo 476,
San Miguel de Tucuman 81, San Pedro 329, San Rafael 627,
Santa Fe 42, Santa Rosa 954, Tandil 293, Viedma 920, Zarate
328
GMT -3 hrs, charge band 10

Armenia 00 7
Erevan 8852, Leninakan 88569
GMT + 4 hrs, charge band 8

Aruba 00 297
GMT -4 hrs, charge band 8
Ascensionlsland 00 247
UK time, charge band 13
Australia 00 61
Adelaide 8 (+9 hrs), Albury 60, Armidale (NSW) 67, Ballarat 53, Bathurst 63, Bendigo 54, Brisbane 7, Broken Hill 80, Bundaberg 71, Cairns 70, Campelltown (NSW) 46, Canberra 6, Cessnock 49, Darwin 89 (+9 hrs), Devonport (TAS) 04, Dubbo 68, Geelong 52, Geraldton 99 (+8 hrs), Gold Coast 75, Goulburn 48, Hobart 02, Kalgoorlie 90 (+8 hrs), Launceston 03, Mackay 79, Maitland (NSW) 49, Melbourne 3, Moe 51, Mt Gambier 87 (+9½ hrs), Newcastle 49, Orange 63, Penrith 47, Perth (WA) 9 (+8 hrs), Red Cliffs 50, Rockhampton 79, Sydney 2, Tamworth 67, Toowoomba 76, Townsville 77, Wagga Wagga 69, Wollongong 42
GMT +10 hrs (except where shown) charge band 6, Telstra Direct 0800 89 0061
Austria 00 43
Baden b. Wien 2252, Bregenz 5574, Dornbirn 5572, Gmunden 7612, Graz 316, Innsbruck 512, Kitzbuhel 5356, Klagenfurt 463, Krems an der Donau 2732, Leoben 3842, Leogang 6583,

Linz, Donau 70, Mayrhofen 5285, St Anton 5446 St Polten 2742, Salzburg 662, Steyr 7252, Traun 7229, Vienna 1, Villach 4242, Wels 7242, Wiener Neustadt 2622, Ziri 5238 (these areas may have more than one valid code)
GMT +1 hr, charge band 2, Austria Direct 0800 87 0043
Azerbaijan 00 994
Baku 12, Nakhichevan 136, Neftechala 153
GMT +1 hr, charge band 8
Azores 00 351
Angra Do Heroismo 95, Horta (Faial) 92, Ponta Delgada (S.Miguel) 96, Santa Cruz (Graciosa) 95, Vila Do Porto 96
GMT -1 hr, charge band 1
Bahamas 00 1 809
GMT -5 hrs, charge band 5, Bahamas Direct 0800 89 0135
Bahrain 00 973
Please take account of business hours when you make your call. Saturday to Thursday am is the working week in Bahrain
GMT +3 hrs, charge band 8, Bahrain Direct 0800 89 0973
Bangladesh 00 880
Bagerhat 401, Barisal 431,Bogra 51,Chittagong 31, Comilla 81, Dhaka 2, Dinajpur 531, Jamalpur 981,Jessore 421, Khulna 41, Kushtia 71, Moulvi Bazar 861, Mymensingh 91, Narayanganj

671, Patvakhali 441, Rajshahi 721, Sylhet 821 GMT +6 hrs, charge band 12

Barbados 00 1 809

GMT -4 hrs, charge band 5

Belarus 00 7

Brest 01622, Gomel 0232, Grodno 0152, Minsk 0172, Mogilev 0222, Vitebsk 0212

GMT +2 hrs, charge band 8

Belgium 00 32

Aalst 53, Antwerp 3, Arlon 63, Ath 68, Bastogne 62, Blankenberge 50, Brugge 50, Brussels 2, Charleroi 71, Chimay 60, Ciney 83, Dendermonde 52, Diest 13, Dinant 82, Durbuy 86, Ghent 9, Hasselt 11, Herentals 14, Huy 85, Ieper 57, Jemelle 84, Kortrijk 56, La Louvière 64, Leuven 16, Libramont 61, Liège 41, Mechelen 15, Mons 65, Namur 81, Ninove 54, Nivelles 67, Ostende 59, Roeselare 51, Ronse-Renaix 55, St Niklaas 3, Stavelot 80, Tienen 16, Tongeren 12, Tournai 69, Turnhout 14, Verviers 87, Veurne 58, Waremme 19, Wavre 10, Zeebrugge 50

GMT +1 hr, charge band 1, Belgium Direct 0800 89 0032

Belize 00 501

Belize City 2, Belmopan 8, Benque Viejo 93, Burrel Boom 28, Caye Caulker 22, Corozal 4, Dangriga 5, Independence 6, Ladyville 25, Orange Walk 3, Punta Gorda 7, San Ignacio 92, San Joaquin 4, San Pedro 26

GMT -6 hrs, charge band 8

Benin 00 229

GMT +1 hr, charge band 10

Bermuda 00 1 809

GMT -4 hrs, charge band 5, Bermuda Direct 0800 89 0123

Bhutan 00 975

GMT +6 hrs, charge band 13

Bolivia 00 591

Beni 46, Buena Vista 932, Cochabamba 42, Cotoca 388, Gral Saavedra 924, La Belgica 923, La Paz 2, Mineros 984, Montero 92, Oruro 52, Portachuelo 924, Potosi 62, Saavedra 924, Santa Cruz 3, Sucre 64, Tarija 66, Trinidad 46, Villamontes 684, Warnes 923

GMT -4 hrs, charge band 13

Bosnia Hercegovina 00 387

Banja Luka 78, Mostar 88, Sarajevo 71, Tuzula 75

GMT +1 hr, charge band 3

Botswana 00 267

GMT +2 hrs, charge band 10

Brazil 00 55

Aracaju 79, Belem 91, Belo Horizonte 31, Brasilia 61, Campinas 192, Curitiba 41, Duque de Caxias 21, Fortaleza 85, Joao Pessoa 83, Londrina 43, Maceio 82, Manaus 92 (-4 hrs), Natal 84, Petropolis 242, Porto Alegre 51, Recife 81, Ribeirao Preto 16, Rio de Janeiro 21, Salvador 71, Santos 132, Sao Luis 98, Sao Paulo 11

GMT -3 hrs (except where shown), charge band 10, Brasil Direto 0800 89 0055

Brunei Darussalam 00 673

Bandar Seri Begawan 2, Kuala Belait 3, Seria 3, Temburong 5, Tutony 4 GMT +8 hrs, charge band 13

Bulgaria 00 359

Blagoevgrad 73, Burgas 56, Devnya 519, Gabrovo 66, Lovetch 68, Plovdiv 32, Rousse 82, Smoliyan 301, Sofia 2, Stara Zagora 42, Varna 52, Veliko Turnovo 62

GMT +2 hrs, charge band 3

Burkina Faso 00 226

UK time, charge band 13

Burundi 00 257

Bubanza 42, Bujumburura 2, Bururi 50, Cibitoke 41, Gitega 40, Muramvya 43, Ngozi 30

158

GMT +2 hrs, charge band 13

Cambodia 00 855

Phnom Penh (only) 23, all other areas are to be accessed via the operator

GMT +7 hrs, charge band 13

Cameroon 00 237

GMT +1 hr, charge band 10

Canada 00 1

Brandon 204 (-6 hrs), Brantford 519, Calgary 403 (-7 hrs), Charlottetown 902 (-4 hrs), Corner Brook 709 (-3½ hrs), Edmonton 403 (-7 hrs) Fredericton 506 (-4 hrs), Gander 709 (-3½hrs), Goose Bay 306 (-4 hrs), Guelph 519, Halifax 902 (-4 hrs), Hamilton 905, Kingston (Ont) 613, Kitchener 519, Lethbridge 403 (-7 hrs), London 519, Medicine Hat 403 (-7 hrs), Moncton 506 (-4 hrs), Montreal 514, Moose Jaw 306 (-6 hrs), New Westminster 604 (-8 hrs), Niagara Falls 416, Oshawa 416, Ottawa 613, Peterborough 705, Prince George 604 (-8 hrs), Quebec City 418, Red Deer 403 (-7 hrs), Regina 306 (-7 hrs), St Catharines 416, St John (NB) 506 (-4 hrs), St Johns (Nfld) 709 (-3½ hrs), Saskatoon 306 (-6 hrs), Sault Ste Marie 705, Sherbrooke 819, Sudbury 705, Sydney 902, Thunder Bay 807, Toronto (Metropolitan) 416, Toronto (all other parts) 905, Van-

couver 604 (-8 hrs)Victoria 604, Whitehorse 403 (-8 hrs), Windsor (Ont) 519, Winnipeg 204 (-6 hrs)
GMT -5 hrs (except where shown) charge band 4, Canada Direct 0800 89 0016

Canary Islands 00 34
Arrecife 28, Lanzarote 28, Las Palmas 28, Santa Cruz 22, Tenerife 22
Current UK time, charge band 1

Cape Verde Islands 00 238
GMT -1 hr, charge band 13

Cayman Islands 00 1 809
GMT -5 hrs, charge band 5

Central African Republic 00 236
Bangui 61
GMT + 1 hr, charge band 13

Chad 00 235
GMT + 1 hr, charge band 13

Chile 00 56
Antofagasta 83, Arica 80, Chillan 42, Concepcion 41, Coquimbo 51, Iquique 81, La Serena 51, Linares 73, Punta Arenas 61, Santiago 2, Temuco 45, Valparaiso 32, Vina del Mar 32
GMT -4 hrs, charge band 10, Chile Direct 0800 89 0056

China 00 86
Beijing 1, Dalian 411, Fuzhou 591, Guangzhou 20, Haikou City 898, Nantong 513, Qingdao 532, Shanghai 21, Shenyang 24, Shenzen 755, Tianjin 22, Wenzhou 577, Xiamen 592
GMT + 8 hrs, charge band 13

Christmas Island 00 672
Followed by numbers beginning with 4
GMT + 7 hrs, charge band 13

Cocos Island 00 672
Followed by numbers beginning with 2
GMT + 6½hrs, charge band 13

Colombia 00 57
Armenia 67, Barranquilla 67, Bogota 1, Bucaramanga 76, Cali 23, Cartagena 53, Cucuta 75, Manizales 68, Medellin 4
GMT -5 hrs, charge band 13, Colombia Direct 0800 89 0057

Comoros 00 269
Anjouan 71, Mohali 72, Moroni 73
GMT + 3 hrs, charge band 10

Congo 00 242
Brazzaville 81, Brazzaville 82, Brazzaville 83, Djambala 86, Gamboma 86, Impfondo 98, Kinkala 85, Loudima 91, Loumbomo 91, Loutete 92, Madingou 92, Makabana 93, Makoua 97,

Mindouli 85, Mouyondzi 92, Nkayi 92, Oyo 97, Ouesso 98, Owando 98, Plateau Region 86, Pointe Noire 94

Following number should consist of 6 digits, GMT + 1 hr, charge band 13

Cook Islands 00 682

GMT -10½ hrs, charge band 13

Costa Rica 00 506

GMT -6 hrs, charge band 10

Cote d'Ivoire 00 225

Current UK time, charge band 10

Croatia 00 38

Bjelovar 43, Daruvar 46, Dubrovnik 50, Gospic 48, Karlovak 47, Krk 532, Kutina 45, Ogulin 401, Osijek 54, Pula 52, Rijeka 51, Sibenik 59, Sisak 44, Split 58, Varzdin 42, Vinkovci 56, Zadar 57, Zagreb 41

GMT + 1 hr, charge band 3

Cuba 00 53

Agramonte 59, Ciego de Avila 33, Cienfuegos 43/432, Cruce de Bacos 225, Enrique G Varona 335, Florencia 335, Gramma 23, Guanajay 686, Havana 7, JA Mella 225, Jaguey Grande 59, Lastunas 31, Mangos de Baragua 225, Matanzas 5/52, Maximo Gomez 335, Moron 335, Plama Soriano 225, Playa Giron 59,

Playa Larga 59, San Jose de Marcos 59, Santa Clara 422, Santiago de Cuba 22/226, Tamarindo 335, Torriente 335, Villa Clara 42

Cyprus 00 357

Akrotiri 5, Ayia Napa 3, Deftera 2, Famagusta 36, Kyrenia 81, Larnaca 4, Limassol 5, Morphou 71, Mosphiloti 2, Nicosia 2, Nicosia (North) 20, Ormidhia 4, Palekhori 2, Paphos 6, Paralimni 3, Polis 6, Stroumbi 6, Zyghi 4

GMT +2 hrs, charge band 2

As an exception to the above, the following area codes should be preceded by 00 905 instead of 00 357 Famagusta 36, Kyrenia 81, Morphou 71, Nicosia (North) 20, charge band 3 applies to numbers beginning with 00 905

Czech Republic 00 42

Brno 5, Ceske Budejovice 38, Hradec Kralove 49, Karlovy Vary 17, Olomouc 68, Ostrava 69, Pardubice 40, Plzen 19, Prague 2, Usti nad labem 47

GMT + 1 hr, charge band 2

Denmark 00 45

GMT + 1 hr, charge band 1, Denmark Direct 0800 89 0045

Djibouti 00 253

160

GMT +3 hrs, charge band 13

Dominica 00 1 809
GMT -4 hrs, charge band 5

DominicanRepublic 00 1 809
Santiago 350
GMT -4 hrs, charge band 5

Ecuador 00 593
Ambato 2, Baba 4, Cuenca 7, Esmeraldas 2, Febres Cordero 4, Guyaquil 4, Machala 4, Manta 4, Mapasingue 4, Mocache 4, Portoviejo 4, Quito 2, Riobamba 2
GMT -5 hrs, charge band 13

Egypt 00 20
Alexandria 3, Ashara Ramadan 15, Assiout 88, Aswan 97, Benha 13, Beni Suef 82, Cairo 2, Damanhour 45, Damietta 57, El Arish 68, Fayoum 84, Giza 2, Heliopolis 2, Ismailiya 64, Kafr el Sheikh 47, Luxor 95, Maeria 3, Manhalla el Kubra 43, Mansoura 50, Marsa Matrah 3, Menia 86, Port Said 66, Pyramids 2, Sacheia 16, Sohag 93, Suez 62, Tanta 40, Zagazig 55
GMT +2 hrs, charge band 9

El Salvador 00 503
GMT -6 hrs, charge band 10

Equatorial Guinea 00 240
GMT +1 hr charge band 13

Eritrea 00 291
Asmara 4, Massawa 4
GMT +3 hrs, charge band 10

Estonia 00 372
Kohtla-Jarve 33, Narva 35, Parnu 44, Rakvere 32, Sillamae 49, Tallinn 2, 64, 65, Tartu 34, 72
GMT +2 hrs, charge band 8

Ethiopia 00 251
Addis Ababa 1, Assab 3, Debre Zeit 1, Dessie 3, Dire Dawa 5, Gondar 8, Harrar 5, Jimma 7, Nazareth 2, Shashemene 6
GMT +3 hrs, charge band 10

FalklandIslands 00 500
GMT -4 hrs, charge band 13

Faroe Islands 00 298
Current UK time, charge band 1

Fiji 00 679
GMT +12 hrs, charge band 13

Finland 00 358
Hameenlinna 17, Hamina 52, Helsinki 0, Hyvinkaa 14, Imatra 54, Joensuu 73, Jyvaskyla 41, Kemi 698, Kotka 52, Kuopio 71,

161

Lahti 18, Lappeenranta 53, Mikkeli 55, Oulu 81, Pori-Bjorneborg 39, Porvoo-Borga 15, Tampere 31, Tornio 698, Turku-Aabo 21, Vaasa-Vasa 61

France 00 33

Note – there are no French area codes. For Paris City and Greater Paris dial 00 331 + 8 digits. For rest of country dial 00 33 + 8 digits, charge band 1. France Direct 0800 89 0033

French Guiana 00 594

GMT -3 hrs, charge band 13

French Polynesia 00 689

Anaa 983, Apataki 961, Fakarava 984, Fangatu 972, Manihi 964, Puka-Puka 974, Tatakoto 975

GMT -10 hrs, charge band 13

Gabon 00 241

GMT +1 hr, charge band 10, Gabon Direct 0800 89 0241

Gambia 00 220

Current UK time, charge band 10

Georgia 00 7

Batumi 88222, Sukhumi 88122, Tbilisi 8832

GMT +4 hrs, charge band 8

Germany 00 49

Aachen 241, Augsburg 821, Berlin 30, Bielefeld 521, Bochum 234, Bonn 228, Bottrop 2041, Braunschweig 531, Bremen 421, Bremerhaven 471, Chemnitz 371, Cologne (Koln) 221, Cottbus 355, Darmstadt 6151, Dessau 340, Dortmund 231, Dresden 351, Duisburg 203, Dusseldorf 211, Eisenach 3691, Erfurt 361, Essen 201, Frankfurt/Main 69, Frankfurt/Oder 335, Freiburg-im-Breisgau 761, Gelsenkirchen 209, Gera 365, Hagen 2331, Halle (Saale) 345, Hamburg 40, Hannover 511, Heidelberg 6221, Herne 2323, Jena 641, Karlsruhe 721, Kassel 561, Kiel 431, Koblenz 261, Krefeld 2151, Leipzig 341, Leverkusen 214, Lubeck 451, Ludwigshafen/Rhein 621, Magdeburg 391, Mainz 6131, Mannheim 621, Monchengladbach 2161, M'gladbach-Rheydt 2166, Mulheim/Ruhr 208, Munich 89, Munster 251, Neuss 2131, Nuremburg 911, Oberhausen 208, Offenbach/Main 69, Oldenburg/Oldb 441, Osnabruck 541, Plauen 3741, Potsdam 331, Recklinghausen 2361, Regensburg 941, Remscheid 2191, Rostock 381, Saarbrucken 681, Solingen 212, Stralsund 3831, Stuttgart 711, Suhl 3681, Torgau 3421, Wiesbaden 611, Wilhelmshaven 4421, Wuppertal 202, Wurzburg 031, Zeitz 3441

GMT +1 hr, charge band 1, Germany Direct 0800 89 0049

Ghana 00 233
*Accra 21, Bolgatanga 72, Cape Coast 42, Koforidua 81, Kumasi
51, Sekondi 31, Takoradi 31, Tamale 71, Tema 221*
Current UK time, charge band 10

Gibraltar 00 350
GMT +1 hr, charge band 1

Greece 00 30
*Alexandroupolis 551, Arta 681, Athens 1, Chios 271, Corfu (City)
661, Iraklion (Crete) 81, Kalamata 721, Kavala 51, Larissa 41,
Mykonos 289, Mytilini 251, Patrai (Patras) 61, Piraeus 1, Pylion
242, Pyrgos Llias 621, Rhodes (Rodos) 241, Syros 281, Thassos
593, Thessaloniki 31, Tripolis 71, Volos 421, Zakynthos 695*
GMT +2 hrs, charge band 1

Greenland 00 299
GMT -3 hrs, charge band 13

Grenada (Including Carriacou) 00 1 809
*Numbers consist of 7 digits, all telephone numbers in Grenada
begin with 44*
GMT -4 hrs, charge band 5

Guadeloupe 00 590
GMT -4 hrs, charge band 8

Guam 00 671
GMT +10 hrs, charge band 13

Guatemala 00 502
*Antigua 932, Guatemala City 2, Mazatenango 97, Quezaltenango
961,* GMT *-6 hrs, charge band 10*

Guinea 00 224
Current UK time, charge band 13

Guinea-Bissau 00 245
Current UK time, charge band 13

Guyana 00 592
*Bartica 5, Cove and John 29, Georgetown 2, Ituni 41, Linden 4,
New Amsterdam 3, Tuschen 60, Vreed en Hoop 64*
GMT -3 hrs, charge band 8

Haiti 00 509
GMT -5 hrs, charge band 8

Honduras 00 504
GMT -6 hrs, charge band 10

Hong Kong 00 852
GMT +8 hrs, charge band 7, Hong Kong Direct 0800 89 0852

Hungary 00 36
*Bakoca 72, Balatonfured 86, Batonyterenye 86, Bekesscaba 66,
Budapestm 1, Debrecen 52, Eger 36, Gyongyos 37, Gyor 96,*

Homokterenye 32, Kaloska 64, Kaposvar 82, Kecskemet 76, Matramindszent 32, Matranovadk 32, Mindszentgodisa 72, Miskolc 46, Nadudfalu 32, Nyiregyhaza 42, Orbottyabn 42, Pecs 72, Pilismarot 33, Salgotarjan 32, Sopron 99, Szeged 62, Szekesfehervar 22, Szolnok 56, Szombathely 94, Tiszaujvaros 49, Tormas 72, Vesprem 88, Zalaegerszeg 92

GMT + 1 hr, charge band 2, Hungary Direct 0800 89 0036

Ibiza (Please see Spain)

Iceland 00 354

Akureyri 6, Hafnarfjoerdur 1, Keflavik 2, Reykjavik 1

Current UK time, charge band 3, Iceland Direct 0800 89 0354

India 00 91

Ahmadabad 272, Bangalore 80, Bombay 22, Calcutta 33, Chandigarh 172, Delhi/New Delhi 11, Hyderabad 42, Jaipur 141, Jullunder 181, Kanpur 512, Lucknow 522, Madras 44, Nagpur 712, Panjim (Goa) 832, Poona 212, Rajkot 281, Varanasi 542

GMT + 5½ hrs, charge band 12

Indonesia 00 62

Balik Papan 542 (+8 hrs), Bandung 22, Banjarmasin 511 (+8 hrs), Denpasar 361 (+8 hrs), Jakarta 21, Manado 431 (+8 hrs), Medan 61, Padang 751, Palembang 711, Semarang 24, Surabaya 31, Ujung Pandang 411 (+8 hrs)

GMT + 7 hrs (except where shown), charge band 13, Indonesia Direct 0800 89 0062

Inmarsat - Customers served by exchanges with digital meter-ing can direct dial their Inmarsat calls 00

Atlantic Ocean (east) 871, Atlantic Ocean (west) 874, Indian Ocean 873, Pacific Ocean 872

Followed by ship's identification number, time difference depend-ent upon ship's position

Iran 00 98

Abadan 631, Ahvaz 61, Arak 2621, Babol 11, Bakhtaran 431, Hamadan 261, Isfahan 31, Kerman 51, Mashad 51, Shiraz 71, Tabriz 41, Tehran 21, GMT + 3½ hrs, charge band 10

Iraq 00 964

Amara 43, Baghdad 1, Baquba 25, Basrah 40, Diwaniya 36, Duhok 62, Erbil 66, Hilla 30, Kerbala 32, Kut 23, Nainawa 60, Najaf 33, Nasiriya 42, Ramadi 24, Samawa 37, Sulaimaniya 53, Tkrit 21

GMT + 3 hrs, charge band 10

Ireland, Republic of 00 353

Arklow 402, Athlone 902, Ballina 96, Bandon 23, Bundoran 72, Carlow 503, Castlebar 94, Cavan 49, Clonmel 52, Cork 21, Donegal 73, Drogheda 41, Dublin 1, Dundalk 42, Ennis 65,

Enniscorthy 54, Galway 91, Kilkenny 56, Killarney 64, Letterkenny 74, Limerick 61, Longford 43, Mallow 22, Monaghan 47, Mullingar 44, Naas 45, Navan 46, Nenagh 67, Portlaoise 502, Rathluirc 63, Roscommon 903, Rosslare 63, Shannon 61, Sligo 71, Thurles 504, Tipperary 62, Tralee 66, Tuam 93, Tullamore 506, Waterford 51, Westport 98, Ireland,Republic of Wexford 53, Wicklow 404, Youghal 24

Current UK time, charged at Irish Republic rate, Ireland Direct 0800 89 0353

Israel (and the occupied territories) 00 972

Afula 6, Ashdod 8, Ashkelon 51, Beer Sheva 7, Ben Gurion Airport 3, Bethlehem 2, Eilat 7, Hadera 6, Haifa 4, Herzlia 9, Hevron 2, Jericho 2, Jerusalem 2, Naharia 4, Nazareth 6, Netania 9, Petah Tikva 3, Raanana 9, Ramalla 2, Ramat Gan 3, Rehovot 8, Safed 6, Tel Aviv 3, Tiberias 6 GMT + 2 hrs, charge band 8a, Israel Direct 0800 89 0972

Italy 00 39

Amalfi 89, Ancona 71, Bari 80, Bologna 51, Bolzano 471, Brescia 30, Brindisi 831, Cagliari 70, Capri 81, Catania 95, Como 31, Ferrara 532, Florence 55, Genoa 10, La Spezia 187, Lecce 832, Livorno 586, Lucca 583, Messina 59, Milan 2, Modena 59, Naples 81, Padua 49, Palermo 91, Parma 521, Perugia 75, Pescara 85, Piacenza 523, Pisa 50, Ravenna 544, Reggio Calabria 965, Reggio Emilia 522, Rimini 541, Rome 6, Salerno 89, San Remo 184, Sassari 79, Siracusa 931, Taranto 99, Terni 744, Trieste 40, Turin 11, Vatican City 66982, Venice 41, Verona 45, Vicenz 444

GMT + 1 hr, charge band 1, Italy Direct 0800 89 0039

Ivory Coast(see Cote d'Ivoire)

Jamaica 00 1 809

GMT -5 hrs, charge band 5

Japan 00 81

Akita 188, Akita (Kumamoto) 96, Chiba 472, Fukuoka 92, Hiroshima 82, Kawasaki (Miyagi) 224, Kawasaki (Kanagawa) 44, Kobe 78, Kyoto 75, Nagasaki 958, Nagoya 52, Okayama 862, Osaka 6, Sakai 722, Sapporo 11, Sendai 22, Tokyo 3, Yokohama 45

GMT +9 hrs, charge band 11, Japan Direct (KDD) 0800 89 0081, Japan Straight (IDC) 0800 89 0080

Jordan 00 962

Amman 6, Aqaba 3, Irbid 2, Jerash 4, Karak 3, Ma'an 3, Salt 5, Um Alamad 8, Zarqa 9

GMT + 2 hr, charge band 9

Kazakhstan 00 7

Almaty *(Alma-Atal)* 3272, Karaganda 3212, Petropavlovsk 3152, Uralsk 31122, Ust-Kamenogorsk 3232

GMT + 5/6 hrs, charge band 8

Kenya 00 254

Athi River 150, Butcre 333, Chuka 166, Diani Beach 127, Eldoret 321, Kabarnet 328, Kagio 163, Keroka 383, Kissi 381, Kisumu 35, Londiani 361, Malindi 123, Mombasa 11, Mukurweini 171, Mwingi 142, Nairobi 2, Nakuru 37, Nanyuki 176, Nyeri 171, Sosiot 361, Thika 151, Turbo 323, Wundanyi 148

GMT + 3 hrs, charge band 10

Kirghizstan 00 7

Bishkek 3312

GMT + 3 hrs, charge band 8

Kiribati 00 686

GMT + 12 hrs, charge band 13

Korea (Peoples Democratic Republic of) (North) 00 850

Pyongyang 2

GMT + 9 hrs, charge band 13

Korea (Republic of) (South) 00 82

Incheon 32, Pusan *(Busan)* 51, Seoul 2, Taegu 53

GMT + 9 hrs, charge band 13, Korea Direct 0800 89 0082,Call Korea (DACOMI0800 89 0820

Kuwait 00 965

Take account of business hours when you make your call, Saturday-Thursday am is the working week in Kuwait

GMT + 3 hrs, charge band 8

Laos 00 856

GMT + 7 hrs, charge band 13

Latvia 00 371

Daugavpils 54, Jelgava 30, Liepaja 34, Rezekne 46, Riga 2, Ventspils 36

GMT + 2 hrs, charge band 8

Lebanon 00 961

Grand Beirut 1, Kerswan and Jbeil 9, Lebanon North 6, Lebanon South 7, Mount Lebanon North 4, Mount Lebanon South 5, Saida 7, Tripoli 6, Tyr 7, Zahle 8

GMT + 2 hrs, charge band 9

Lesotho 00 266

GMT + 2 hrs, charge band 10

Liberia 00 231

Current UK time, charge band 10

Libya 00 218
Benghazi 61, Benina 63, Derna 81, Sabratha 24, Tripoli 21,
Tripoli (Int Airport) 22, Zawia 23, Zuara 25
Liechtenstein 00 41 75
GMT + 1 hr, charge band 3
Lithuania 00 370
Kaunas 7, Klaipeda 61, Panevežys 54, Siauliai 14, Vilnius 2
GMT + 2 hrs, charge band 8
Luxembourg 00 352
GMT + 1 hr, charge band 1, Luxembourg Direct 0800 89 0352S
Macao 00 853
GMT + 8 hrs, charge band 13, Macao Direct 0800 89 0853
Macedonia 00 389
Bitola 97, Kicevo 95, Kocani 903, Kumanovo 901, Ohrid 96,
Prilep 98, Skopje 91, Stip 92, Strumica 902, Tetovo 94, Titov
Veles 93
GMT + 1 hr, charge band 3
Madagascar 00 261
Antananarivo 2
GMT + 3 hrs, charge band 13

Madeira 00 351 91
Current UK time, charge band 1
Malawi 00 265
Domasi 531, Namadzi 534, Njuli 664, Thondwe 533
GMT + 2 hrs, charge band 10
Malaysia 00 60
Ipoh 5, Johor Bahru 7, Kota Kinabalu 88, Kuala Lumpur 3,
Kuantan 9, Kuching 82, Malacca (Melaka) 6, Penang 4, Port
Dickson 6, Sandakan 89, Sibu 84, Taiping 5
GMT + 8 hrs, charge band 13, Malaysia Direct 0800 89 0060
Maldives 00 960
Hulule Airport 32, Male Island 32, North Male Atoll 34, South
Male Atoll 34
GMT + 5 hrs, charge band 13
Mali 00 223
Current UK time, charge band 13
Malta 00 356
GMT + 1 hr, charge band 2
Marshall Islands 00 692
Ebeye 329,Majuro 625
GMT + 12 hrs, charge band 13

167

Martinique 00 596
GMT -4 hrs, charge band 8

Mauritania 00 222
Current UK time, charge band 13

Mauritius (including Rodriguez Island) 00 230
GMT +4 hrs, charge band 10

Mayotte 00 269
GMT +3 hrs, charge band 10

Mexico 00 52
Acapulco 748, Aguascalientes 491 (-7 hrs), Campeche 981, Chihuahua 14, Ciudad Obregon 641 (-7 hrs), Cuernavaca 73, Culiacan 671, Durango 181 (-7 hrs), Guadalajara 36 (-7 hrs), Hermosillo 621 (-7 hrs), Irapuato 462, Jalapa Veracruz 281, Leon 47, Matamoros (Tamaulipas) 891, Mazatlan 678 (7 hrs), Merida 99, Mexicali 65, Mexico City 5, Monterrey 83, Morelia 451, Nogales (Sonora) 631, Nuevo Laredo 871, Oaxaca 951, Puebla 22, Reynosa 892, Saltillo 841, San Luis Potosi 481, Tampico 12, Tijuana 66 (-8 hrs), Toluca 721, Torreon 17, Tuxpan (Veracruz) 783, Veracruz 29, Villahermosa 931
GMT -6 hrs (except where shown) charge band 13

Micronesia 00 691
Kosrae 370, Ponape 320, Truk 330 (+10 hrs), Yap 350 (+10

hrs)
GMT +11 hrs (except where shown) charge band 13

Midway Island
GMT -11 hrs, charge band 13

Minorca (see Spain)

Moldova 00 373
Kishinev 2

GMT +2 hrs, charge band 8

Monaco 00 33 93
GMT +1 hr, charge band 1

Mongolia
GMT +8 hrs, charge band 13

Montserrat 00 1 809
GMT -4 hrs, charge band 5

Morocco 00 212
Agadir 8, Casablanca 2, El Jadida 3, Essaouira 47, Fes 5, Kenitra 7, Larache 91, Marrakech 4, Meknes 5, Mohammedia 32, Oujda 68, Rabat 7, Safi 4, Sale 7, Tangier 9, Tetouan 9, Tinrhir 4, Zagora 4
Current UK time, charge band 3

Mozambique 00 258
Beira 3, Chimoio 51, Chokwe 21, Maputo 1, Nampula 6,

Qualimane 4, Tete 52, Xai Xai 22
GMT + 2 hrs, charge band 13

Myanmar 00 95
Bassein 42, Mandalay 2, Moulmein 32, Yangon (Rangoon) 1
GMT + 6½, charge band 13

Namibia 00 264
Gobabis 681, Grootfontein 673, Industria 61, Keetmanshoop 631, Luderitz 6331, Swakopmund 641, Tsumeb 671, Walvis Bay 642, Windhoek Airport 626
GMT + 2 hrs, charge band 10

Nauru 00 674
GMT + 12 hrs, charge band 13

Nepal 00 977
Bhairawa 71, Bhaktapur 1, Biratnagar 21, Birgunj 51, Dhangarhi 91, Janakpur 41, Kathmandu 1, Nepalgunj 81, Patan 1, Phokhara 61
GMT + 5¾ hrs, charge band 13

Netherlands 00 31
Aerdenhout 23, Alkmaar 72, Almelo 5490, Almere 36, Amersfoort 23, Amstelveen 20, Amsterdam 20, Apeldoorn 55, Arnhem 85, Assen 5920, Bergen op Zoom 1640, Bithoven 30, Breda 76, Bussum 2159, Delft 15, Delfzijl 5960, Den Helder 2230, Deventer 5700, Dordrecht 78, Eindhoven 40, Emmen 5910, Enschede 53, Ermelo 3417, Geleen 46, Goirle 13, Gouda 1820, s-Gravenhage 70, Groningen 50, Haarlem 23, Hague 70, Harlingen 5178, Heemstede 23, Heerlen 45, Helmond 4920, Hengelo (Overijssel) 74, s'Hertogenbosch 73, Hilversum 35, Hoek van Holland 1747, Ijmuiden 2550, Kampen 5202, Katwijk a/d Rihn 1718, Kerkrade 45, Leeuwarden 58, Leiden 71, Maassluis 1899, Maastricht 43, Middelburg 1180, Nijmegen 80, Oss 4120, Renkum 8373, Rheden 8309, Rijswijk (Gelderland) 3452, Rijswijk Z'Holland 70, Roermond 4750, Roosendaal 1650, Rotterdam 10, Scheveningen 70, Schiedam 10, Sittard 46, Soest 2155, Terneuzen 1150, Tiel 3440, Tilburg 13, Ulvenhout 76, Utrecht 30, Veendam 5987, Venlo 77, Vlaardingen 10, Vlissingen 1184, Voorburg 70, Wassenaar 1751, Weert 4950, Zaandam 75, Zeist 3404, Zoetermeer 79, Zutphen 5750, Zwolle 38
GMT + 1 hr, charge band 1, Nederlands Direct 0800 89 0031

Nevis (see St. Kitts and Nevis)

New Caledonia 00 687
GMT + 11 hrs, charge band 13

New Zealand 00 64
Ashburton 3, Auckland 9, Blenheim 3, Christchurch 3, Dunedin 3, Gisborne 6, Gore 3, Hamilton 7, Hastings 6, Invercargill 3,

Lyttelton 3, Marton 6, Masterton 6, Napier 6, Nelson 3, New Plymouth 6, Palmerston North 6, Rotorua 7, Taupo 7, Taurengam 7, Timaru 3, Waitangi (Chatham Island) 3, Wanganui 6, Wellington 4, Whangarei 9

GMT + 12 hrs, charge band 6, NZ Direct 800 89 0064, NZ Clear Comms 0800 89 0640

Nicaragua 00 505

Bluefields 82, Chinandega 341, Corinto 342, Diriamba 42, Granada 55, Jinotega 63, Leon 311, Managua 2, Masaya 52, Matagalpa 61, Rivas 461, San Marcos 43

GMT -6 hrs, charge band 10

Niger 00 227

GMT + 1 hr, charge band 13

Nigeria 00 234

Abeokuta 39, Abuja 9, Akure 34, Amuwo 1, Bauchi 77, Benin City 52, Birnin-Kebbi 68, Calabar 87, NigeriaEbute-Metta 1, Enugu 42, Ibadan 22, Ikeja 1, Ilorin 31, Jos 73, Kaduna 62, Kano 64, Katsina 65, Lagos 1, Maiduguri 76, Makurdi 44, Minna 66, Owerri 83, Oyo 38, Port Harcourt 84, Shomolu 1, Sokoto 60, Yola 75, Zaria 69

GMT + 1 hr charge band 10

Niue 00 683

GMT -11 hrs, charge band 13

Norfolk Island 00 6 72

GMT +11½ hrs, charge band 13

NorthernMarianas 00 670

Rota 532, Tinian 433, Saipan (Capitol Hill) 322, Saipan (Susupe City) 234

GMT + 10 hrs, charge band 13

Norway 00 47

GMT + 1 hr, charge band 2, Norway Direct 0800 89 0047

Oman 00 968

GMT + 4 hrs, charge band 8

Pakistan 00 92

Faisalabad 411, Gujranwala 431, Hyderabad 221, Islamabad51, Jhelum 5941, Karachi 21, Lahore 42, Multan 61, Peshawar 521, Quetta 81, Rawalpindi 51, Sialkot 432, Sukkur 71

GMT + 5 hrs, charge band 12

Palau 00 680 9

GMT + 9 hrs, charge band 13

Panama 00 507

GMT -5 hrs, charge band 10

Papua NewGuinea 00 675
GMT +10 hrs, charge band 13

Paraguay 00 595
Asuncion 21, Ciudad Del Este 61, Concepcion 31, Coronel Oviedo
521, Encarnacion 71, PJ Cabellero 36, Villarica 541
GMT -4 hrs, charge band 10

Peru 00 51
Abancay 84, Arequipa 54, Cajamarca 44, Cerro de Pasco 64,
Chiclayo 74, Cuzco 84, Iquitos 94, Lima 14, Piura 74,
PeruTarapoto 94, Trujillo 44
GMT -5 hrs, charge band 10

Philippines 00 63
Bacolod 34, Cagayan De Oro 8822, Cebu 32, Dagupan 75, Davao
82, Iloilo 33, Manila 2, San Pablo 93
GMT +8 hrs, charge band 13, Philippines Direct 0800 89 0063

Pitcairn Island
GMT -8½ hrs, charge band 13

Poland 00 48
Bedzin 3, Bialystok 85, Bydgoszcz 52, Bytom 3, Chojnice 531,
Chorzow 32, Czestochowa 34, Elblag 50, Gdansk 58, Gdynia
58, Gliwice 32, Grudziadz 51, Katowice (6 digit nos) 32, (7
digit nos) 3, Kielce 41, Komertel 3912, Krakow 12, Leszno 65,

Lodz 42, Lublin 81, Myslowice 3, Plock 24, Poznan 61, Radom
48, Ruda Slaska 32, Rzeszow 17, Siedlce 25, Sopot 58,
Sosnowiec 3, Szczecin 91, Tarnow 14, Torun 56, Tychy 3,
Warsaw (6 digit nos) 2, (7 digit nos) 2, Wloclawek 54, Wroclaw
71, Zabrze 3
GMT +1 hr, charge band 2

Portugal 00 351
Almada 1, Amadora 1, Amarante 55, Arcos de Valdevez 58,
Aveiro 34, Barreiro 1, Beja 84, Braga 53, Braganca 73, Castelo
Branco 72, Chaves 76, Coimbra 39, Covilha 75, Elvas 68, Evora
66, Faro 89, Figueira da Foz 33, Fundao 75, Guarda 71,
Guimaraes 53, Lagos 82, Lamego 54, Leiria 44, Lisbon 1, Loule
89, Mafra 61, Matosinhos 2, Oporto 2, Penafiel 55, Pombal,
36, Portalegre 45, Portimao 82, Santarem 43, Seia 38, Setubal
65, Tavira 81, Torres Vedras 61, Viana do Castelo 58, Vila Real
59, Viseu 32
GMT +1 hr, charge band 1, Portugal Direct 0800 89 0351

Puerto Rico 00 1 809
GMT -4 hrs, charge band 5

Qatar 00 974
*Please take account of business hours, Saturday to Thursday
am is the working week in Qatar, GMT +3 hrs, charge band 8*

Reunion 00 262
GMT +4 hrs, charge band 13

Rodriguez Island (see Mauritius)

Romania 00 40
Arad 57, Bacau 34, Baia Mare 99, Botosani 31, Braila 39, Brasov 68, Bucharest 1, Buzau 38, Cluj-Napoca 95, Constanta 41, Craiova 94, Focsani 939, Gaesti 92, Galati 36, Giurgiu 46, Hunedoara 54, Iasi 32, Lugoj 96, Mamaia 91, Oradea 99, Petrosani 93, Pitesti 97, Ploiesti 97, Roman 93, Sacele 92, Satu-Mare 61, Sibiu 69, Suceava 30, Timisoara 96, Tirgu-Mures 954, Turda 95, Zarnesti 92
GMT +2 hrs, charge band 8

Russian Federation 00 7
Arkhangelsk 818, Chelyabinsk 3512, Ekaterinburg 3432 (+5 hrs), Irkutsk 3952, Kaliningrad 0112, Khabarovsk 421, Kursk 071, Moscow 095, Naberezhyne Chelny 84329, Nizhny Novgorod 8312, Novosibirsk 3832 (+7hrs), Omsk 38112, Perm 3422, Petropavlovsk-Kamchatsky 415, Rostov-on-Don 8632, Samara 8462, St Petersburg 812, Sochi 862, Stavropol 86522, Toliatti 8480, Tula 0872, Tyumen 3452, Ufa 347, Vladivostok 4232 (+10 hrs), Volgograd 8442 (+4 hrs), Voronezh 0732, Yakutsk 41122, Yuzhno-Sakhalinsk 424

GMT + 2/12 hrs (except where shown) charge band 8

Rwanda 00 250
GMT + 2 hrs, charge band 13

St Helena 00 290
Current UK time, charge band 13

St Kitts and Nevis 00 1 809
All numbers in St Kitts commence 465, all numbers in Nevis commence 469

St Lucia 00 1 809
GMT -4 hrs, charge band 5

St Pierre and Miquelon 00 508
GMT -3 hrs, charge band 5

St Vincent and The Grenadines 00 1 809
GMT -4 hrs, charge band 5

Saipan (see Northern Marianas)

Samoa (USA) 00 684
GMT -11 hrs, charge band 13

Samoa(Western) 00 685
Calls available to Apia only, GMT -11 hrs, charge band 13

San Marino 00 378
GMT + 1 hr, Charge band 1

172

Sao Tome and Principe 00 239
Current UK time, Charge band 2

Saudi Arabia 00 966

Abha 7, Abqaiq 3, Bukayriyah 6, Dammam 3, Dhahran 3, Hail 6, Hawiyah 2, Hofur 3, Jeddah 2, Jubal 3, Layla 1, Mecca 2, Medina 4, Qatif 3, Rabigh 2, Ras Tanurah 3, Riyadh 1, Shaqra 1, Tabuk 4, Taif 2, Yanbu 4.

Please note business hours, Saturday to Thursday am is the working week in Saudi Arabia, GMT +3 hrs, charge band 8

Senegal 00 221
Current UK time charge band 10

Seychelles 00 248
GMT +4 hrs, charge band 10

Sierra Leone, 00 232

Bo 32, Freetown 22, Juba 24, Kenema 42, Kono 53, Lungi 25, Makeni 52, Wellington 23

Current UK time, charge band 10

Singapore 00 65
GMT +8 hrs, charge band 7, Singapore Direct 0800 89 0065

Slovakia 00 42

Banska Bystrica 88, Bratislava 7, Kosice 95, Nitra 87, Poprad 92, Presov 91, Trencin 831, Zilina 89

173

GMT +1 hr, charge band 2

Slovenia 00 386

Kranj 64, Ljubjana 1, Maribor 62, Postojna 67
GMT +1 hr, charge band 3

Solomon Islands 00 677
GMT +11 hrs, charge band 13

Somalia 00 252

Mogadiscio 1
GMT +3 hrs, charge band 10

South Africa 00 27

Aliwal North 551, Allanridge 1723, Amanzimtoti 31, Beaufort West 201, Bellville 21, Bethal 1361, Bethlehem 1431, Bisho 401, Bloemfontein 51, Bothaville 1414, Britz 1211, Caledon 281, Capetown 21, Ceres 233, Cradock 481, Dannhauser 344, De Aar 571, Despatch 422, Dundee 341, Durban 31, East London 431, Empangeni 351, Ermelo 1341, Figrove 24, George 441, Glencoe 341, Gordon's Bay 24, Graff Reinet 491, Grahamstown 461, Heidelberg 151, Johannesburg 11, Kimberley 531, King William's Town 433, Klerksdrop 18, Kroonstad 1411, Ladysmith 361, Lichtenburg 1441, Lydenburg 1323, Malmesbury 224, Middelburg, Cape Province 483, Middelburg, Tvl 132, Mossel Bay 4441, Newcastle 3431, Oudtshoorn 4431,

Paarl 2211, Parow 21, Parys 1601, Pietermaritzburg 331, Pietersburg 1521, Pinetown 31, Port Elizabeth 41, Portchefstroom 148, Pretoria 12, Queenstown 451, South Africa Rustenburg 1421, Sasolburg 16, Scottburgh 323, Simonstown 21, Somerset West 24, Standerton 1331, Stellenbosch 2231, Strand 24, Thohoyandou 15581, Uitenhage 422, Umtata 471, Vanderbijlpark 16, Vereeniging 16, Virginia 1722, Vryburg 1451, Vryheid 381, Welkom 171, Wellington 2211, Worcester 231, Yzerfontein 2245

GMT + 2 hrs, charge band 8, South Africa Direct 0800 89 0027

Spain 00 34

Aguilas 68, Albacete 67, Alcira 6, Alcoy 65, Algeciras 56, Alicante 65, Almeria 50, Avila 20, Aviles 85, Badajoz 24, Badalona 3, Barcelona 3, Benidorm 65, Bilbao 4, Burgos 47, Caceres 27, Cadiz 56, Cartagena 68, Castellon de la Plana 64, Ceuta 56, Ciudad Real 26, Cordoba 57, Cuenca 69, Gandia 65, Gerona 27, Gijon 85, Granada 58, Guadalajara 49, Huelva 59, Ibiza 71, Irun 43, Jaen 53, Jerez de la Frontera 56, La Coruna 81, Las Palmas 28 (time as GMT), Leon 87, Lerida 73, Linares 53, Logrono 41, Lorca 68, Lugo 82, Madrid 1, Mahon 71, Malaga 52, Marbella 52, Merida 24, Murcia 68, Orense 88, Oviedo 85, Palencia 79, Palma de Mallorca 71, Pamplona 48, Pontevedra 86, Reus 77, Sabadell 3, Sagunto 6, Salamanca 23, San Feliu de Llobregat 3, San Sebastian 43, Santa Cruz de Tenerife 22 (Time as GMT), Santander 42, Santiago de Compostela 81, Segovia 21, Sevilla 54, Tarragona 77, Tarrasa 3, Tenerife 22, (time as GMT) Teruel 78, Toledo 25, Torremolinos 52, Tortosa 77, Valencia 6, Valladolid 83, Vigo 86, Vitoria 45, Zamora 80, Zaragoza 76,

GMT + 1 hr, charge band 1, Spain Direct 0800 89 0034

Sri Lanka 00 94

Colombo (Central) 1, Dehiwela 1, Galle 9, Jaffna 21, Kandy 8, Katunayake (Int Airport) 30, Kurunegala 37, Moratuwa 1, Negombo 31, Nuwara Eliya 522, Panadura 34, Trincomalee 26

GMT + 5½ hrs, charge band 12

Sudan 00 249

Khartoum 11, all other area codes via operator

GMT + 2 hrs, charge band 10

Suriname 00 597

Swaziland 00 268

GMT + 2 hrs, charge band 10

Sweden 00 46

Arboga 589, Boras 33, Eskilstuna 16, Falkenberg 346, Falun

23, Galve-Sandviken 26, Gothenburg 31, Halmstad 35, Harnosand 611, Helsingborg 42, Hudiksvall 650, Jonkoping 36, Kalix 923, Kalmar 480, Karlshamn 454, Karlskrona 455, Karlstad 54, Kristianstad 44, Landskrona 418, Lidkoping 510, Lulea 920, Lund 46, Malmo 40, Mariestad 501, Norrkoping 11, Nykoping 155, Orebro 19, Ornskildsvik 660, Oskarshamn 491, Ostersund 63, Oxelosund 155, Piteaa 911, Ronneby 457, Skelleftea 910, Skovde 500, Soderhamn 270, Sodertalje 755, Stockholm 8, Stromstad 526, Sundsvall 60, Trelleborg 410, Trollhatten 520, Uddevalla 522, Umeaa 90, Uppsala 18, Varberg 340, Vasteraas 21, Vastervik 490, Visby Voir Gotland 498, Ystad 411

GMT + 1 hr, charge band 2, Sweden Direct 0800 89 0046S

Switzerland 00 41

Aarau 64, Aigle 25, Baden 56, Basle 61, Bellinzona 92, Berne 31, Bienne 32, Brig 28, Burgdorf 34, Chaux de Fonds, La 39, Chur 81, Davos 81, Faido 94, Frauenfeld 54, Fribourg 37, Geneva 22, Grenchen 65, Grindewald 36, Herisau 71, Interlaken 36, Koniz 31, Langenthal 63, Lausanne 21, Locarno 93, Locle, Le 39, Lucerne 41, Lugano 91, Montreux 21, Neuchatel 38, Olten 62, Rapperswill 55, Rorschach 71, St Gallen 71, St Moritz 82, Schaffhausen 53, Schwyz 43, Sion 27, Solothurn 65, Sursee 45, Thun 33, Uster 1, Vevey 21, Winterthur 52, Yverdon 24, Zermatt 28, Zug 42, Zurich 1, Zweisimmen 30

GMT + 1 hr, charge band 1

Syria 00 963

Aleppo 21, Banias 43, Damascus 11, Deir Ezzor 51, Deraa 51, Edleb 23, Hama 33, Hassakah 52, Homs 31, Jebleh 41, Jisr Ash-Shughur 44, Kamichly 53, Kordaha 44, Kuneitra 14, Lattakia 41, Manbej 25, Ma'arret Al Nouman 24, Nabek 12, Palmayra 34, Raqqah 22, Safita 32, Sweida 16, Tartous 43, Zabadani 13, Zweisimmen 30

GMT + 2 hrs, charge band 9

Tadzhikistan 00 7

Dushanbe 3772

GMT + 3 hrs, charge band 8

Taiwan 00 886

Hualien 38, Kaohsiung 7, Keelung 32, Nantou 49, Pingtung 8, Taichung 4, Tainan 6, Taipei 2

GMT + 8 hrs, charge band 13, Taiwan Direct 0800 89 0886

Tanzania 00 255

Arusha 57, Chake Chake 54, Dar es Salaam 51, Dodoma 61, Iringa 64, Kilimanjaro Airport 575, Mbeya 65, Mkoani 54, Morogoro 56, Moshi 55, Mtwara 59, Mwanza 68, Tabora 62, Tanga 53, Wete 54, Zanzibar 54

GMT + 3 hrs, charge band 10
Thailand 00 66
Bangkok 2, Chieng Mai 53, Khon Kean 43, Nakhon Pathom 34, Nakhon Ratchasima 44, Suphanburi 35, Udon Thani 42
GMT +7 hrs, charge band 13, Thailand Direct 0800 89 0066
Togo 00 228
Current UK time, charge band 10
Tonga 00 676
GMT + 13 hrs, charge band 13
Trinidad and Tobago 00 1 809
GMT -4 hrs, charge band 5
Tristan da Cunha
Current UK time, charge band 13
Tunisia 00 216
Bizerte 2, Carthage 1, Gabes 5, Hammamet 2, Haouaria 2, Kairouan 7, Mahdia 3, Marsa 1, Menzel Bourguiba 2, Monastir 3, Nabeul 2, Sfax 4, Sousse 3, Tunis 1
GMT + 1 hr, charge band 3
Turkey 00 90
Adana 322, Ankara 312, Antalya 242, Aydin 256, Bursa 224, Denizli 258, Diyarbakir 412, Erzurum 442, Eskisehir 222, Gaziantep 342, Istenderum 881, Isparta 246, Istanbul 216, Izmir

232, Izmit 262, Kayseri 352, Konya 332, Kozan 7341, Kusadasi 6361, Malatya 422, Mersin 324, Samsun 362, Trabzon 462, Zonguldak 372
GMT + 2 hrs, charge band 3, Turkey Direct 0800 89 0090
Turkmenistan 00 7
Ashgabad 3632
GMT 5 hrs, charge band 8
Turks and Caicos Islands 00 1 809
GMT -5 hrs, charge band 5
Tuvalu 00 688
GMT + 12 hrs, charge band 13
Uganda 00 256
Entebbe 42, Fort Portal 493, Jinja 43, Kampala 41, Kasese 493, Lugazi 44, Masaka 481, Mbale 45, Mbarara 485, Tororo 45
GMT +3 hrs, charge band 10
Ukraine 00 7
Dnepropetrovsk 0562, Donetsk 0622, Kharkov 0572, Kiev 044, Lvov 0322, Odessa 0482, Sevastopol 0692, Simferopol 0652, Yalta 0654
GMT + 2 hrs, charge band 8
United Arab Emirates 00 971
Abu Dhabi 2, Ajman 6, Al Ain 3, Al Saad 3, Aweer 4, Dhayd 6,

Dubai 4, Fujairah 9, Jebel Ali 84, Jebel Dhana 81, Kalba 9, Khor Fakkan 9, Ras al Khaimah 7, Sadiyat 2, Sharjah 6, Umm al Quwain 6

Take account of business hours, Saturday to Thursday am is the working week in United Arab Emirates, GMT +4 hrs, charge band 8, UAE Direct 0800 89 0971

Uruguay 00 598

Las Piedras 32, Maldonado 42, Melo 462, Mercedes 532, Minas 442, Montevideo 442, Pando 392, Paysandu 722, Punta del Este 42, Rivera 622, Salto 732, San Jose De Carrasco 38, Tacuarembo 632

GMT -3 hrs, charge band 10

USA 00 1

Alaska 907 (-10/11 hrs), Albuquerque (NM) 505 (-7 hrs), Anchorage 907 (-8 hrs), Atlanta (GA) 706, Atlantic City (NJ) 609, Austin (TX) 612 (-6 hrs), Baltimore (MD) 410, Baton Rouge (LA) 504 (-6 hrs), Battle Creek (MI) 616, Birmingham (AL) 205 (-6 hrs), Bloomfield (NJ) 201, Boston (MA) 617, Bridgeport (CT) 203, Buffalo (NY) 716, Burbank (CA) 818 (8 hrs), Charleston (SC) 803, Charlotte (NC) 704, Chattanooga (TN) 615 (-6 hrs), Chicago (IL) 312 (-6 hrs), Cincinnati (OH) 513, Cleveland (OH) 216, Colorado Springs (CO) 719 (-7 hrs), Columbia (SC) 803, Columbus (MS) 601 (-6 hrs), Columbus (OH) 614, Corpus Christi (TX) 512 (-6 hrs), Dallas (TX) 214 (-6 hrs), Denver (CO) 303 (-7 hrs), Des Moines (IO) 515 (-6 hrs), Detroit (MI) 313, El Paso (TX) 915 (-7 hrs), Fort Lauderdale (F/A) 305, Fort Worth (TX) 817 (-6 hrs), Grand Rapids (MI) 616, Hartford (CT) 203, Hawaii 808 (-10 hrs), Hollywood (CA) 213 (-8 hrs), Honolulu (HI) 808 (-10 hrs), Houston (TX) 713 (-6 hrs), Indianapolis (IN) 317, Jackson (MS) 601 (-6 hrs), Jersey City (NJ) 201 (-6 hrs), Kansas City (MO) 816 (-6 hrs), Las Vegas (NV) 702, Long Beach (CA) 310 (-8 hrs), Los Angeles (CA) 213 (-8 hrs), Louisville (KY) 502, Memphis (TN) 901 (-6 hrs), Miami (FL) 305, Milwaukee (WI) 414 (-6 hrs), Minneapolis (MN) 612 (-6 hrs), Mobile (AL) 205 (-6 hrs), Nashville (TN) 615 (-6 hrs), Newark (NJ) 201, New Haven (CT) 203, New Orleans (LO) 504 (-6 hrs), New York City (NY) Bronx 718, Brooklyn 718, Manhattan 212, Queens 718, Staten Island 718, Norfolk (VA) 804, Oklahoma City (OK) 405 (-6 hrs), Omaha (NE) 402 (-6 hrs), Orlando (FL) 407, Palm Springs (CA) 619 (-8 hrs), Pasadena (CA) 818 (-8 hrs), Philadelphia (PA) 215, Phoenix (AZ) 602 (-7 hrs), Pittsburgh (PA) 412, Portland (OR) 503 (-8 hrs), Providence (RI) 401, Richmond (VA) 804, Rochester (NY) 716, Rockford (IL) 815 (-6 hrs), Sacramento (CA) 916 (-8 hrs), St Louis (MO) 314 (-6 hrs), St Paul (MN) 612

[-6 hrs), Salt Lake City (UT) 801 (-7 hrs), San Diego (CA) 619 (-8 hrs), San Francisco (CA) 415 (-8 hrs), Seattle (WA) 206 (-8 hrs), Springfield (MA) 413, Syracuse (NY) 315, Tampa (FL) 813, Toledo (OH) 419, Tulsa (OK) 918 (-6 hrs), Washington DC 202, Wichita (KS) 316 (-6 hrs), Wilmington (DE) 302, Yonkers 914, Youngstown (OH) 216

GMT -5 hrs (except where shown), charge band 4, AT & T USA Direct 0800 89 0011, Hawaii Direct 0800 89 0808, MCI call USA 0800 89 0222, USA Sprint Express 0800 89 0877, Phone USA TRT 0800 89 0456

USSR

For international codes for Estonia, Latvia, Lithuania, Armenia, Azerbaidzan, Belarus, Georgia, Kazakhstan, Russian Federation, Kurghistan, Moldova, Turkmenistan, Uzbekistan and Ukraine consult the new entries under those country names.

Uzbekistan 00 7
Bukhara 36522, Samarkand 36622, Tashkent 3712
GMT +5 hrs, charge band 8

Vanuatu 00 678
GMT +11 hrs, charge band 13

Vatican City (See Italy)

Venezuela 00 58
Barquisimeto 51, Caracas 2, Ciudad Bolivar 85, Cumana 93, Maracaibo 61, Maracay 43, Maturin 91, Merida 74, Puerto Cabello 42, Puerto La Cruz 81, San Cristobal 76, Valencia 41, Valera 71
GMT -4 hrs, charge band 10

Vietnam 00 84
GMT +7 hrs, charge band 13

Virgin Islands (UK) 00 1 809 4
GMT -4 hrs, charge band 5

Virgin Islands (US) 00 1 809
GMT -4 hrs, charge band 5

Wake Island
GMT +12 hrs, charge band 13

Wallis and Futuna
GMT +12 hrs, charge band 13

Yemen 00 967]5
Aden Governate 1, Attaq 46, Baidah 6, Hajja 7, Hodeidah 3, Ibb 4, Jaar 32, Lahej 22, Mareb 63 when followed by a 4 digit customer's number, Mareb 7 when followed by a 6 digit customer's number, Nisab 42, Qatn 8, Sadaa 51, Sanaa 1, Seiyun 84, Shihr 56, Taiz 4, Tarim 8, Zingibar 2

GMT + 3 hrs, charge band 10

Yugoslavia 00 381

Belgrade 11, *Kragujevac* 34, *Krusevac* 37, *Leskovac* 16, *Novi Sad* 21, *Pec* 39, *Skopje* 91, *Titograd* 81

GMT + 1 hr, charge band 3, for codes for Sarajevo in Bosnia-Hercegovina, Zagreb in Croatia and Ljubljana in Slovenia, consult the entries under those names

Zaire 00 243

Kinshasa 12, *Lubumbashi* 2 (+2 hrs)

GMT + 1 hr (except where shown), charge band 13

Zambia 00 260

Chililabombwe 2, *Chingola* 2, *Itimpi (Garneton)* 2, *Kabompo* 8, *Kabwe* 5, *Kasempa* 8, *Kitwe* 2, *Livingstone* 3, *Luanshya* 2, *Lusaka* 1, *Mansa* 2, *Mazabuka* 32, *Mbala* 4, *Mufulira* 2, *Mungwi* 4, *Mwinilunga* 8, *Ndola* 2, *Solwezi* 8

GMT + 2 hrs, charge band 10

Zimbabwe 00 263

Beitbridge 86, *Bulawayo* 9, *Chipinge* 27, *Chitungwiza* 70, *Colleen Bawn* 16, *Filabussi* 17, *Glendale* 758, *Gweru* 54, *Harare* 4, *Hwange (Wankie)* 81, *Juliasdale* 29, *Kadoma (Gatooma)* 68, *Kariba* 61, *Kwekwe* 55, *Marondera* 79, *Masvingo (Mazoe)* 75, *Murambinda* 21, *Mutare (Umtali)* 20, *Mvurwi* 77, *Norton* 62, *Plumtree* 80, *Ruwa* 73, *Selous* 628, *Triangle* 33, *Victoria Falls* 13, *Zvishavane* 51

GMT + 2 hrs, charge band 10

179

999 — *Emergency*

Fire • **Police** • **Ambulance**
Coastguard *(sea and cliff rescue)*
Mountain rescue • **Cave rescue**

How to call the Emergency Services

• Lift the telephone handset and press or dial 999

• Tell the BT operator which emergency service you want

• You may be asked for the number of the telephone you are using

• WAIT for the BT operator to connect you to the emergency service

• Tell the emergency service –
  WHAT the trouble is
  WHERE it is
  WHERE you are telephoning from

NEVER MAKE A FALSE CALL
It could risk the lives of others who really need help and it is against the law. It can also be traced immediately to the phone where the call came from.

Childline – *Freefone 0800 1111*
The Samaritans – *Lo-call 0345 909090*

Your personal telephone numbers

Name	Number

Your personal telephone numbers

Name	Number

Your personal telephone numbers

Name	Number

Your personal telephone numbers

Name	Number

Your personal telephone numbers

Name	Number

Your personal telephone numbers

Name	Number

Your personal telephone numbers

Name	Number

Your personal telephone numbers

Name	Number

Your personal telephone numbers

Name   *Number*

Your personal telephone numbers

Name	Number

Your personal telephone numbers

Name	Number

Your personal telephone numbers

Name   *Number*